VE
ON
THOUSAND
RED&
199FIVE

T ECR ATI

L S RA IC

L

B OK NET

IN HU D

NI ETY5

CONTENTS

THE CREATIVE ILLUSTRATION BOOK / BLACK BOOK MARKETING GROUP

BBMG HEADQUARTERS
866 Third Avenue
New York, New York 10022
Phone 212 702.9700
Facsimile 212 605.4808

SALES OFFICES
DALLAS 214 320.3434
CHICAGO 312 944.5115
MINNEAPOLIS 612 338.9044
SAN FRANCISCO 415 543.4100

CHAIRMAN | William F. Achtmeyer
PRESIDENT & PUBLISHER | H. Huntington Stehli
VICE PRESIDENT/ASSOCIATE PUBLISHER | Donna L. LeVan
VICE PRESIDENT FINANCE | Laura Branchini
NATIONAL ILLUSTRATION DIRECTOR | Alison Davis Chaitman
NATIONAL PHOTOGRAPHY DIRECTOR | Diane Casey

NEW YORK
MARKETING CONSULTANT - ILLUSTRATION | David Hoffman
ILLUSTRATION COORDINATORS | Brett Schaeffer
SENIOR MARKETING CONSULTANT - PHOTOGRAPHY | Erica Sturdevant
PHOTOGRAPHY COORDINATOR | Brodi Zimmer
MULTIMEDIA DIRECTOR | David Epstein
MULTIMEDIA COORDINATOR | David Watson

CHICAGO
MARKETING CONSULTANT - ILLUSTRATION | Adrian Hessel
MARKETING CONSULTANT – PHOTOGRAPHY | Sandy Markus
SALES COORDINATORS | Katie Neary, Melissa Kowalski

DALLAS
MARKETING CONSULTANT - ILLUSTRATION & PHOTOGRAPHY | Mary Preussel

LOS ANGELES
SENIOR MARKETING CONSULTANT - PHOTOGRAPHY | Françoise Dubois
SALES COORDINATOR | Marcy Renga

MINNEAPOLIS
MARKETING CONSULTANT - ILLUSTRATION | Linda McNally Cail
MARKETING CONSULTANT - PHOTOGRAPHY | Julia Millan

SAN FRANCISCO
MARKETING CONSULTANT - ILLUSTRATION | Lenore Cymes
MARKETING CONSULTANT - PHOTOGRAPHY | Breeze Carlile
SALES COORDINATOR | Maggie Kenny

PRODUCTION
PRODUCTION MANAGERS | Dana Grossman, Jason Taback
SENIOR PRODUCTION COORDINATORS | Christina Holbrook, Melissa Moss
PRODUCTION COORDINATOR | Mary Prevosti
TRAFFIC COORDINATOR | William F. Dolan
PROMOTION & CREATIVE COORDINATOR | Mimi Weisel
PRODUCTION ASSISTANT | Jason Sturdevant

DISTRIBUTION & LISTINGS
DISTRIBUTION & LISTINGS MANAGER | John Siemens
ASSISTANT LISTINGS MANAGER | Robert Sefcik
LISTINGS COORDINATOR | Cynthia Thomas
DISTRIBUTION COORDINATOR | Lisa Gotlib

ADMINISTRATION
SENIOR ACCOUNTANTS | Stanley Gong, Gayle Walker
SENIOR ACCOUNTANT / ACCOUNTS RECEIVABLE MANAGER | Steven Schmidt
ACCOUNTING CLERK | Farida Dhanji
EXECUTIVE ASSISTANT TO THE PUBLISHER | Cynthia V. Riley

The Creative Illustration Book was printed in Hong Kong by Everbest Printing Co., Ltd., through Four-Colour Imports, Ltd. Color separations by Universal Colour Scanning, Ltd.

The Creative Illustration Book is distributed in the U.S. and Canada by Black Book Marketing Group Inc., New York.

The Creative Illustration Book is distributed outside of the U.S. and Canada by Hearst Books International, 1350 Avenue of the Americas, New York, New York, 10019. Phone 212-261-6770, Facsimile 212-261-6795.

"The Creative Illustration Book" is a trademark of Black Book Marketing Group, Inc.

Copyright 1995 Black Book Marketing Group, Inc. All rights reserved. We are not responsible for errors or omissions.

ISBN 0-916098-90-7 | ISSN 1045-9855

Much of the artwork contained in this publication is protected by prior copyright in the name of the artist, and is reproduced here with permission. No art shown in this publication may be reproduced in any form without first obtaining the permission of the artist.

BOOK DESIGNER | Martin Solomon
TYPOGRAPHIC COORDINATOR | Alexa Nosal
Martin Solomon, Co.
303 Park Avenue South
New York, NY 10010
T: 212 477.3300 F: 212 677.7023

TO OUR READERS

Is producing an illustration annual similar to producing fine wine?

Though I am not a vintner, having produced several editions of Creative Illustration, I feel that the analogy is apt.

The elements of wine production include soil, weather, grapes and knowledge of the art of winemaking. The elements of this illustration annual include you the creative, the economic climate, the illustrators, and the people at Black Book Marketing Group who proudly present this edition to you.

Through six years of producing The Creative Illustration Book, we have established roots with buyers and producers of illustration. This period has enabled us to provide you with an illustration annual of exceedingly high caliber. The illustrators are those with whom you often work, and those you will be delighted to discover.

In the process of making a great wine, the grapes may suffer and rebound from not enough rain, or not enough sun, or not enough of some other element. This has been the climate for illustration this year. There were either not enough assignments, budgets not as big as one would like, or not as much creative freedom as one would desire. I have heard these sentiments expressed by creatives and illustrators. Yet the strained conditions you faced with your clients challenged illustrators who responded with their best work.

This edition of Creative Illustration has been graced with conditions that would produce vintage wine. However unlike vintage wine, this edition should be consumed immediately, and we hope that you will use it to excess, this year, and for many years to come.

Cheers.

Alison Davis Chaitman
National Illustration Director

Martin Solomon, Co., "A through (Z)ero".

Martin Solomon, Co., 303 Park Avenue South, New York, NY 10010 / Tel: 212 477.3300 Fax: 212 677.7023
Designer of the 1995 Creative Illustration Book

JANUARY

Call for entries, The 29th Belding Awards, The Ad Club of LA

Judging, Art Directors Club 74th Annual Exhibition, The Art Directors Club of New York

Call for Entries, American Illustration 14th Annual Competition

JANUARY 31

Deadline for entries, The One Show, New York

FEBRUARY 11 - MARCH 15

Exhibition of the 37th Annual Showing of American Illustrators, (Editorial & Book Categories), The Society of Illustrators, New York

MARCH

AR100 Deadline for Entries, Black Book Marketing Group, New York

Showing and Awards, The Belding Awards, The Ad Club of LA

EVENTS & AWARDS

Call for entries, ADDY Awards, American Advertising Federation, Washington, DC

MARCH 16th

Deadline for entries, Illustration Annual, Communication Arts Magazine

MARCH 15 - APRIL 15

Exhibition of the 37th Annual Showing of American Illustrators, (Advertising & Institutional), The Society of Illustrators, New York

MARCH 24 - APRIL 22

Communication Graphic Show, AIGA

APRIL

Presentation/Awards, Art Directors Club 73rd Annual Exhibition, The Art Directors Club of New York

Deadline for entries, ADDY Awards, American Advertising Federation

Judging, American Illustration 14th Annual Competition

APRIL 14

Deadline for entries, Book Show, AIGA

MAY

Call for entries, Illustration West Competition, Society of Illustrators, LA Awards Presentation, ANDY Awards, The Ad Club of New York

MAY

Show Presentation The One Show, New York

MAY 5-JUNE 3

Book Show, AIGA

JUNE

Deadline for Entries, Applied Arts Award Annual, Applied Arts Magazine, Ontario, Canada

JUNE 1-4

National Ad Conference Begins, ADDY Awards, American Advertising Federation Washington DC

JUNE 22nd

Deadline for entries, Design and Advertising Annual, Communications Arts Magazine

JULY

Deadline for entries, Annual Art Exhibition, The Art Directors Club of LA

AUGUST

San Francisco Society of Illustrators Annual Show (through September)

SEPTEMBER

Showing, Illustration West Competition, Society of Illustrators, LA

Call for entries, Art Directors Club 74th Annual Exhibition, The Art Directors Club of New York

OCTOBER

Presentation of Hall of Fame Inductees The Art Directors Club of New York

OCTOBER 1

Deadline for entries, 37th Annual Showing of American Illustrators, The Society of Illustrators, New York

NOVEMBER

Judging, Annual Exhibition, The Art Directors Club of LA

Deadline for entries, Art Directors Club 74th Annual Exhibition, The Art Directors Club of New York

DECEMBER

Deadline for entries, ANDY Awards, The Ad Club of New York

1995

JANUARY 1
New Year's Day

JANUARY 16
Martin Luther King, Jr. Day

FEBRUARY 14
Valentine's Day

FEBRUARY 20
President's Day

MARCH 1
Ash Wednesday

MARCH 17
St. Patrick's Day

APRIL 9
Palm Sunday

APRIL 14
Good Friday

APRIL 15
Passover

APRIL 16
Easter Sunday

MAY 14
Mother's Day

MAY 29
Memorial Day(Obsvd)

JULY 4
Independence Day

AUGUST 16
Elvis Day

SEPTEMBER 4
Labor Day

SEPTEMBER 25
Rosh Hashanah

OCTOBER 4
Yom Kippur

OCTOBER 9
Columbus Day (Obsvd)

OCTOBER 31
Halloween

NOVEMBER 7
Election Day

NOVEMBER 11
Veteran's Day

NOVEMBER 23
Thanksgiving Day

DECEMBER 18
Hannukah Begins

DECEMBER 25
Christmas Day

1996

JANUARY 1
New Year's Day

JANUARY 15
Martin Luther King, Jr. Day

FEBRUARY 14
Valentine's Day

FEBRUARY 19
President's Day

FEBRUARY 21
Ash Wednesday

MARCH 17
St. Patrick's Day

MARCH 31
Palm Sunday

APRIL 4
Passover

APRIL 5
Good Friday

APRIL 7
Easter Sunday

MAY 12
Mother's Day

MAY 27
Memorial Day(Obsvd)

JULY 4
Independence Day

AUGUST 16
Elvis Day

SEPTEMBER 2
Labor Day

SEPTEMBER 14
Rosh Hashanah

SEPTEMBER 23
Yom Kippur

OCTOBER 14
Columbus Day (Obsvd)

OCTOBER 31
Halloween

NOVEMBER 5
Election Day

NOVEMBER 11
Veteran's Day

NOVEMBER 28
Thanksgiving Day

DECEMBER 6
Hannukah Begins

DECEMBER 25
Christmas Day

1995

	S M T W T F S	S M T W T F S	S M T W T F S	S M T W T F S	S M T W T F S	S M
JANUARY	1 2 3 4 5 6 7	8 9 10 11 12 13 14	15 **16** 17 18 19 20 21	22 23 24 25 26 27 28	29 30 31	
FEBRUARY	1 2 3 4	5 6 7 8 9 10 11	12 13 **14** 15 16 17 18	19 **20** 21 22 23 24 25	26 27 28	
MARCH	**1** 2 3 4	5 6 7 8 9 10 11	12 13 14 15 16 **17** 18	19 20 21 22 23 24 25	26 27 28 29 30 31	
APRIL	1	2 3 4 5 6 7 8	**9** 10 11 12 13 **14 15**	**16** 17 18 19 20 21 22	23 24 25 26 27 28 29	30
MAY	1 2 3 4 5 6	7 8 9 10 11 12 13	14 15 16 17 18 19 20	21 22 23 24 25 26 27	28 **29** 30 31	
JUNE	1 2 3	4 5 6 7 8 9 10	11 12 13 14 15 16 17	18 19 20 21 22 23 24	25 26 27 28 29 30	
JULY	1	2 3 **4** 5 6 7 8	9 10 11 12 13 14 15	16 17 18 19 20 21 22	23 24 25 26 27 28 29	30 31
AUGUST	1 2 3 4 5	6 7 8 9 10 11 12	13 14 15 **16** 17 18 19	20 21 22 23 24 25 26	27 28 29 30 31	
SEPTEMBER	1 2	3 **4** 5 6 7 8 9	10 11 12 13 14 15 16	17 18 19 20 21 22 23	24 **25** 26 27 28 29 30	
OCTOBER	1 2 3 **4** 5 6 7	8 **9** 10 11 12 13 14	15 16 17 18 19 20 21	22 23 24 25 26 27 28	29 30 **31**	
NOVEMBER	1 2 3 4	5 6 7 8 9 10 **11**	12 13 14 15 16 17 18	19 20 21 22 **23** 24 25	26 27 28 29 30	
DECEMBER	1 2	3 4 5 6 7 8 9	10 11 12 13 14 15 16	17 **18** 19 20 21 22 23	24 **25** 26 27 28 29 30	31

1996

	S M T W T F S	S M T W T F S	S M T W T F S	S M T W T F S	S M T W T F S	S M
JANUARY	1 2 3 4 5 6	7 8 9 10 11 12 13	14 **15** 16 17 18 19 20	21 22 23 24 25 26 27	28 29 30 31	
FEBRUARY	1 2 3	4 5 6 7 8 9 10	11 12 13 **14** 15 16 17	18 **19** 20 **21** 22 23 24	25 26 27 28 29	
MARCH	1 2	3 4 5 6 7 8 9	10 11 12 13 14 15 16	**17** 18 19 20 21 22 23	24 25 26 27 28 29 30	31
APRIL	1 2 3 **4** **5** 6	**7** 8 9 10 11 12 13	14 15 16 17 18 19 20	21 22 23 24 25 26 27	28 29 30	
MAY	1 2 3 4	5 6 7 8 9 10 11	**12** 13 14 15 16 17 18	19 20 21 22 23 24 25	26 **27** 28 29 30 31	
JUNE	1	2 3 4 5 6 7 8	9 10 11 12 13 14 15	16 17 18 19 20 21 22	23 24 25 26 27 28 29	30
JULY	1 2 3 **4** 5 6	7 8 9 10 11 12 13	14 15 16 17 18 19 20	21 22 23 24 25 26 27	28 29 30 31	
AUGUST	1 2 3	4 5 6 7 8 9 10	11 12 13 14 15 **16** 17	18 19 20 21 22 23 24	25 26 27 28 29 30 31	
SEPTEMBER	1 **2** 3 4 5 6 7	8 9 10 11 12 13 **14**	15 16 17 18 19 20 21	22 **23** 24 25 26 27 28	29 30	
OCTOBER	1 2 3 4 5	6 7 8 9 10 11 12	13 **14** 15 16 17 18 19	20 21 22 23 24 25 26	27 28 29 30 **31**	
NOVEMBER	1 2	3 4 **5** 6 7 8 9	10 **11** 12 13 14 15 16	17 18 19 20 21 22 23	24 25 26 27 **28** 29 30	
DECEMBER	1 2 3 4 5 **6** 7	8 9 10 11 12 13 14	15 16 17 18 19 20 21	22 23 24 **25** 26 27 28	29 30 31	

1995 GRAPHIC ARTISTS GUILD GUIDELINES

In an effort to encourage better business relations between design and illustration professionals and art buyers, the Code of Fair Practice for the Graphic Communications Industry has been included in The 1995 Creative Illustration Book. The Code is widely accepted and agreed upon within the graphics community and serves as a voluntary guide for the conduct of its members. By making this information easily accessible to art buyers as well as to graphic artists, we hope to encourage improved communication between the groups.

In 1948, the Joint Ethics Committee formulated the original Code of Fair Practice in order to provide the graphic communications industry with accepted standards of ethics and professional conduct. Since then, the Code has been revised twice. The version reprinted here is the most recent. Sponsoring institutions of the Committee are the American Society of Magazine Photographers, the Committee of the American Institute of Graphic Arts, the Graphic Artists Guild, the Art Directors Club, the Society of Illustrators and the Society of Photographers and Artists Representatives.

The Committee's influence is derived from widespread acceptance and, while it has neither judicial nor police powers, its performance has made it an effective and respected tribunal. Judgments and decisions of the Committee are supported by the professions represented in the Committee. For further information, as well as assistance, please contact the local chapter of any of the above-mentioned organizations.

Joint Ethics Committee Code of Fair Practice for the Graphic Communications Industry

In 1945 a group of artists and art directors in New York City, concerned with growing abuses and misunderstandings – as well as with an increasing disregard – of uniform standards of conduct, met to consider possibilities for improvement. They realized that any efforts must have the most widespread backing, and further, that it must be a continuing, not a temporary, activity. On their recommendation, three leading New York art organizations together established and financed a committee known as the Joint Ethics Committee, which wrote and published a Code of Fair Practice for the graphic communications industry in 1948. In 1989 the committee revised the code.

Formulated in 1948, the Code was conceived to promote equity for those engaged in creating, selling, buying and using graphic arts. The Code has been used successfully since its formulation by thousands of industry professionals to establish equitable relationships in the practices of selling and buying art. Each artist should individually decide whether to enter art contests or design competitions, provide free services, work on speculation or work on a contingent basis. Each artist should independently decide how to price his or her work.

Relations between Artists and Buyers

The word "artist" should be understood to include creative people in the field of visual communications such as illustration, graphic design, photography, film and television. This code provides the graphic communications industry with an accepted standard of ethics and professional conduct. It presents guidelines for the voluntary conduct of persons in the industry which may be modified by written agreement between the parties.

ARTICLE I

Negotiations between an artist or the artist's representative and a client should be conducted only through an authorized buyer.

ARTICLE 2

Orders or agreements between an artist or artist's representative and buyer should be in writing and shall include the specific rights which are being transferred, the specific fee arrangement agreed to by the parties, delivery date and a summarized description of the work.

ARTICLE 3

All changes or additions not due to the fault of the artist or artist's representative should be billed to the buyer as an additional and separate charge.

ARTICLE 4
There should be no charges to the buyer for revisions or retakes made necessary by errors on the part of the artist or the artist's representative.

ARTICLE 5
If work commissioned by a buyer is postponed or cancelled, a "kill-fee" should be negotiated based on time allotted, effort expended and expenses incurred.

ARTICLE 6
Completed work shall be paid for in full and the artwork shall be returned promptly to the artist.

ARTICLE 7
Alterations shall not be made without consulting the artist. Where alterations or retakes are necessary, the artist shall be given the opportunity of making such changes.

ARTICLE 8
The artist shall notify the buyer of any anticipated delay in delivery. Should the artist fail to keep the contract through unreasonable delay or non-conformance with agreed specifications, it will be considered a breech of contract by the artist.

ARTICLE 9 *

ARTICLE 10
There shall be no undisclosed rebates, discounts, gifts, or bonuses requested by or given to buyers by the artist or representative.

ARTICLE 11
Artwork and copyright ownership is vested in the hands of the artist.

ARTICLE 12
Original artwork remains the property of the artist unless it is specifically purchased. It is distinct from the purchase of any reproduction rights. ** All transactions shall be in writing.

ARTICLE 13
In case of copyright transfers, only specified rights are transferred. All unspecified rights remain vested with the artist. All transactions shall be in writing.

ARTICLE 14
Commissioned artwork is not to be considered "work for hire."

ARTICLE 15
When the price of work is based on limited use and later such work is used more extensively, the artist shall receive additional payment.

ARTICLE 16
If exploratory work, comprehensives, or preliminary photographs from an assignment are subsequently used for reproduction, the artist's prior permission shall be secured and the artist shall receive fair additional payment.

ARTICLE 17
If exploratory work, comprehensives, or photographs are bought from an artist with the intention or possibility that another artist will be assigned to do the finished work, this shall be in writing at the time of placing the order.

ARTICLE 18
If no transfer of copyright ownership ** has been executed, the publisher of any reproduction of artwork shall publish the artist's copyright notice if the artist so requests at the time of agreement.

ARTICLE 19
The right to remove the artist's name on published artwork is subject to agreement between artist and buyer.

ARTICLE 20
There shall be no plagiarism of any artwork.

ARTICLE 21
If an artist is specifically requested to produce any artwork during unreasonable working hours, fair additional renumeration shall be paid.

ARTICLE 22
All artwork or photography submitted as samples to a buyer should bear the name of the artist or artists responsible for the work. An artist shall not claim authorship of another's work.

ARTICLE 23
All companies and their employees who receive artist portfolios, samples, etc. shall be responsible for the return of the portfolio to the artist in the same condition as received.

ARTICLE 24
An artist entering into an agreement with a representative, studio, or production company for an exclusive representation shall not accept an order from nor permit work to be shown by any other representative or studio. Any agreement which is not intended to be exclusive should set forth the exact restrictions agreed upon between the parties.

ARTICLE 25
No representative should continue to show an artist's samples after the termination of an association.

ARTICLE 26
After termination of an association between artist and representative, the representative should be entitled to a commission for a period of six months on accounts which the representative has secured, unless otherwise specified by contract.

ARTICLE 27
Examples of an artist's work furnished to a representative or submitted to a prospective buyer shall remain the property of the artist, should not be duplicated without the artist's consent and shall be returned promptly to the artist in good condition.

ARTICLE 28 *

ARTICLE 29
Interpretation of the Code for the purposes of mediation and arbitration shall be in the hands of the Joint Ethics Committee and is subject to changes and additions at the discretion of the parent organizations through their appointed representatives on the Committee. Submitting to mediation and arbitration under the auspices of the Joint Ethics Committee is voluntary and requires the consent of all parties to the dispute.

* Articles 9 and 28 have been deleted from this publication because, at press time, they are the subject of a Department of Justice investigation.

** Artwork ownership, copyright ownership and ownership rights transferred after January 1, 1978 are to be in compliance with the Federal Copyright Revision Act of 1976.

THE CREATIVE ILLUSTRATION BOOK   INDEX TO ADVERTISERS

A Priori Art & Media
PO Box 11510, Honolulu, HI 96828
808 949.2708

A&A
PO Box 330008, Ft Worth, TX 76163
817 292.1855

A.I.R. Studio
353 W 53rd St, NYC, NY 10019
212 582.0023
fax 212 582.0090
page 146

A.I.R. Studio
203 E Seventh St, Cincinnati, OH 45202
513 721.1193

Aardema, John
2601 Kieffer Ct, Valparaiso, IN 46383
219 464.1982

Abalone Design Group
990 A St, San Rafael, CA 94901
415 454.9446

Abboud, David
PO Box 1607, Monument, CO 80132
719 488.0757

ABC Calligraphy
1903 Broderick, San Francisco, CA 94115
415 668.8832

Abe, George
21531 NE 144th Pl,
Woodinville, WA 98072
206 788.5304
fax 206 788.1180
page 49

Abraham, Daniel
372 Fifth Ave, Brooklyn, NY 11215
718 499.4006

Abrams, Jodell
PO Box 925, Julian, CA 92036
619 765.2615

Abrams, Kathie
548 Ninth St, Brooklyn, NY 11215
718 499.4408

ABZ Art
4435 E Patterson Rd, Dayton, OH 45430
513 426.2363

Accardo, Anthony
8123 Seventh Ave, Brooklyn, NY 11228
718 680.2288

Accornero, Franco
620 Broadway, NYC, NY 10012
212 674.0068

Ace, Katherine
4017 SW 41st Pl, Portland, OR 97221
503 274.2543

Acerno, Jerry
3455 Jasmine Ave, L.A., CA 90034
310 842.9728

Acme Arts
2554 Como Ave, St Paul, MN 55108
612 644.2418

Action Studio
362 Quintard St, Chala Vista, CA 91911
619 476.6629

Acuna, Ed
232 Madison Ave, NYC, NY 10016
212 889.8777

Adams, Beth
151 E 20th St, NYC, NY 10003
212 677.2768

Adams, Gil
1440 Terrace Dr, Tulsa, OK 74104
918 749.2424

Adams, Jeanette
PO Box 130, Acworth, NH 03601
603 835.2984

Adams, Jenny
724 N Robinson St, L.A., CA 90026
213 655.6155

Adams, Kathryn
512 Richmond St E, Toronto, ON,
Canada M5A 1R3
416 367.2446

Adams, Lisa
40 Harrison St, NYC, NY 10013
212 691.3238

Adams, Mark
1766 E Third St, Long Beach, CA 90802
310 435.0344

Adams, Neal
4710 W Magnolia Blvd, Burbank, CA 91505
818 980.8852

Adams, Norman
211 E 51st St, NYC, NY 10022
212 755.1365

Adams, Tony
4203 Montrose Blvd, Houston, TX 77006
713 522.1555

Ade & Associates
700 W St Claire St, Cleveland, OH 44113
216 241.4990

Adigard, Erik
237 San Carlos Ave, Sausalito, CA 94965
415 331.1022

Adler, Steve
217 E 86th St, NYC, NY 10028
212 355.0910

Adrian Studios
Pier 46, San Francisco, CA 94107
415 543.3127

Advertising Arts
2309 Mt View Dr, Boise, ID 83706
208 377.2447

Advertising Graphics
27 S Forge St, Akron, OH 44304
216 535.2525

Africa, Eli
943 Solano Ave, Albany, CA 94706
510 528.2709

Agrell, Lewis
PO Box 12024, Prescott, AZ 86304
602 445.7038

Ahle, Dorothy
Eight Grimshaw St, Malden, MA 02148
617 321.8302

Airbrush Ink Studio
58 Forest Ave, Ronkonkoma, NY 11779
516 471.2728

Aitken, Doug
49 Ann St, NYC, NY 10038
212 608.1965

Aizawa, Kaz
6140 Monterey Rd, L.A., CA 90042
213 254.3362

Ajhar, Brian
PO Box 521, Canadensis, PA 18325
717 595.3782

AKA Design Inc
1605 S Ninth St, St Louis, MO 63104
314 621.6070

Akgulian, Nishan
42-29 64th St, Woodside, NY 11377
718 565.6936

Akimoto, George
6389 Embarcadero Dr, Stockton, CA 95219
209 476.0483

Akins, Kelly
29023 Rolando Rd, Lake Elsinore, CA 92530
909 674.6124

Akiometrics
77 W 15th St, NYC, NY 10011
212 807.8832

Akiyama, Meg
2330 Schoolside Ave,
Monterey Park, CA 91754
818 584.4137

Al Doggett Studio
1734 34th Ave, Seattle, WA 98122
206 329.5563

Alaimo, Terry M Studio
2233 Martin St, Irvine, CA 92715
714 724.8899

Alanen, Erkki
161 Country Rd, El Paso, TX 79932
915 581.2272

Alavezos, Gus
19050 Merrymen Cir, Monument, CO 80132
719 488.9078

Albers, Dave
6549 11th Ave NW, Seattle, WA 98117
206 781.7933

Albrecht, Anne
68 E Wacker Pl, Chicago, IL 60601
312 951.5181

Albury-Noyes, Mary
1413 Muir Ln, Burnsville, MN 55337
612 894.6727

Alcala, Alfredo P
740 Cochran Ave, L.A., CA 90036
213 938.8675

Alcorn, Stephen
112 W Main St, Cambridge, NY 12816
518 677.5798

Alden, Anne
2248 22nd St, Santa Monica, CA 90405
310 450.3788

Alder, Kelynn
430 W 14th St, NYC, NY 10014
212 431.4673

Aldridge Reps
758 Brookridge Dr, Atlanta, GA 30306
404 872.7980

Alexander & Turner
322 Madison ave, NYC, NY 10016
212 889.8777

Alexander, Pat
19 E 83rd St, NYC, NY 10028
212 288.3345

Alexander/Pollard
1841 Lake Cypress Dr,
Tampa Bay, FL 30306
813 725.4438 800 347.0734
pages 163-169

Alexander/Pollard
848 Greenwood Ave NE,
Atlanta, GA 30306
404 875.1363 800 347.0734
fax 404 875.9733
pages 163-169

Alfano, Wayne
15 W 72nd St, NYC, NY 10028
212 799.2231

Alkire, Betty Jo
Historic Taneywood,
Rockaway Beach, MO 65740
417 561.8106

Allaux, Jean-François
RD 2 Box 119, Thompson, PA 18465
717 756.3033

Alleman, Hans
301 Cherry St, Phila, PA 19106
215 829.9442

Alleman, Keith
1185 Bethel Rd, Columbus, OH 43220
614 459.8863

Allen, Barbara
81 Elm St, Woburn, MA 01801
617 932.9472

Allen, Dave
18108 Martin Ave, Homewood, IL 60430
708 798.3283

Allen, Julian
41 Union Sq W, NYC, NY 10003
212 929.5590

Allen, Kelly
2811 McKinney Ave, Dallas, TX 75204
214 922.9080

Allen, Mark Design & Associates
129 20th Street, Manhattan Beach, CA 90266
310 796.1443

Allen, Pat
4510 Alpine Rd, Portola Valley, CA 94028
415 851.3116

Allen, Rick
2222 E Third St, Duluth, MN 55812
218 724.4861
page 315

Allen, Terry
164 Daniel Low Ter,
Staten Island, NY 10301
718 727.0723
fax 718 727.0927
page 459

Allen, Thomas B
1201 W Campus Rd, Lawrence, KS 66044
913 864.4401

Allen, Victoria
31 Walker St, NYC, NY 10013
212 334.0120
page 60

Allison, Drew
1840 Massachusetts Ave, Lexington, MA 02173
617 674.2327

Allison, John
7645 Jarboe, Kansas City, MO 64114
816 444.7782
page 458

Allshouse, William
3279 Daleford Rd, Shaker Heights, OH 44120
216 751.1038

Almquist, Don
353 W 53rd St, NYC, NY 10019
212 582.0023
fax 212 582.0090
page 145

Alper, AJ
224 Elizabeth St, NYC, NY 10012
212 522.7697

Alpert, Olive
9511 Shore Rd, Brooklyn, NY 11209
718 833.3092

Alstad & Associates
3625 Colfax Ave S, Mpls, MN 55409
612 827.4148

Altamore, Vincent
152-48 Melbourne Ave, Flushing, NY 11367
718 263.2264

Alterio, Caroline
430 Ventura Pl, Vero Beach, FL 32963
617 236.1920

Amatrula, Michele
259 W Tenth St, NYC, NY 10014
212 255.7413

Amber Enterprises
4130 La Jolla Village Dr, La Jolla, CA 92037
619 755.0847

Ambrosi & Associates Inc
1100 W Washington Blvd, Chicago, IL 60607
312 666.9200

Ambroson, Rodd
8402 SW Woods Creek Ct,
Portland, OR 97219
503 246.9511

Ameijide, Ray
108 E 35th St, NYC, NY 10016
212 889.3337

American Art Studio
124 W 24th St, NYC, NY 10011
212 633.1466

American Artists
353 W 53rd St, NYC, NY 10019
212 582.0023
fax 212 582.0090
pages 142-147

Americonsult
7855 NW 125th St, Miami, FL 33126
305 717.3300

Amicosante, Vincent
370 Junipero Ave, Pacific Grove, CA 93950
408 648.8849

Amit, Emmanuel
4322 Sunset Ave, Montrose, CA 91020
818 249.1739

Amorosi, Teresa
Six Compton St, East Rockaway, NY 11518
516 596.0160

Ampah, Felix
6814 18th Ave S, Mpls, MN 55423
612 861.7380

Anastas, Nicolette
1833 N Hudson Ave, Chicago, IL 60614
312 664.4754

Anatoly
716 Montgomery St, San Francisco, CA 94111
415 433.1222

Anderson, A Richard
927 Franklin Ave, River Forest, IL 60305
708 366.5661

Anderson, Michael
11843 S Nottingham Ct, Houston, TX 77071
713 493.5939

Anderson, Sara
3131 Western Ave, Seattle, WA 92121
206 285.1520

Anderson, Tim
1826 Asheville Pl, Charlotte, NC 28203
704 372.6007

Andrea, Pat
18 rue Henri Regnault, Paris, France 75014
011 33.1.454.54423

Andrews, Joanne
40 Waterford Way, Fairport, NY 14450
716 223.9023

Andrews, John
1500 Calico Ln, Sun Prairie, WI 53590
608 837.4235

Angel Arts Productions
11203 Emelita St, North Hollywood, CA 91601
818 907.2660

Angelagraphics/Angela Kamstra
529 S Seventh St, Mpls, MN 55415
612 332.1832

Angelini, George
Four Churchill St, Ossining, NY 10562
914 923.4029

Angelo
1449 Longfellow Ave, Bronx, NY 10459
718 617.2907

Angle, Scott
21051 Barbados Cir,
Huntington Beach, CA 92646
714 960.8485

Angrisani, Chris
6095 N Ninth Rd, Arlington, VA 22205
703 241.3739

Anka, Adam
10724 1/2 Valley Spring Ln,
North Hollywood, CA 91602
818 985.7071

Annino, Michael
2616 N Highland Ave, Arlington Hts, IL 60004
708 255.1359

Annis, Scott
PO Box 22582, Denver, CO 80222
303 758.7905

Another Girl Rep
PO Box 421443,
San Francisco, CA 94142
415 647.5660
fax 415 285.1102
pages 378-381, 464

Anselmo/Chromatics/Colorfast
211 E 51st St, NYC, NY 10022
212 753.1606

Ansley, Frank
414 Jackson St, San Francisco, CA 94111
415 989.9614

Anthony, Tony
132 Rumson Rd NE, Atlanta, GA 30305
404 237.9836

Anton, Jerry
119 W 23rd St, NYC, NY 10011
212 633.9880

Antonios, Tony
60 E 42nd St, NYC, NY 10165
212 682.1490

Anzalone, Lori
35-02 Berdan Ave, Fair Lawn, NJ 07410
201 796.5588

Anzilotti, Ed
230 Ashley Cir, Danville, CA 94526
510 743.0698

Apple Slide & Design Inc
639 Howard St, San Francisco, CA 94105
415 974.5395

Applebee, Angie
6628 Floyd St, Overland Park, KS 66202
913 236.8332

Appleoff, Sandy
4323 Bluffview Blvd, Dallas, TX 75209
214 352.9192

Appleton, Wayne
2100 W Big Beaver Rd, Troy, MI 48084
810 643.6000

Arbas, Rasa
823 19th St, Santa Monica, CA 90403
310 828.3761

Arbogast, Shane
177 Seventh Ave, Brooklyn, NY 11215
718 832.0149

Arbour, Dennis
PO Box 512, Belfast, ME 04915
207 338.5245

Archambault, Matthew
15 W 72nd St, NYC, NY 10023
212 799.2251

Archey, Rebecca
63 Madrone Ave, Larkspur, CA 94939
415 924.9000

Architectural Arts
2145 SW Second Ave, Ft Lauderdale, FL 33315
305 523.1312

Arday, Don
616 Arbor Creek Dr, DeSoto, TX 75115
214 223.6235

Arden Graphics
1232 The Alameda, Berkeley, CA 94709
510 524.5994

Arditti, Sara
3840 Marcasel Ave, L.A., CA 90066
310 397.6445

Arena
144 Royal College St,
London, England NW1 0TA
011 71.267.9661
fax 011 71.284.0486
pages 34-35

Arendt, David C Graphic Design
7651 Sunset Dr, Elmwood Park, IL 60635
708 452.9156

Ariail, Alan
20 W Hubbard, Chicago, IL 60610
312 222.1361
fax 312 222.0753
pages 422-423

Arisman, Marshall
314 W 100th St, NYC, NY 10025
212 967.4983

Arkle, Dave
1010 S Robertson Blvd, L.A., CA 90035
310 652.7322

Armendariz, David
3240 Fay Ave, L.A., CA 90034
310 559.6816

Armes, Steve
1509 Glenbrook Dr, Irving, TX 75061
214 721.0614

Arnet, Angela
400 Central Park W, NYC, NY 10025
212 865.0966

Aronson, Ben
33 Wayside Inn Rd, Framingham, MA 01701
508 788.1455

Arrco Medical Art & Design
909 Beacon St, Boston, MA 02215
617 266.2680

Arrowood, Scott
2137 Texas St, Salt Lake City, UT 84109
801 322.0433

Arroyo, Andrea
509 Cathedral Pky, NYC, NY 10025
212 864.6648

Arroyo, Fian
7123 SW 115th Pl, Miami, FL 33173
305 274.3812

Art & Commerce
755 Washington St, NYC, NY 10014
212 206.0737

The Art Agency
2405 NW Thurman St,
Portland, OR 97210
503 225.9687
fax 503 228.6030
pages 233-235

Art Attack
5309 Coldwater Canyon Ave,
Sherman Oaks, CA 91401
818 907.8626

The Art Collection
266 Fulham Rd, London, England SW10 9EL
011 44.71.376.7773

The Art Company
720 Washington St, Hanover, MA 02339
617 829.0011

The Art Depot Creative Agency
432 E St, San Diego, CA 92101
619 696.6545

Art Directions
91 McBride Rd, Wales, MA 01081
413 267.5024

Art Directions
812 Huron Rd, Cleveland, OH 44115
216 621.5388

The Art Director's Studio
419 Park Ave S, NYC, NY 10016
212 689.9888

Art for Advertising Inc
566 W Adams St, Chicago, IL 60601
312 939.3393

The Art of the Pen
1220 S Bedford St, L.A., CA 90035
310 271.4909

The Art Rep
PO Box 1122, La Habra, CA 90631
310 694.0838

The Art Source
PO Box 2193, Grapevine, TX 76099
817 481.2212
fax 817 481.2908
pages 358-359

Art Source/Diane Barkley
Box 257, Pleasantville, NY 10570
914 747.2220

Artability
152 Village Sq, Orinda, CA 94563
510 254.4616

Artco
232 Madison Ave, NYC, NY 10016
212 889.8777

Artco
227 Godfrey Rd, Weston, CT 06883
203 222.8777

Artech-Illustration
934 Carlson Dr, Brea, CA 92621
714 275.1750

Artemis
721 Emerson St, Palo Alto, CA 94301
415 325.6596

Arthur Art Studio
990 Illinois Rd, Lake Forest, IL 60445
708 234.2225

Artique Design
18155 Karen Dr, Tarzana, CA 91356
818 345.7357

Artistix
66 Sentinel, Aliso Viejo, CA 92656
714 362.5242

Artists Inc
193 E Waterloo Rd, Akron, OH 44319
216 773.0396

Artists International
320 Bee Brook Rd, Washington, CT 06777
203 868.1011

Arts & Letters
3214 Hewitt St, Falls Church, VA 22042
703 560.1717

The Artsmith
PO Box 391, Athens, GA 30603
706 543.5555

The Artworks Freelance Group
4409 Maple Ave, Dallas, TX 75219
214 521.2121

Artworks Illustration
270 Park Ave S, NYC, NY 10010
212 260.4153

Aru, Agnes
498 Manning Ave, Toronto, ON,
Canada M6G 2V7
416 532.9861
fax 416 532.9861
page 392

Arvidson, Glenn
8923 Marion, Morton Grove, IL 60053
312 938.1900

Asbaghi, Zita
104-40 Queens Blvd,
Forest Hills, NY 11375
718 275.1995
page 159

Asciutto Art Representatives
1712 E Butler Cir, Chandler, AZ 85225
602 899.0600

Asesa Studio
PO Box 140012, Irving, TX 75014
214 550.9073

Ash, Susan
3301A S Jefferson Ave, St Louis, MO 63118
314 773.2600

Asher, Neal & Audette
601 N Park Blvd, Grapevine, TX 76051
817 481.3961

Asher, Terri
21800 Schoenborn St, Canoga Park, CA 91304
818 348.4278

Ashton Art & Design
86 Lackawanna Ave, West Paterson, NJ 07424
201 256.6636

Asmussen, Don
3975 Hortensia St, San Diego, CA 92110
619 298.0414

Aspinall, Neal
1255 Martha Washington Dr,
Milwaukee, WI 53213
414 774.3808

Assel, Steven
29-54 143rd St, Flushing, NY 11354
718 539.5776

Astro Graphics
124 N Park Ave, Westmont, IL 60559
708 969.5854

Atkeson, Ed
292 Lark St, Albany, NY 12210
518 436.9498

Atkins, Bill
31568 First Ave, Laguna Beach, CA 92677
714 499.3857

Atkinson, Janet
359 Ovington Ave, Brooklyn, NY 11209
718 836.9335

Atkinson, Steve
3077 Dundee Ln, Mound, MN 55364
612 472.5938

Ator, Robin
2405 NW Thurman St, Portland, OR 97210
503 225.9687

Atteberry, Kevan
13000 Bel-Red Rd, Bellevue, WA 98005
206 453.6010

Attebery, Craig
1812 Wollam St, L.A., CA 90065
213 227.4120

Auckland, Jim
30166 Chapala Ct, Laguna Niguel, CA 92677
714 495.3664

Auerbach Italic Calligraphy
611 Frederick St, San Francisco, CA 94117
415 661.8060

Austin, Cary
1537 S Main, Silic, UT 84115
801 484.6775

Austin, Dona
2205 Broadlawn, Houston, TX 77058
713 480.3814

Austin, Michael
2006 Broadway, Boulder, CO 80302
303 444.6880

Avery Illustration/Design/Adv
3471 W Spruce, Fresno, CA 92646
209 261.2622

Aveto, Michael
280 Madison Ave, NYC, NY 10016
212 545.9155

Avishai, Susan
28 Marlboro St, Newton, MA 02158
617 969.5451

Axelrod, Dale
3415 22nd St, San Francisco, CA 94110
415 824.1549

Axis Design
5807 N Tobias Ave, Van Nuys, CA 91411
818 781.8848

Ayers, Alan
Three Copper Hill Dr, Guilford, CT 06437
203 453.3925

Ayerst, Deborah Artists Agent
2546 Sutter, San Francisco, CA 94115
415 567.3570

Ayriss, Linda Holt
507 Browning St, Mill Valley, CA 94941
415 383.4039

Azar, Joe
3935 N Fourth St, Arlington, VA 22203
703 527.1443

Azzinaro, Lew
11872 St Trinians Ct, Reston, VA 22091
703 620.5155

B2 Creative Consultants
PO Box 34952, Phoenix, AZ 85067
602 254.7220

Babb, Paul
823 Yosemite, Glendale, MO 63122
314 968.8843

Babb, Phil
6705 Kemman, Hebron, IL 60034
815 648.4375

Bachem, Paul
46 Soundview Ave, Locust Valley, NY 11560
516 671.8604

Bacher, Nancy
2654 Rodeo Dr NE, Blaine, MN 55449
612 786.1200
pages 172-173

Bachor, Jim
18200 Harwood, Homewood, IL 60430
708 798.2056

Bachtell, Tom
202 S State St, Chicago, IL 60604
312 939.6603

Bacigalupi, David
348 Florence Ave, Sebastopol, CA 95472
707 829.7980

Backes, Nick
PO Box 421443,
San Francisco, CA 94142
415 647.5660
fax 415 285.1102
page 378

Backhaus, Kenn
6989 Sconfinato Dr, Hartford, WI 53027
414 673.9233

Badin, Andy & Ella Leffler
50 W 72nd St, NYC, NY 10023
212 877.2390

Badonsky, Kathy
251 Kings Hwy, Decatur, GA 30030
404 373.6377

Badyrka, Miriam
7456 N Fiske St, Portland, OR 97203
503 285.8322

Baechli, George
6550 Hillcroft, Houston, TX 77081
713 771.7836

Bailey & Associates
139 Grandville Ave SW,
Grand Rapids, MI 49503
616 451.8374

Bailey, Kevin
4203 Montrose Blvd, Houston, TX 77006
713 522.1555

Bailey, Pat
24 Lincoln St, Jamestown, RI 02835
401 461.9172

Baird, Edward
1402 Santa Rosa Dr, Santa Fe, NM 87501
505 989.4783

Baker, Don
2814 NW 72nd St, Seattle, WA 98117
206 784.1136
fax 206 784.1171
page 48

Baker, Garin
478 Union Ave, New Windsor, NY 12533
914 562.7802

Baker, Joe
35 Wooster St, NYC, NY 10013
212 925.6555
page 320

Baker, Kolea
2814 NW 72nd St, Seattle, WA 98117
206 784.1136
fax 206.784.1171
pages 48-49

Baker, Louise
3436 N Racine Ave, Chicago, IL 60657
312 327.7286

Baker, Richard
4230 W Porter Ave, Fullerton, CA 92633
714 994.0459

Baker, Skip
731 N 24th St, Phila, PA 19130
215 232.6666
fax 215 232.6585
page 326

Balboni, Timothy
54 W 82nd St, NYC, NY 10024
212 877.0591

Balbus, Sydney
9600 Van Nuys Blvd, Panorama City, CA 91402
818 891.1370

Baldini Associates
14095 Orchid Ave, Poway, CA 92064
619 486.1993

Baldino Design
64 Vernon Dr, Scarsdale, NY 10583
914 723.4001

Baldridge Illustration/Design
PO Box 18972, Oklahoma City, OK 73154
405 843.8876

Baldwin, Christopher
601 Valley St, Seattle, WA 98109
206 284.8553
fax 206 281.8293
page 126

Ball, David
142 E 16th St, NYC, NY 10003
212 979.2371

Ball, H/Smile Face Creator
340 Main St, Worcester, MA 01608
508 752.9154

Ball, John
2100 W Big Beaver Rd, Troy, MI 48084
810 643.6000

Ballard, Dan Visual Communications
PO Box 85187, Seattle, WA 98145
206 634.0084

Ballsun, John
5325 Newcastle Ave, Encino, CA 91316
818 345.4398

Bamundo, David
66 Carreau Ave, Staten Island, NY 10314
718 370.7726

Banashek, Jill
578 29th Ave, San Francisco, CA 94121
415 751.5336

Banaszak, Pat
15 W 72nd St, NYC, NY 10028
212 799.2231

Bane, Jeff
8950 Cal Ctr Dr, Sacramento, CA 95826
916 362.0400

Banner, Shawn
25 W 25th St, NYC, NY 10001
212 398.9540

Banta, Susan
17 Magazine St, Cambridge, MA 02139
617 876.8568

Banthien, Barbara
127 Leland Way, Tiburon, CA 94920
415 381.0842

Baquero, George
Four Westley Ln, New Milford, NJ 07646
201 261.6011

Baradat, Sergio
210 W 70th St, NYC, NY 10023
212 721.2588

Barbaria, Steve
1990 Third St, Sacramento, CA 95814
916 442.3200

Barber, Rob
1963 Esperanza Dr, Concord, CA 94519
510 674.9069

Barbier, Suzette
124 Winchester St,
Newton, MA 02161
617 527.8388
fax 617 244.0266
page 406

Barbour, Karen
PO Box 1210, Point Reyes Sta, CA 94956
415 663.1100

Barcelow, Rick
2299 Pearl St, Boulder, CO 80302
303 447.9164

Barker & Lee Graphic Design
3248 Minnesota Ave, Costa Mesa, CA 92626
714 850.1935

Barkley, Jim
444 Bedford Rd, Pleasantville, NY 10570
914 747.2220

Barnard, Bryn
914 Rockmoss Ave, Newark, DE 19711
302 456.3909

Barnes, Barry
3825 Valley Blvd, Walnut, CA 91789
909 594.5979

Barnes, Kim
735 Cypress Rd, Severna Park, MD 21146
410 544.4644

Barnes, Lois
1344 Palos Verdes Dr W,
Palos Verdes Est, CA 90274
310 373.5045

Barnes, Michelle
165 Perry St, NYC, NY 10014
212 219.9269

Barnes, Suzanne
430 Ventura Pl, Vero Beach, FL 32963
617 236.1920

Barnes-Murphy, Rowan
420 Lexington Ave, NYC, NY 10017
212 986.5680

Barnet, Nancy
8928 Shady Vista Ct, Elk Grove, CA 95624
916 685.4147

Barnett, Juanita
6226 Secret Hollow Ln, Centreville, VA 22020
703 266.0012

Barnhart, Duane Cartooning
5505 Prospect Ave,
White Bear Lake, MN 55110
612 429.7660

Baron, Dolores
14044 Petronella Dr, Libertyville, IL 60048
312 467.6380

Barr, Elissa
PO Box 483, Brookline Vlg, MA 02147
617 731.4487

Barr, Glenn
307 W Sixth St, Royal Oak, MI 48067
810 541.5167

Barr, Ken
420 Lexington Ave, NYC, NY 10170
212 697.8525

Barr, Kevin
35 Stillman St, San Francisco, CA 94107
415 543.6881

Barr, Marilynn Grant
5721 Wildberry Dr, Greensboro, NC 27409
910 852.4287

Barrall, Tim
372 Bleecker St, NYC, NY 10014
212 243.9003

Barrett, Debby
49 Hamilton St, Everett, MA 02149
617 387.2031

Barrett, Robert
Pine Rd HCR, Neversink, NY 12765
914 985.2936

Barrett, Ron
2112 Broadway, NYC, NY 10023
212 874.1370

Barrett, Tom
7118 Wayne Ave, Upper Darby, PA 19082
215 352.9530

Barrington, Brian
308 W Third St, Tustin, CA 92680
714 731.8538

Barry Enterprises
21005 Tamarack Cir, Southfield, MI 48075
810 356.8946

Barry, Ron
165 E 32nd St, NYC, NY 10016
212 686.3514

Barson, Jeff
60 E 42nd St, NYC, NY 10017
212 867.8092

Barsotti, Charles
419 E 55th St, Kansas City, MO 64110
816 444.1108

Barta, Dorothy
3151 Chapel Downs, Dallas, TX 75229
214 352.8246

Bartalos, Michael
30 Ramona Ave, San Francisco, CA 94103
415 863.4569

Bartashev, Igor
3033 Brighton 13th St, Brooklyn, NY 11235
718 648.2989

Bartczak, Peter
PO Box 7709, Santa Cruz, CA 95060
408 426.4247

Bartek, Shelly
8522 Izard, Omaha, NE 68114
402 399.5251
page 154

Bartell, George
23890 Madison St, Torrance, CA 90505
310 375.9541

Bartels, Ceci Associates
NYC, NY
212 912.1877
page 321

Bartels, Ceci Associates
3286 Ivanhoe, St Louis, MO 63139
314 781.7377
fax 314 781.8017
page 321

Bartels, Ceci Associates
Chicago, IL
312 786.1560
page 321

Bartholomew, Beth
486 Graham Ave, Brooklyn, NY 11222
718 384.0162

Barton, Kent
5378 Pinecrest Ln, Youngharris, GA 30582
305 431.4652

Bartos, Adam
55 W 11th St, NYC, NY 10011
212 243.9490

Baruffi, Andrea
341 Hudson Ter, Piermont, NY 10968
914 359.9542

Baseman, Gary
442 12th St, Brooklyn, NY 11215
718 499.9358

Basso, Bill
38 Ogden Ln, Englishtown, NJ 07726
908 431.5497

Batcheller, Keith
1438 Calle Cecilia, San Dimas, CA 91773
818 331.0439

Batelman, Kenneth
47-16 39th Ave, Sunnyside, NY 11104
718 392.3483

Bates, Byron R
9167 1/2 Las Tunas Dr, Temple City, CA 91780
818 309.0425

Bates/Prieur
8143 Hihn Rd, Ben Lomond, CA 95005
408 336.3661

Batik Illustration
400 N First St, Mpls, MN 55401
612 371.0153

Battles, Brian
6316 Dissinger Ave,
San Diego, CA 92139
619 267.3182
fax 619 267.6649
page 348

Bauer, Carla Design
156 Fifth Ave, NYC, NY 10010
212 807.8305

Bauer, Stephen
3000 Chestnut Ave, Baltimore, MD 21211
410 243.0643

Baughman, Christi
467 Clearfield, Garland, TX 75043
214 270.5925

Bauman, Jill
PO Box 150152, Jamaica, NY 11415
718 886.5616

Baumgart, Ted
2425 Mountain Ave, La Crescenta, CA 91214
818 957.1071

Bautista, Vincent
2113 Parkside Ave, L.A., CA 90031
213 222.9408

Baviera, Rocco
1888 Century Park E, L.A., CA 90067
310 826.1332
fax 310 284.3290
page 265

Baviera, Rocco
41 King William St, Hamilton, ON,
Canada L8R 1A2
905 570.0004
fax 905 385.0047
page 265

Beach, Lou
215 Park Ave S, NYC, NY 10017
212 674.8080

Beach, P Illustration
83 Moseley Ave, Newburyport, MA 01950
508 462.4275

Beach, Pearl
11936 W Jefferson Blvd,
Culver City, CA 90230
310 390.8663

Beatman, Josh
628 E 14th St, NYC, NY 10009
212 353.0834

Beaudoin, Mario
22 E 36th St, NYC, NY 10016
212 685.4580

Beaupre, Judy
200 New Castle Ave, Portsmouth, NH 03801
603 431.0177

Beck Visual Communications
2525 E Franklin Ave, Mpls, MN 55406
612 338.8642

Beck, David
4042 Appletree Ct, Cincinnati, OH 45247
513 741.1228

Beck, Jenny
222 Poplar St, Buffalo, MN 55313
612 682.4016

Becker, Pamela
PO Box 173, Stinson Beach, CA 94970
415 868.1111

Becker, Paula
6017 Ebonwood, Corpus Christi, TX 78412
512 993.0164

Bedrick, Jeffrey K
2852 California St, San Francisco, CA 94115
415 923.1122

Bee, Johnee
30166 Chapala Ct, Laguna Niguel, CA 92677
714 495.3664

Beerworth, Roger
1723 S Crescent Hts Blvd, L.A., CA 90035
213 933.9692

Beha, Philippe
18 McKinley St, Rowayton, CT 06853
203 866.3734
fax 203 857.0842
page 17

Beha, Philippe
NYC, NY
212 581.8338
page 17

Behrens, Mark
1444 Pacific Ave, San Francisco, CA 94109
415 771.8454

Behum, Cliff
26384 Aaron Ave, Euclid, OH 44132
216 261.9266

Beilfuss, Kevin
420 Lexington Ave, NYC, NY 10170
212 986.5680
fax 212 818.1246
page 82

Bekke, Doug
700 Third St S, Mpls, MN 55415
612 338.5417

Belcastro, Mario
2946 Sebolt Rd, Library, PA 15129
412 835.8470

Bell, Andrea
2306 Harriman Ln, Redondo Beach, CA 90278
310 376.3945

Bell, James Design
692 Washington Ave, Brooklyn, NY 11238
718 230.0107

Bell, Jill
2501 Clark Ln, Redondo Beach, CA 90278
310 372.4204

Bell, Karen
1700 Decker Canyon Rd, Malibu, CA 90265
310 457.3943

Bellantuono, Jeffrey
292 Britannia St, Meriden, CT 06450
203 639.0665

Bellerose, Mark
275 Newbury St, Boston, MA 02116
617 276.0618

Bemus, Bart
353 W 53rd St, NYC, NY 10019
212 682.2462

Bendell, Norm
31 S Finley Ave, Basking Ridge, NJ 07920
908 221.9030

Bender, Mark
930 N Lincoln Ave, Pittsburgh, PA 15233
412 321.3266

Benjamin, Christine
1057 Broadway Ave, San Jose, CA 95125
408 297.6431

Benny, Mike Illustration
2773 Knollwood Ave,
Cameron Park, CA 95682
916 677.9142

Benoit
155 W 15th St, NYC, NY 10011
212 989.8770

Bensen, Linda
270 Park Ave S, NYC, NY 10017
212 260.4135

Benson, Elaine
PO Box 470818, San Francisco, CA 94147
415 383.9026

Benson, Phil
149 Carnegie Ct, St Louis, MO 63088
314 225.1517

Bensusen, Sally J
932 S Walter Reed Dr, Arlington, VA 22204
703 979.3931

Benton, Mary
282 Thayer St, Providence, RI 02900
508 675.6104

Bentz, Charles
110 W 40th St, NYC, NY 10018
212 302.9088

Berasi, Teresa
427 Third St, Brooklyn, NY 11215
718 965.2231

Berendsen & Associates
2233 Kemper Ln, Cincinnati, OH 45206
513 861.1400

Berg, David
14021 Marquesas Way,
Marina del Rey, CA 90292
310 822.6531

Berg, Jeanne
250 Sylvan Rd, N Babylon, NY 11703
516 669.2366

Berg, Ron Illustration
71 Hewitt Ave, Toronto, ON,
Canada M6R 1Y4
416 537.4069
fax 416 539.8840
page 90

Berge, Kay
2413 W 157th St, Gardena, CA 90249
213 770.3872

Bergendorff, Roger
1010 S Robertson Blvd, L.A., CA 90035
310 652.7322

Berger, Susan
853 N Alta Vista Blvd, L.A., CA 90046
213 930.2165

Bergherr, Mary
2520 W 22nd St, Mpls, MN 55405
612 377.0996

Bergin, Tom Studios
708 E University Blvd, Tucson, AZ 85719
602 884.1618

Berglund, Cindy
5275 E Lake Bch Ct, Shoreview, MN 55126
612 490.5141

Bergman, Eliot
41 Union Sq W, NYC, NY 10003
212 929.5590
page 244

Berkson, Nina
Two Silver Ave, Toronto, ON,
Canada M6R 3A2
416 530.1500
fax 416 530.1401
page 461

Bernard, Gary
3640 S Sepulveda Blvd, L.A., CA 90034
310 842.9583

Bernard, Nancy
906 Hyde Ave, Cupertino, CA 95014
408 253.7804

Bernardin, James
23632 Hwy 99, Edmonds, WA 98026
206 517.4953

Bernath, Paul Anthony
127 W Third St, Frederick, MD 21701
301 620.0600

Bernetti, Larry
Box 257, Pleasantville, NY 10570
914 747.2220

Bernhard, Durga
28 Broadview Rd, Woodstock, NY 12498
914 679.4940

Bernstein & Andriulli
60 E 42nd St, NYC, NY 10165
212 682.1490
fax 212 286.1890
page 354

Bernstein, Saul
649 Encino Vista Dr,
Thousand Oaks, CA 91362
805 497.7967

Berran, Bob
60 E 42nd St, NYC, NY 10017
212 867.8092

Berrett, Lisa
1450 Morning Glory Dr, Petaluma, CA 94954
707 763.7254

Berrett, Randy
716 Montgomery St, S. F., CA 94111
415 433.1222

Berrit, Grynan
1125 Landwehr Rd, Northbrook, IL 60062
708 498.8936

Berry, Rick
93 Warren St, Arlington, MA 02174
617 648.6375

Berryhill, Gene
PO Box 1429, Laguna Beach, CA 92652
800 576.2328

Berson, Julie Handlettering
Ten Westfair Dr, Westport, CT 06880
203 255.9431

Berta, Michael Graphic Design
590 Hull Ave, San Jose, CA 95125
408 293.6779

Bertram, Bob
837 Pebblefield Ter, Ballwin, MO 63021
314 256.0405

Beserra, Joe
2613 Rutherford Dr, L.A., CA 90068
213 469.2890

Best Evidence
2820 Camino del Rio S, San Diego, CA 92108
619 297.2378

Best, Diane
PO Box 282, Big Bear City, CA 92314
909 585.5785

Bettoli, Delana
PO Box 400, Silverton, OR 97381
503 873.8257

Betz, Karen
887 W Marietta St, Atlanta, GA 30318
404 875.8225

Bevill, Jennifer
106 Prospect Pk W, Brooklyn, NY 11215
718 369.2758

Beylerian & Connor Design
3329 Garfield Dr NE, Mpls, MN 55418
612 781.1748

Bialek, David
230 N Michigan Ave, Chicago, IL 60601
312 368.8777

Bianco, Peter
348 Manning St, Needham, MA 02192
617 444.9077

Biddle, Meg
160 via Paraiso, Monterey, CA 93940
408 373.7443

Bieck, Kathy
5183 Overland Ave, Culver City, CA 90230
310 558.3325

Biedrzycki, David
60 E 42nd St, NYC, NY 10165
212 682.4190

Biers, Nanette
123 Willow Ave, Corte Madera, CA 94925
415 927.1531

The Big Pixel
3188 Airway Ave, Costa Mesa, CA 92626
714 433.7400

Biles, Robin
4318 Presto Cir, Grand Prairie, TX 75052
214 641.2525

Billingskog, Goran
597 Riverside Ave, Westport, CT 06880
203 226.4724

Billout, Guy
225 Lafayette St, NYC, NY 10012
212 431.6350

Bilmes, Semyon
420 Lexington Ave, NYC, NY 10170
212 697.8525

Bilter, Lori
Nashville, TN
615 297.3930
page 46

Binder, Pat
2713 Prairie Creek, Dallas, TX 75075
214 596.5275

Biomedia Corp
Two Northfield Plz, Northfield, IL 60093
708 501.5560

Biomedical Illustrations Inc
804 Columbia St, Seattle, WA 98104
206 682.8197

Birchard, Margaret
327 Second Ave W, Seattle, WA 98119
206 283.6289

Birkey, Randall
635 S Home St, Oak Park, IL 60304
708 386.5150

Birling, Paul
Box 257, Pleasantville, NY 10570
914 747.2220

Birmingham, Lloyd
500 Peekskill Hollow Rd,
Putnam Valley, NY 10579
914 528.3207

Birnbaum, M Dianne
17301 Elsinore Cir,
Huntington Beach, CA 92647
714 847.7631

Bischel, Mark
112 W Ninth St, Kansas City, MO 64105
816 421.4473

Bishofs, Maris
251-16 Northern Blvd, Little Neck, NY 11363
718 229.7570

Bishop, Drew
120 W Third St, NYC, NY 10012
212 533.2070

Bishop, John
Two Prebend St, London, England
011 44.71.359.6291

Bissaillon, Laurie
30 Exchange St, Portland, ME 04101
207 828.0441

Bissonnette, Dina
17845 Skypark Cir, Irvine, CA 92714
714 261.6786

Bittman, Monika
PO Box 186, El Rito, NM 87530
505 581.4681

Bjorck, Liselotte
444 Fresno Ave, Morro Bay, CA 93442
805 772.0546

Björkman, Steve
501 Fifth Ave, NYC, NY 10017
212 490.2450
fax 212 697.6828
page 292

BK Graphics
1638 Eastern Pky, Louisville, KY 40204
502 459.0295

Black Box Studio
2435 E North St, Greenville, SC 29615
803 244.1369

Black, Dave
100 Bleecker St, NYC, NY 10012
212 982.6533

Black, Richard H
205 Foxridge Dr, Dayton, OH 45429
513 293.9001

Blackbird Fly Design
1212 N Ashland Ave, Chicago, IL 60622
312 772.0224

BlackDog
239 Marin St, San Rafael, CA 94901
415 258.9663

Blackshear, Ami
220 Elm Cir, Colorado Spgs, CO 80906
719 636.5009

Blackshear, Lisa
208 W 23rd St, NYC, NY 10011
212 675.1083

Blackshear, Thomas
1428 Elm Dr, Novato, CA 94947
415 897.9486

Blackwell, Garie
60 E 42nd St, NYC, NY 10165
212 682.1490

Blackwell, Patrick
Pond Rd PO Box 324, North Truro, MA 02652
508 487.3336

Blair, Bob
12121 Wilshire Blvd, L.A., CA 90025
310 826.9378

Blair, Dru
22 E 36th St, NYC, NY 10016
212 685.4580

Blake, Marty
PO Box 266, Jamesville, NY 13078
315 492.1332

Blank, Jerry
1048 Lincoln Ave, San Jose, CA 95125
408 289.9095
fax 408 289.8532
page 316

Blasutta, Mary Lynn
156 Huguenot St,
New Paltz, NY 12561
914 256.0830
fax 914 256.0831
page 456

Blechman, RO
Two W 47th St, NYC, NY 10036
212 869.1630

Bleck, Cathie
2270 Chatfield Dr, Cleveland Hts, OH 44106
216 932.4910

Bleck, Linda
642 W Aldine, Chicago, IL 60657
312 281.0286
fax 312 281.4955
page 345

Blessen, Karen
6327 Vickery Blvd, Dallas, TX 75214
214 827.3257

Bliss, Harry
1727 S 13th St, Phila, PA 19148
215 334.5744

Bliss, Jim
265 Westminster Rd, Rochester, NY 14607
716 244.6956

Bliss, Phil
22 Briggs Ave, Fairport, NY 14450
716 377.9771

Blitt, Barry
34 Lincoln Ave, Greenwich, CT 06830
203 622.2988

Bloch, A Calligraphy / Design
854 W 181st St, NYC, NY 10033
212 927.6856

Bloch, Alexander
139 E 33rd St, NYC, NY 10016
212 532.3374

Blockey, Gloria
100 Wyndham Cir W,
New Brighton, MN 55112
612 631.2353

Blower, Gale Holiday
420 Lexington Ave, NYC, NY 10017
212 687.3460

Blubaugh, Susan M
NYC, NY
212 406.3652
page 211

Blue Sky Studios
95 Richard Ct, Pomona, NY 10970
914 354.3085

Blumen, Irina
2265 S Bascom Ave, Campbell, CA 95008
408 377.3872

Blumrich, Christoph
149 Broadway, Greenlawn, NY 11740
516 757.0524

Blythe, Amy
3150 Livernois, Troy, MI 48083
313 689.6620

Boatwright, Phil
2342 Stillwater, Mesquite, TX 75181
214 222.2399

Bobbette, Dawn
8137 Walpole Ave, California City, CA 93505
619 373.7810

Bober, Kathleen
5706 16th St NW, Wash, DC 20011
202 829.7704

Bobnick, Dick
9801 Dupont Ave S, Bloomington, MN 55431
612 881.1008

Bockos, Patrice
500 N Michigan, Chicago, IL 60611
312 661.1717
fax 312 661.0043
page 355

Boddy, Joe
5375 Skyway Dr, Missoula, MT 59801
406 251.3587
fax 406 251.3587
page 431

Boddy, William
609 N Tenth St, Sacramento, CA 95814
916 443.5001

Bodoff, Janet
1614 Ashurst Rd, Phila, PA 19151
215 877.3093

Boege, Kimberly
1115 E McLellan, Phoenix, AZ 85014
602 265.4389

Boehm, Roger
31726 Fourth Ave, South Laguna, CA 92677
714 499.6230

Boer, Jan-Willem
2654 Rodeo Dr NE, Blaine, MN 55449
612 780.4085
page 173

Boerger, Andrew
2350 Taylor St, San Francisco, CA 94133
415 776.3833

Bogan, Paulette
40 W 11th St, NYC, NY 10011
212 243.1694

Boggs, Marv
2964 Tomahawk Ln, Eugene, OR 97401
503 683.3885

Bohbot, Michel
3823 Harrison St, Oakland, CA 94611
510 547.0667
fax 510 547.0667
page 367

Bohn Illustration
14 North First Ave, St Charles, IL 60174
708 513.1269

Bohn, Rex
138 Millbrook Ln, Wilmette, IL 60091
312 401.7247

Boie, Chuck
925 Elm Grove Rd,
Elm Grove, WI 53122
414 785.1940
fax 414 785.1611
page 218

Boies, Alex
126 N Third St, Mpls, MN 55401
612 333.2418

Boise, Kathyjean
1233 De Haro St, San Francisco, CA 94107
415 285.3014

Bold Impressions Inc
6990 E Main, Scottsdale, AZ 85251
602 990.2093

Boldman, Craig
PO Box 18128, Fairfield, OH 45018
513 868.2874

Boles, Terry
8145 Hearthside Rd S,
Cottage Grove, MN 55016
612 459.9820
page 361

Boll, Maxine
200 Aquetong Rd,
New Hope, PA 18938
215 862.2091
fax 215.862.2641
page 279

Boll, Tom Illustration
9500 Wyoming Ave S, Bloomington, MN 55438
612 942.6119

Bolling, Bob
2395 NE 185th St, N Miami Beach, FL 33180
305 931.0104

Bollinger, Peter
232 Madison Ave, NYC, NY 10016
212 889.8777

Bolster, Rob
Seven Hope St, Walpole, MA 02081
508 660.1751

Bolton, Andrea
1724 State St, South Pasadena, CA 91030
818 441.0620

Bomar, Morgan
2518 Drexel, Houston, TX 77027
713 960.0808

Bomba, Ron
421 N 36th St, Seattle, WA 98103
206 634.0777

Bond, Bob & Associates
202 Lewis St, Lynn, MA 01902
617 595.4201

Bond, Denny
6481 Miriam Cir, East Petersburgh, PA 17520
717 569.5823

Bondante, Chris
3015 W Speedway Blvd, Tucson, AZ 85745
602 624.5994

Bone, Fred
28 Farm Ct, New Britain, CT 06051
203 827.8418

Bonilla, Michael
4743 Shaunee Creek, Dayton, OH 45415
513 275.7071

Bonk, Christopher
1400 N Elmhurst Rd, Mt Prospect, IL 60056
708 577.5157

Bono, Mary
288 Graham Ave, Brooklyn, NY 11211
718 387.3774

Bono, Peter
63 Stark Rd, Columbia, NJ 07832
908 496.8524

Booker, George
5183 Overland Ave, Culver City, CA 90230
310 558.3325

Bookwalter, Tom
405 N Wabash Ave, Chicago, IL 60611
312 321.1336

Boonthanskit, Ted
1400 N Hayworth Ave,
West Hollywood, CA 90046
213 851.7737

Booth, George
PO Box 3005, Stamford, CT 06905
203 329.8769

Booth, Martha Anne
PO Box 208, Montara, CA 94037
415 728.8332

Bootman, Colin
866 UN Plaza, NYC, NY 10017
212 644.2020

Boquel, Beth
31 First St, Rumson, NJ 07760
908 842.9162

Borda, Juliette
114 Carnegie Pl, Pittsburgh, PA 15208
412 441.7188
fax 412 247.9908
page 274

Borge, Rich
124 Maney Ave, Asheville, NC 28804
704 251.1795

Borgioli, Linda M
47 Fawn Ct, Buffalo, NY 14227
716 683.1826

Boris, Lusana
1850 Titus, San Diego, CA 92110
619 296.0466

Bornstein, Dean
170 W 81st St, NYC, NY 10024
212 496.2695

Bornstein, Peter
474 Fifth St, Brooklyn, NY 11215
718 768.0443

Borowski, Diane
848 Greenwood Ave NE,
Atlanta, GA 30306
404 875.1363 800 347.0734
fax 404 875.9733
page 168

Borum, Rick
16403 Azimuth St, Crosby, TX 77532
713 328.6757

Bory, Lou
108 E 35th St, NYC, NY 10016
212 889.3337

Borzotta, Joseph
234 Garden St, Hoboken, NJ 07030
201 420.0293

Boskovich, John
PO Box 4191, Santa Rosa, CA 95402
707 523.3049

Boston, David
9824 Bent Branch Ln, Dallas, TX 75243
214 503.1371

Boswick, Steven
331 Oak Cir, Wilmette, IL 60091
708 251.1430

Botero, Kirk
278 Tenth St, Idaho Falls, ID 83404
208 524.3959

Bourne, Adrian
1131 Oddstad Dr, Redwood City, CA 94063
415 599.9473

Bovy, Deb
10415 N 38th St, Phoenix, AZ 85028
602 257.0097

Bowden, Jane
1636 N Thorne Ave, Fresno, CA 93704
209 266.8547

Bower, Joel
2164 Elysian Pl, Cincinnati, OH 45219
513 651.9280

Bower, Tim
2121 Bryant, S.F., CA 94110
415 821.2046

Bowers, David
100 Scott Way, Carnegie, PA 15106
412 276.7224

Bowler, Jean
PO Box 1854, Orinda, CA 94563
510 256.9923

Bowles, Doug
Seven W 70th Ter,
Kansas City, MO 64113
816 523.6324
fax 816 523.0188
page 187

Bowles, Doug
716 Sanchez St,
San Francisco, CA 94114
415 285.8267
fax 415 285.8268

Bowman, Eric
11605 SW Terra Linda St,
Beaverton, OR 97005
503 644.1016
page 157

Bowman, Rich
3215 Central, Kansas City, MO 64111
816 756.0925
page 374

Boyd, Silvia
3219 Autumn Bridge Ln, Houston, TX 77084
713 578.3971

Boyer, Bill
HCR 1 Box 1535-S, Tucson, AZ 85736
602 822.9320

Boyer-Pennington, Lyn
4281 Baywood Dr, Traverse City, MI 49684
616 938.1911

Boyle, Neil
1239 Dover Ave, Thousand Oaks, CA 91360
805 496.6008

Bozzini, James
501 Fifth Ave, NYC, NY 10017
212 490.2450
fax 212 697.6828
page 294

Bozzo, Frank
400 E 85th St, NYC, NY 10028
212 535.9182

Bracken, Laura / LoArt
852 W Roscoe, Chicago, IL 60657
312 281.4663

Bradbury, Jack
130 Casa Verde Ct, Sonoma, CA 95476
707 938.2975

Braddick, Wayne
5410 Worth St, Dallas, TX 75214
214 823.7573

Bradford / Cout & Jansen Design
9933 N Lawler, Skokie, IL 60077
708 673.4777

Bradley, Barbara
750 Wildcat Canyon Rd, Berkeley, CA 94708
510 525.5496

Brady, Elizabeth Illustration
1444 Holbrook St, L.A., CA 90041
213 340.8026

Bragg, Shokie
Five Oklahoma Ave, Wilmington, DE 19803
302 761.9144

Bralds, Braldt
119 Wykeham Rd, Washington, CT 06793
203 868.7577

Bramhall, William
885 Duckfarm Rd, Fairfield, CT 06340
203 259.0258

Bramsen, David
4376A Cuna Dr, Santa Barbara, CA 93110
805 683.0912

Brancato, Ron
72 Cascade Dr, Rochester, NY 14614
716 262.4450

Brandon, Bill
425 W 23rd St, NYC, NY 10011
212 242.6367

Brandt, Joan
15 Gramercy Park S, NYC, NY 10003
212 473.7874

Brandts, Dirk
PO Box 23808, Santa Barbara, CA 93121
805 682.4659

Brashear, Aaron
269 Vanderbilt, Brooklyn, NY 11205
718 398.9634

Braswell, Amy
3721 Steve Dr NW, Marietta, GA 30064
404 426.4230

The Brauer Co
2735 Hereford, St Louis, MO 63139
314 776.7650

Brault, Gene
2115 Hyperion Ave, L.A., CA 90027
213 664.3034

Braun, Marty
265 Pleasant Ave,
Peaks Island, ME 04108
207 766.9726
page 4

Breakey, John
611 Broadway, NYC, NY 10012
212 982.0188

Bredemeier, Bob
10170 SW Todd St, Portland, OR 97225
503 297.9301

Breeden, Don
PO Box 5686, Brownsville, TX 78523
210 542.5193

Breedlove City Studios
710 13th St, San Diego, CA 92101
619 271.3662

Bremmer, Mark
7155 W Walden Pl, Littleton, CO 80123
303 932.8759

Brenda, Aminah
791 Sunbury Rd, Columbus, OH 43147
614 252.4771

Brennan, Dan Illustration
120 N Illinois St, Chicago, IL 60610
312 822.0887

Brennan, Steve
420 Lexington Ave, NYC, NY 10170
212 986.5680

Brenno, Vonnie
5183 Overland Ave, Culver City, CA 90230
310 558.3325

Brevoort, Dick
26571 Normandale Dr, Lake Forest, CA 91263
714 770.3205

Brewster, John Creative Services
597 Riverside Ave,
Westport, CT 06880
203 226.4724
fax 203 454.9904
pages 62-69

Brice, Jeff
2416 NW 60th St, Seattle, WA 98107
206 281.7352

Brickey, Brodie
263 Belmont Ave, Long Beach, CA 90803
310 438.5473

Brickman, Robin
32 Ft Hoosac Pl, Williamstown, MA 01267
413 458.9853

Bridewell, Elizabeth
5360 Kester Ave, Sherman Oaks, CA 90803
310 438.5473

Bridges, Gregory
60 E 42nd St, NYC, NY 10165
212 682.1490

Bridy, Dan
72 Rocklynn Pl, Pittsburgh, PA 15228
412 531.4044

Briers, Stuart
108 E 35th St, NYC, NY 10016
212 889.3337

Brigham, Derek
4512 Harriet Ave S, Mpls, MN 55409
612 827.3431
page 172

Briles, Patty
8238 Billowvista Dr, Playa del Rey, CA 90293
310 823.5594

Brillhart, Ralph
60 E 42nd St, NYC, NY 10017
212 867.8092

Brindak, Hermine
Three Lockwood Ave,
Old Greenwich, CT 06870
203 698.1732

Brindle, Carolyn Illustration
203 E 89th St, NYC, NY 10128
212 534.4177

Bringham, Sherry
1804 Arlington, El Cerrito, CA 94530
510 235.2859

Brion, David
28 Cheever Pl, Brooklyn, NY 11231
718 858.0362

Brisette·Gendron
41 Union Sq W, NYC, NY 10003
212 929.5590
page 250

Brisker, Robin
600 N Bishop Ave, Dallas, TX 75208
214 946.6569

Bristol, Suzanne
409 Leland Ave, Palo Alto, CA 94306
415 324.4235

Britt, Stephanie
PO Box 818, Hanalei, HI 96714
808 826.9746

Britt, Suzanne
1225 N Wilson, Pasadena, CA 91104
818 797.3876

Britt, Tracy
PO Box 421443,
San Francisco, CA 94142
415 647.5660
fax 415 285.1102
page 379

Broad, David
100 Golden Hinde, San Rafael, CA 94903
415 479.5505

Broda, Ron
420 Lexington Ave, NYC, NY 10170
212 697.8525

Brodner, Steve
120 Cabrini Blvd, NYC, NY 10033
212 740.8174

Brody, Sam
15 W Terrace Rd, Great Neck, NY 11021
516 482.2835

Bronikowski, Ken
925 Elm Grove Rd,
Elm Grove, WI 53122
414 785.1940
fax 414 785.1611
page 217

Brooke & Co
4323 Bluffview, Dallas, TX 75209
214 352.9192

Brooker, Krysten
558 Seventh St, Brooklyn, NY 11215
718 788.5221

Brooks, Andrea
99 Bank St, NYC, NY 10014
212 633.1477

Brooks, Lou
415 W 55th St, NYC, NY 10019
212 245.3632

Brooks, Nan
825 Greenleaf, Wilmette, IL 60091
708 256.2304

Brooks, Rob
NYC, NY
212 490.2450
fax 212 697.6828
page 305

Brothers, Barry
1920 E 17th St, Brooklyn, NY 11229
718 336.7540

Broussard, Edwin Scott
43 E Grand Ave, Montvale, NJ 07645
201 391.0226

Brown, Bill
2020 Euclid Ave, Cleveland, OH 44115
216 694.2020

Brown, Bradford
175 Prospect St, East Orange, NJ 07017
201 678.9205

Brown, Calef
770 E 73rd St, Indpls, IN 46240
317 255.1197

Brown, Charley
716 Montgomery St, San Francisco, CA 94111
415 433.1222

Brown, Dan
270 Park Ave S, NYC, NY 10017
212 260.4153

Brown, Dennis
662 Shoppers Ln Plz, Covina, CA 91723
818 339.8289

Brown, Heather
315 Washington Ave HM,
Rensselaer, NY 12144
518 449.2836

Brown, Judith Gwyn
522 E 85th St, NYC, NY 10028
212 288.1599

Brown, Mark Kingsley
1400 N Hwy 101, Leucadia, CA 92024
619 753.5196

Brown, Michael David
932 Hungerford Dr, Rockville, MD 20850
301 762.4474

Brown, Peter D
235 E 22nd St, NYC, NY 10010
212 684.7080

Brown, Rick
60 E 42nd St, NYC, NY 10165
212 682.1490

Brown, Rick
4290 Upper Mt Rd, Furlong, PA 18925
215 794.8186

Brown, Sue Ellen
Seven Ivy Hill Rd, Ridgefield, CT 06877
203 438.8386

Brown, Susan
604 Park Bend Dr, Richardson, TX 75081
214 699.9442

Brown-Farney, Tina
2227-E Rexford Rd, Charlotte, NC 28211
704 527.6985

Browne, Pema Ltd
Pine Rd HCR, Neversink, NY 12765
914 985.2936

Brownson, Matt
1863 S Pearl St, Denver, CO 80210
303 733.0128
fax 303 733.8154
page 149

Bruce, Sandra
13997 Emerald Ct, Grass Valley, CA 95945
916 477.1909

Bruce, Tim
1826 Asheville Pl, Charlotte, NC 28203
704 372.6007

Bruck & Moss
333 E 49th St, NYC, NY 10017
212 980.8061

Bruckstein, Donald
43 E 19th St, NYC, NY 10003
212 254.4996

Bruemmer, Betsy
PO Box 667, Chilmark, MA 02535
508 645.3158

Brugger, Bob
1930 Robinson St, Redondo Beach, CA 90228
310 372.0135

Brun, Robert
76 State St, Newburyport, MA 01950
508 462.1948

Bruneau Studio Inc
901 W McDowell Rd, Phoenix, AZ 85007
602 253.0014

Brunettin, Alan
337 Sherman Ave, Evanston, IL 60602
708 869.4180

Bruning, Bill
118 E 26th St, Mpls, MN 55404
612 871.4539

Brunke, Ruth Roman
125 N Oak, Wood Dale, IL 60191
708 616.8590

Brunkus, Denise
62 Perryville Rd, Pittstown, NJ 08867
908 735.2671

Brunnick, Jeanne
1233 Hermosa Ave, Hermosa Beach, CA 90254
310 798.2771

Brush Images
8522 Izard St, Omaha, NE 68114
402 399.5251

Bryan, Mike G
828 S Keniston Ave, L.A., CA 90005
213 934.6719

Bryant Lettering & Design
7305 Kenneth Dr, Richmond, VA 23228
804 262.7133

Bryant, Amy
10520 Gooding Dr, Dallas, TX 75229
214 350.5822
fax 214 902.0163
page 362

Bryant, Rick J
18 W 37th St, NYC, NY 10018
212 594.6718

Bubar, Lorraine
12748 Indianapolis St, L.A., CA 90066
310 390.2938

Buchanan, Yvonne
18 Lincoln Pl, Brooklyn, NY 11217
718 783.6682

Buchanon, Jill
168 Ludlow St, NYC, NY 10002
212 228.2452

Buchs, Thomas
925 Elm Grove Rd,
Elm Grove, WI 53122
414 785.1940
fax 414 785.1611
pages 213, 219

Buck & Kane
566 Seventh Ave, NYC, NY 10003
212 221.8090
fax 212 221.8092
page 386

Buck, Steven
14630 Saticoy St, Van Nuys, CA 91405
818 989.9112

Budwine, Olden
7706 White Fir Dr, Houston, TX 77088
713 448.4696

Bull, Michael H
2350 Taylor St, San Francisco, CA 94133
415 776.7471

Bullock, Max
3064 Cederwood Ln, Falls Church, VA 22042
703 534.1441

Bulthuis, Henri
932 Francisquito, West Covina, CA 91790
818 918.0755

Bumas, Jonathan
99-44 67th Rd, Forest Hills, NY 11375
718 486.8136

Bunnell, Deb Troyer
346 Lincoln St, Carlisle, PA 17013
717 249.0937

Bunting, Mary
15621 N Hillcrest, Eden Prairie, MN 55346
612 937.2921

Burchard, Michelle
2269 India St, L.A., CA 90039
213 664.5036

Burckhardt, Marc
1101 Shoal Creek Blvd,
Austin, TX 78701
512 474.9781
fax 512. 474.9781
page 404

Burdzinski, Ray
12121 Wilshire Blvd, L.A., CA 90025
310 826.9378

Burgard, Tim
1400 N Hayworth Ave,
West Hollywood, CA 90046
213 851.7737

Burgard, WC
2785 Heather Way, Ann Arbor, MI 48104
313 971.3014

Burger, Robert
145 Kingwood Stockton Rd,
Stockton, NJ 08559
609 397.3737

Burgess, Tom
25-A Parkway Rd, Grainville, MD 20770
301 474.4725

Burgio, Trish
8205 Santa Monica Blvd, L.A., CA 90046
310 274.5787

Burgos, George
2100 W Big Beaver Rd, Troy, MI 48084
810 643.6000

Burgoyne, John
26 Staler Rd, Belmont, MA 02178
617 489.4960

Burk Studios
7733 Roe Ave, Prairie Vlg, KS 66208
913 649.7264

Burke, Dianne O'Quinn
1131 16th St, Baywood Park, CA 93402
805 528.6754

Burke, Michael
1131 16th St, Los Osos, CA 93402
805 528.6754

Burke, Phillip
163 College St, Buffalo, NY 14201
716 882.9054

Burkey Studios
1526 Edison St, Dallas, TX 75207
214 746.6336

Burkhart, Amelia
63 Hawthorne St, Lennox, MA 01240
413 637.4951

Burn, Ted
56 Cliff Dr, Fairhope, AL 36532
205 990.8159

Burnett, Lindy
476 Loridans Dr, Atlanta, GA 30342
404 875.1363 800 347.0734
fax 404 875.9733
page 164

Burns, Brad
495 Carolina St, San Francisco, CA 94107
415 863.4969

Burns, Jim
11 Kings Ridge Rd, Long Valley, NJ 07853
908 813.8718

Burns, Mark Design
6925 Casa Loma Ave, Dallas, TX 75214
214 319.9903

Burrell, Chris
PO Box 2676, Vineyard Haven, MA 02568
508 696.8257

Burris, Jimm
350 W 39th St, NYC, NY 10018
212 239.6767

Burton, Brian Design
Irvine, CA
714 852.9059

Burton, Caroline
330 Eighth St, Jersey City, NJ 07302
201 656.6502

Burzynski, Mary
1535 N Western Ave, Chicago, IL 60622
312 227.6755

Busch, Cynthia
978 Lorimer St, Brooklyn, NY 11222
718 383.3160

Busch, Lon
6959 Seaburt, St Louis, MO 63123
314 353.8021

Bustamante, Gerald
2400 Kettner Blvd, San Diego, CA 92101
619 234.8803

Butler, Chris
319 29th St, Boulder, CO 80303
303 494.4118

Butler, David
15090 Upper Fredericktown,
Fredericktown, OH 43019
614 694.6117

Butler, Nate Studio
PO Box 27470, Albuquerque, NM 87125
505 268.6869

Butterfield, Ned
278 Cedar Ave, Islip, NY 11751
516 277.3151

Buttram, Andy
1636 Hickory Glenn Dr,
Miamisburg, OH 45342
513 859.7428

Byram, Stephen
52 68th St, Guttenberg, NJ 07093
201 869.7493

Byrd, David Edward
654 Pier Ave, Santa Monica, CA 90405
310 392.4877

Byrne, Robert
6135 Reseda Blvd, Reseda, CA 91335
818 342.3766
page 263

The Cabat Studio
627 N Fourth Ave, Tuscon, AZ 85705
602 622.6362

Cable, Jerry
133 Kuhl Rd, Flemington, NJ 08822
908 788.8673

Cable, Mark
2018 Maryland Ave, Louisville, KY 40205
502 451.4228

Cabossel, Jannine
104A E Barcelona Rd,
Santa Fe, NM 87501
505 983.4099
fax 505 983.4026
page 109

Cacy, Michael Studio
537 SE Ash St, Portland, OR 97214
503 233.7715

Cadman, Joel
41-15 50th Ave, Sunnyside, NY 11104
718 784.1267

Caged Beagle Productions
24 Elizabeth St, Port Chester, NY 10573
914 939.3999

Caggiano, Thom
83-25 Dongan Ave, Elmhurst, NY 11373
718 651.8993

Cagle Design
5353 Hinton Ave, Woodland Hills, CA 91367
818 340.2887

Cain, David
200 W 20th St, NYC, NY 10011
212 633.0258

Cain, Janan
520 W Erie, Chicago, IL 60610
312 664.0006

Cain, Kevin
2847 SW Adams St, Seattle, WA 98126
206 933.0759

Cairnes, Brian
22 King St, Glasgow, Scotland G15 QP
011 44.41.522.7543

Caito, Mike
5315 Ville Angela, St Louis, MO 63042
314 770.1938

Calabrese, Russell
454 Myrtle Ave, Brooklyn, NY 11205
718 643.1923

Calderwood & Preg
16 River Office Park, Braintree, MA 02184
617 848.1190

Caldwell, John
152 Barrett St, Schenectady, NY 12305
518 393.6211

Caldwell, Kirk
1033 Battery, San Francisco, CA 94111
415 398.7553

Caldwell, Margaret
2233 Kemper Ln, Cincinnati, OH 45206
513.861.1400

Calhoun, Dia
731 N 24th St, Phila, PA 19130
215 232.6666

Calhoun, Paul
1220 A Broughton Blvd, Florence, SC 29501
803 678.9270

Calibey, Greg
51 Old Kings Hwy, Old Greenwich, CT 06870
203 637.3484

Call, Greg
18909 Cabral St, Santa Clarita, CA 91351
805 252.4068

Call, Ken
1836 N Winchester, Chicago, IL 60622
312 489.2323

Callanan, Brian
Three Hidden St, Providence, RI 02904
401 421.2344

Callanan, Maryjane Begin
866 United Nations Plz, NYC, NY 10017
212 644.2020

Calleja, Bob
490 Elm Ave, Bogota, NJ 07603
201 488.3028

Calligraphers II
345 S La Peer Dr, Beverly Hills, CA 90211
310 278.5370

Calligraphic Arts
4232 Herschel Ave, Dallas, TX 75219
214 522.4731

CalliGraphics by Julie Ann
54200 W Prickly Pear Rd, Maricopa, AZ 85239
602 531.5747

Calligraphy by Domenica
1010 E Lois Ln, Phoenix, AZ 85020
602 395.9786

Calligraphy Studio
5294 Mayfield Rd, Lyndhurst, OH 44124
216 473.5505

Calligraphy West Studio & Shop
3101 Federal Ave, L.A., CA 90066
310 837.3604

Callow Calligraphy
1686 Union St, San Francisco, CA 94123
415 928.3303

Callygraphics
15453 Plantation Oaks Dr, Tampa, FL 33647
813 977.8483

Calsbeek, Craig
1316 Third St, Santa Monica, CA 90401
310 394.6037

Calver, Dave
70 Stoneham Dr, Rochester, NY 14625
716 383.8996

Camarro, Paul
36 Bank St, Sussex, NJ 07461
201 875.2092

Camejo, Daniel
2440 Ocean Park Blvd,
Santa Monica, CA 90405
310 452.2276

Cameron Graphics Pasadena
34 W Dayton St, Pasadena, CA 91105
818 796.2647

Campbell, DJ
2809 Folsom Ln, Bowie, MD 20715
301 262.3062

Campbell, Franklin
1456 N Dayton St, Chicago, IL 60622
312 649.9144

Campbell, Jenny
731 N 24th St, Phila, PA 19130
215 232.6666
fax 215 232.6585
page 338

Campbell, Jim
420 Lexington Ave, NYC, NY 10170
212 986.5680

Cannon, William
3340 36th Ave S, Mpls, MN 55406
612 722.4778

Canny, Thomas
7471 Melrose Ave, L.A., CA 90046
213 653.4421

Canty, Bill
PO Box 1053, South Wellfleet, MA 02663
508 349.7549

Capalungan, David
780 Monroe Dr NE, Atlanta, GA 30308
404 876.1230

Caplan, Dan
2905 Seay St, Alexandria, VA 22314
703 461.7182

Caporale, Wende
Studio Hill Farm, North Salem, NY 10560
203 226.4724

Cappello, Fred Studios
58 Brookmont St, Irvine, CA 92714
714 559.1365

Capstone Studios
5371 Wilshire Blvd, L.A., CA 90036
213 936.1156

Caras, George
Ten Parkview Dr, St Peters, MO 63376
314 279.2234

Caravello Studios
165 W 18th St, NYC, NY 10011
212 532.0928

Carbone, Kye
202 Carroll St, Brooklyn, NY 11231
718 802.9143

Carbone, Lynne
146 Boylston St, Watertown, MA 02172
617 924.1790

Cardella, Elaine
24 Elizabeth St, Port Jervis, NJ 12771
914 856.8889

Carden, Vincent
2308 E Glenoaks Blvd, Glendale, CA 91206
818 956.0807

Cardillo, Dan
330 Mountain Way, Rutherford, NJ 07070
201 935.4986

Carey, Sue/Claymatrix
1700 Bush St, San Francisco, CA 94109
415 441.7046

Caricatures by Drum
Eight Ninth St, Medford, MA 02155
617 395.2778

Caricatures by Sherry Lane
155 Bank St, NYC, NY 10014
212 675.6224

Carling, Nancy
60 E 42nd St, NYC, NY 10165
212 682.1490

Carlson, Frederick H
118 Monticello Dr, Monroeville, PA 15146
412 856.0982

Carlson, Lisa
407 14th Ave SW, Rochester, MN 55902
507 252.0311

Carmichael, Dennis
19355 Pacific Coast Hwy, Malibu, CA 90265
310 456.5915

Carnabuci, Anthony
92 Village St, S Easton, MA 02375
508 238.4231

Carnase
30 E 21st St, NYC, NY 10010
212 777.1500

Carr, Alan
51 Dean St, Brooklyn, NY 11201
718 596.8850

Carr, Barbara
245 E 40th St, NYC, NY 10016
212 370.1663

Carr, Bill
1713 Catalina Ave, Seal Beach, CA 90740
310 430.0904

Carranza, Steve
22868 Via Pimiento, Mission Viejo, CA 92691
714 770.6338

Carreiro, Ron
Six Hillside Dr, Plymouth, MA 02360
508 224.9290

Carroll, Justin
1316 Third St, Santa Monica, CA 90401
310 458.7600

Carroll, Michael
520 N Michigan Ave, Chicago, IL 60611
312 527.0351

Carrozza, John
56 Maquan St, Pembroke, MA 02359
617 293.358

Carruthers, Roy
270 Fifth St, Brooklyn, NY 11215
718 965.1330

Carsello Design & Illustration
117 S Morgan, Chicago, IL 60607
312 733.5709

Carson, Cliff
114 N Almont Dr, Beverly Hills, CA 90211
310 858.3859

Carson, Jim
11 Foch St, Cambridge, MA 02140
617 661.3321
fax 617 661.3321
page 442

Carson, Lynn
12165 SE Foster Pl, Portland, OR 97266
503 760.8987

Carter, Alice
828 Pine Hill Rd, Stanford, CA 94305
415 424.9886

Carter, Ben
PO Box 959, Ridgefield, CT 06877
203 438.8386

Carter, Brian Frank
649 Edgewood Ave, Mill Valley, CA 94941
415 388.4071

Carter, Bunny
828 Pine Hill Rd, Stanford, CA 94305
415 424.9886

Carter, Mary
PO Box 421443,
San Francisco, CA 94142
415 647.5660
fax 415 285.1102
page 378

Carter, Penny
12 Stuyvesant Oval, NYC, NY 10009
212 473.7965

Carver, Steve
102 E State St, Ithaca, NY 14850
607 272.9150

Casale, Paul
5304 11th Ave, Brooklyn, NY 11219
718 871.6848

Case, Bob
12811 S 45th St, Phoenix, AZ 85044
602 957.6636

Cashwell, Charles
1728 N Rock Spgs Rd, Atlanta, GA 30324
404 874.2014

Casilla, Robert
365 Walnut St, Yonkers, NY 10701
914 965.8258

Cassady, Jack
PO Box 340568, Tampa, FL 33694
813 264.4346

Cassano, Rose
863 Carolina St, San Francisco, CA 94107
415 550.1402

Cassidy, Michael
237 Barbara Ave, Solana Beach, CA 92075
619 755.6290

Cassler, Carl
420 Lexington Ave, NYC, NY 10017
212 986.5680

Castellanos, Carlos
13174 80th Ln N, West Palm Beach, FL 33412
407 791.7993

Castelo, Elizabeth
1504 N Commonwealth Ave, L.A., CA 90027
213 666.9717

Castigliano, Christine
18485 Harris Ave NE, Suaquamish, WA 98392
206 598.3846

Catalano, Dominic
PO Box 959, Ridgefield, CT 06877
203 438.8386

Catalano, Sal
114 Boyce Pl, Ridgewood, NJ 07450
201 447.5318

Cathey, Kirsten
3854 N Southport, Chicago, IL 60613
312 348.8501

Caton Creative Services
15 Warrenton Ave, Hartford, CT 06105
203 523.4562

Cavette, Mike
22840 Jorgenson Ln, Red Bluff, CA 96080
916 529.0825

Ceballos, John
1047 Broadmoor Dr, Napa, CA 94558
707 226.1026

Ceccarelli, Chris
3427 Folsom Blvd, Sacramento, CA 95816
916 455.0569

Celestial Talent
3311 Oak Lawn Ave, Dallas, TX 75219
214 443.9111
fax 214 443.9112
pages 236, 273

Celio, Jim
15015 S La Condesa Dr, La Mirada, CA 90638
714 994.1350

Celusniak, Chris Design
6918 Shavelson, Houston, TX 77055
713 688.4120

Centeno, Vidal
1734 Madison Ave, NYC, NY 10029
212 365.9749

Centre Grafik
900 W Valley Rd, Wayne, PA 19087
215 688.2949

Ceribello, Jim
221 Butler Ave, Staten Island, NY 10307
718 967.5344

Cervantes, William
2558 Winthrop Ct, Simi Valley, CA 93065
805 581.0168

Chabrian, Deborah
28 Spooner Hill Rd, South Kent, CT 06785
203 927.4945

Chadwick, Paul
162 Cornwall Rd, Warren, CT 06754
203 868.9261

Chaffee, James
5400 Colusa Way, Sacramento, CA 95841
916 348.6345

Chaffee, Randy
230 N Michigan Ave, Chicago, IL 60601
312 368.8777

Chalmers, Cheryl
Ten Mitchell Pl, NYC, NY 10017
212 826.3716

Chambers, Dave
20435 Osage Ave, Torrance, CA 90503
310 542.2060

Chamelon, A Design Firm
1937 McJenkin Dr, Atlanta, GA 30340
404 352.4555

Champagne, Tony
8608 Palmetto St, New Orleans, LA 70118
504 486.0161

Chan, Harvey
200 W 15th St, NYC, NY 10011
212 243.4209

Chan, Ron
110 Sutter St, San Francisco, CA 94104
415 441.4384
fax 415 395.9809
page 275

Chandler, Jean
385 Oakwood Dr, Wyckoff, NJ 07481
201 891.2381

Chandler, Karen
80 Lattington Rd, Locust Valley, NY 11560
516 671.0388

Chandler, Roger
597 Riverside Ave,
Westport, CT 06880
203 226.4724
fax 203 454.9904
page 66

Chang, Warren
17 N Union Ave, Cranford, NJ 07016
908 272.6929

Chap, Louis
RD 2 Box 1252, Bethel, VT 05032
802 234.9352

Chapman, Shirley
20 Espada Ct, Fremont, CA 94539
510 792.8986

Chappell, Ellis
111 Madison Ave, Memphis, TX 38103
901 527.0496

Charles, Milton
904 Ravine Rd, Califon, NJ 07830
908 832.7076

Charmatz, Bill
25 W 68th St, NYC, NY 10023
212 595.3907

Charpentier, Russ
51 Oakwood St, San Francisco, CA 94110
415 553.8943

Chase, Margo Design
2255 Bancroft Ave, L.A., CA 90039
213 668.1055

Chase, Scott
2554 Como Ave, St Paul, MN 55108
612 644.2418

Chau, Tungwai
18439 Lost Knife Cir, Gaithersburg, MD 20879
301 208.0279

Chaves, Leslie
121.12 115th Ave,
South Ozone Park, NY 11420
718 845.2915

Chayette, Jeff
803 N Lafayette Park Pl, L.A., CA 90026
213 353.0125

Cheadle, Nancy
142 E 49th St, NYC, NY 10017
213 371.3015

Chelsea, David
43 W 27th St, NYC, NY 10001
212 889.6196

Chen, David
15013 Emory Ln, Rockville, MD 20853
301 460.6575
fax 301 460.5351
page 410

Chen, Tony
241 Bixley Heath, Lynbrook, NY 11563
516 596.9158

Cheney, May
6220 N 14th Pl, Phoenix, AZ 85014
602 279.2840

Chernishov, Anatoly
Four Willowbank Ct, Mahwah, NJ 07430
201 327.2377

Cherry, Jim
341 W Vernon, Phoenix, AZ 85003
602 252.5072
fax 602 252.5073
page 209

Chesak, Lina
2265 Idylwood Station Ln,
Falls Church, VA 22043
703 573.4230
fax 703 560.5651
page 128

Chesterman, Adriane
270 Park Ave S, NYC, NY 10017
212 260.4135

Chestnutt, David
415 Carlton St, Toronto, ON,
Canada M5A 2M3
416 921.8700

Cheung, Phil
2149 Lyon St, San Francisco, CA 94115
415 921.7140

Chezem, Douglas R
3613 Cornell Rd, Fairfax, VA 22030
703 591.5424

Chi Kwan, Stella
666 Azure Hills Dr, Simi Valley, CA 93065
805 582.0937

Chiaramonte, Vincent
4300 N Narragansett, Chicago, IL 60634
708 670.0912

Chiba, Lisa
2256 NW Quimby St, Portland, OR 97210
503 223.3849

Chid
55 Desmond Ave, Bronxville, NY 10708
914 793.5220

Child's Eye
37 Wenham Rd, Topsfield, MA 01983
408 887.0173

Chin, Gerald
7305 Shelter Creek Ln, San Bruno, CA 94066
415 583.8760

Chinchar, Alan
1718 Capstan St, Houston, TX 77062
713 480.3227

Chirko, Gail
3490 Piedmont Rd., Atlanta, GA 30305
404 262.1209

Chironna, Ron
122 Slosson Ave, Staten Island, NY 10314
718 720.6142

Chislovsky, Carol Design Inc
853 Broadway, NYC, NY 10003
212 677.9100
fax 212 353.0954
pages 185, 382-383

Chiu, Calvin
9242 Beverly Blvd, Beverly Hills, CA 90210
310 280.0569

Cho, Sun-Kyung
220 W 21st St, NYC, NY 10011
212 242.9469

Chodos-Irvine, Margaret
311 First Ave S, Seattle, WA 98104
206 624.2480

Choi, Jae
70 Clark St, Brooklyn, NY 11201
718 237.0216

Chorney, Steve
420 Lexington Ave, NYC, NY 10170
212 986.5680
fax 212 818.1246
page 89

Choudoir, Peggy
305 E Main St, Fremont, WI 54940
414 446.3756

Chouinard, Roger
1026 Montana Ave, Santa Monica, CA 90403
310 451.0771

Chow, Rita Asia
280 Madison Ave, NYC, NY 10016
212 545.9155

Christiana, Dave
731 N 24th St, Phila, PA 19130
215 232.6666

Christensen, Kent
518 E 80th St, NYC, NY 10021
212 744.3050

Christensen, Wendy
3443 Wade St, L.A., CA 90066
310 390.9595

Christiansen, Cheryl
3443 Wade St, L.A., CA 90066
310 390.9595

Christiansen, Lee
817 Westwood Dr S, Mpls, MN 55416
612 374.3169

Christmas, Edward
64 Glen Eyrie Ave, San Jose, CA 95125
408 287.7231

Christopher, Everett
725 E Romie Ln, Salinas, CA 93901
408 422.6396

Christopher, Tom
11-51 30th Road, L.I.C., NY 11102
718 278.4661

Chu, Michael
5009 Woodman Ave,
Sherman Oaks, CA 91423
818 788.3835

Chui, John
1500 Laurel Ave, Richmond, CA 94805
510 233.2333

Chun, Jeff
2434 W 250th St, Lomita, CA 90717
310 214.6271

Church, Maude
1970 Hopkins St, Berkeley, CA 94707
510 526.7430

Churchill, Marilyn
1470 Prospect Ave, Capitola, CA 95010
408 475.6382

Chwast, Seymour
215 Park Ave S, NYC, NY 10003
212 674.8080

Ciardiello, Joseph
2182 Clove Rd, Staten Island, NY 10305
718 727.4757

Cibere, Joe
12121 Wilshire Blvd, L.A., CA 90025
310 826.9378

Ciccarelli, Gary
317 Elmwood, Dearborn, MI 48124
313 278.3504

Ciesiel, Christine G
80 Pierrepont St, Brooklyn, NY 11201
718 237.6036

Cigliano, Bill
501 Fifth Ave, NYC, NY 10017
212 490.2450
fax 212 697.6828
page 303

Cirocco, Frank
2042 Casa Mia Dr, San Jose, CA 95124
408 371.0337

Claff Design & Illustration
121 Concord Rd, Sudbury, MA 01773
508 443.6795

Claire, Geneviève
200 Aquetong Rd,
New Hope, PA 18938
215 862.2091
fax 215 862.2641
page 282

Clar, David Austin
104 Loyalist Ave, Rochester, NY 14624
716 247.2050

Clare, Pam Represents
7535 Bradley Blvd, Wash, DC 20817
301 365.5422
fax 301 365.1653
pages 142.143

Clark, Bob
3934 NE Royal Ct, Portland, OR 97232
503 236.1600

Clark, Bradley H
36 Haggerty Hill Rd, Rhinebeck, NY 12572
914 876.2615

Clark, David
PO Box 991, Arlington, VA 22216
703 524.9076

Clark, Johnston
1210 Gregory Ave, Wilmette, IL 60091
708 251.2444

Clark, Roger
1310 Richmond Ct, Richmond, TX 77469
713 939.2211

Clarke, Bob
55 Brook Rd, NYC, NY 14534
212 686.3514

Clarke, Greg
844 Ninth St, Santa Monica, CA 90403
310 395.7958

Clarke, Tim
1256 25th St, Santa Monica, CA 90404
310 202.1044

Classen, Martin
321 E 153rd St, Bronx, NY 10451
718 665.7579

Classic Art Concepts
44 Forest St, Hartford, CT 06105
203 278.3225

Clayton, Christian
543 Sycamore Ave, LA, CA 90038
303 337.5952

Clee, Suzanne
7520 Crittenden St, Phila, PA 19119
215 247.8883

Clegg, Dave
3571 Aaron Sosebee Rd, Atlanta, GA 30130
404 255.1430

Cleland, Janet
One Mono Ln, San Anselmo, CA 94960
415 457.1049

Clement, Cameron
2445 E 19th St, Tulsa, OK 74104
918 749.9424

Clementson, John
11 Kings Ridge Rd,
Long Valley, NJ 07853
908 813.8718
fax 908 813.0076
page 34

Clemmensen, Denise
10047 Columbus Ave, Mission Hills, CA 91345
818 893.3298

Cleveland, Thomas
10730 Glenora Dr, Houston, TX 77065
713 894.6546

Clifford, Judy
24 W 90th St, NYC, NY 10024
212 799.9040

Cline, Donna
PO Box 664, Sierra Madre, CA 91025
818 355.9481

Clownbank Studio
PO Box 7709, Santa Cruz, CA 95060
408 426.4247

Clubb, Rick Clubb Illustration
310 S Hale St, Wheaton, IL 60187
708 690.5554

Clyne, Dan
20 W Hubbard, Chicago, IL 60610
312 222.1361

Coakes Illustration & Design
4415 W Harrison, Hillside, IL 60162
708 449.0333

Coats, Laura Jane
335 Prentiss, San Francisco, CA 94110
415 821.0457

Cobane, Russell
1863 S Pearl, Denver, CO 80210
303 733.0128

Cobb, Patricia
21 Brington Rd, Brookline, MA 02146
617 277.0810

Cober, Alan
95 Croton Dam Rd, Ossining, NY 10562
914 941.8696

Cober-Gentry, Leslie
150 Huntington Ave, Boston, MA 02115
617 266.0228

Cocca-Leffler, Maryann
Five Edison St, Saugus, MA 01906
617 233.3512

Cochran, Bobbye
11936 W Jefferson Blvd,
Culver City, CA 90230
310 390.8663

CoConis, Ted
Box 758, Cedar Key, FL 32625
904 543.5720

Cocozza, Chris
Nine Woodbury Pl, Woodbury, CT 06798
203 263.2061

Codner, Ellen
1966 W Roselawn, Falcon Heights, MN 55113
612 644.8474

Cody, Dale
186 1/2 First St, Hermosa Beach, CA 90254
310 374.3277

Coe, Wayne
920 N Douglas St, L.A., CA 90026
213 977.0449

Coffelt, Ken
4791 Regalo Rd, Woodland Hills, CA 91364
818 224.4274

Cogbill, Sharon
3138 N Seminary, Chicago, IL 60657
312 348.6541

Cohen, Adam
96 Greenwich Ave, NYC, NY 10011
212 691.4074

Cohen, Eleanor
Ten Lyon St, San Francisco, CA 94117
415 552.1752

Cohen, Jim Illustration
107 Miller Rd, Hawthorn Woods, IL 60047
708 726.8979

Cohen, M E
357 W 12 St, NYC, NY 10014
212 627.8033

Cohen, Santiago
705 Park Ave, Hoboken, NJ 09030
201 420.7275

Cohen, Shari
33522 Heritage Hills Dr,
Farmington Hills, MI 48331
810 661.5005

Colalillo, Giovannina
19 East Dr, Toronto, ON,
Canada M6N 2N8
416 604.0057
fax 416 604.0057
page 397

Colby, Garry
6375 Indian Wells Blvd,
Boynton Beach, FL 33437
407 731.1759

Cold Springs Design
1494 Cold Springs Rd,
Pottstown, PA 19464
610 326.8038
fax 610 326.6173
page 438

Cole Studios
847 W Jackson Blvd, Chicago, IL 60607
312 455.0911

Cole, Aaron
108 E 35th St, NYC, NY 10016
212 889.3337

Cole, Dick
21925 Hyde Rd, Sonoma, CA 95476
707 935.6757

Cole, Lynn
191 Berkeley Pl, Brooklyn, NY 11217
718 622.2207

Cole, Olivia
PO Box 212 Rt 96, East Boothbay, ME 04544
207 633.6030

Coleman, Gail Simon
54 W Gennessee St, Skaneateles, NY 13152
315 685.3123

Coleman, Mark
230 N Michigan Ave, Chicago, IL 60601
312 368.8777

Coleman-Renoe, Mary Lynn
5475 W 85th Ter, Prairie Village, KS 66207
913 381.0026

Collage Design
216 E 45th St, NYC, NY 10017
212 697.6260

Colleen
25 Stanton Rd, Brookline, MA 02146
617 731.6959

Colley, Michael
4170 S Arbor Cir, Marietta, GA 30066
404 924.4793

Collicott, Sharleen
201 Ocean Ave, Santa Monica, CA 90402
310 458.6616

Collier, Jan
PO Box 470818,
San Francisco, CA 94147
415 383.9026
fax 415 383.9037
pages 2-3, 253-255

Collier, John
8329 San Leandro, Dallas, TX 75218
214 324.2879

Collier, Michele
2769 Canterbury Dr, Santa Rosa, CA 95405
707 544.3246

Collignon, Daniele
200 W 15th St, NYC, NY 10011
212 243.4209
page 424

Collins, Brigid
11 Kings Ridge Rd,
Long Valley, NJ 07853
908 813.8718
fax 908 813.0076
page 35

Collins, Britt Taylor
1728 N Rock Spgs Rd, Atlanta, GA 30324
404 874.2014

Collins, Daniel
50 Dunster St, Jamaica Plain, MA 02130
617 983.0888

Collins, Daryll
2969 Ensley Ct, Maineville, OH 45039
513 683.9335
fax 513 683.9335
page 433

Collins, Martha
30166 Chapala Ct, Laguna Niguel, CA 92677
714 495.3664

Collyer, Frank
Ten Knapp Rd, Stony Point, NY 10980
914 947.3050

Colquhoun, John
367 Collins Ave, Mt Vernon, NY 10552
914 699.1788

Colvin, Rob
1351 North 1670 West, Farmington, UT 84035
801 451.6858

Combs, Jonathan
716 Montgomery St, San Francisco, CA 94111
415 433.1222

Command Arts
308 Prince St, St Paul, MN 55101
612 291.1954

Commander, Bob
1565 Village Round Dr, Park City, UT 84060
801 649.4356

Comp Art Plus
49 W 45th St, NYC, NY 10036
212 921.1199

Comport, Sally Wern
750 94th Ave N, St Petersburg, FL 33702
813 579.4499

Comrie, Elace
Barton Hill Rd, Delanson, NY 12053
518 895.2645

Conahan, Jim
822 Charles Ave, Naperville, IL 60540
708 961.1478

Conant, Pat
13 Heritage Ln, Westfield, MA 01085
413 568.3843

Condon, Ken
126 Ashfield Mtn Rd, Ashfield, MA 01330
617 628.4042

Cone, William
640 Clayton, San Francisco, CA 94117
415 255.9450

Coney, Geraldine
60 Evergreen Ave, Lynbrook, NY 11563
516 599.0132

Conge, Bob
28 Harper St, Rochester, NY 14607
716 473.0291

Connally, Connie
8827 Kingsley Rd, Dallas, TX 75231
214 503.1344

Connelly, Gwen Design
840 D Forest, Evanston, IL 60202
708 869.8643
312 943.4477
fax 708 869.8653
page 435

Connelly, Jim
7421 Harmon Ln, Jenison, MI 49428
616 669.5043

Conner, Mona
One Montgomery Pl, Brooklyn, NY 11215
718 636.1527

Connolly, Jim
25 Cedar St, Hingham, MA 02043
617 749.0825

Connor, Todd
223 Prospect, Seattle, WA 98109
206 282.8558
fax 206 285.4304
page 131

Connor, Tom
912 President St, Brooklyn, NY 11215
718 230.0391

Conrad, James & Associates
2149 Lyon Ave,
San Francisco, CA 94115
415 921.7140
fax 415 921.3939
page 410

Conran, Kevin
1010 S Robertson Blvd, L.A., CA 90035
310 652.7322

Consing, Raymond
1400 N Hayworth Ave,
West Hollywood, CA 90046
213 851.7737

Consing, Robert
1400 N Hayworth Ave,
West Hollywood, CA 90046
213 851.7737

Continuity Studios
4710 W Magnolia Blvd, Burbank, CA 91505
818 980.8852

Cook, Anne
96 Rollingwood Dr, San Rafael, CA 94901
415 454.5799

Cook, Jeff
731 N 24th St, Phila, PA 19130
215 232.6666

Cook, Jerry Studio
1000 E Walnut St, Pasadena, CA 91106
818 568.3232

Cook, John
101 Ranney Dr, Dallas, TX 75067
214 317.3729

Cook, Peter
140 N Gardner St, L.A., CA 90036
213 930.1156

Cook, Steve
731 N 24th St, Phila, PA 19130
215 232.6666

Cook, Timothy
4014 S Eighth St, Arlington, VA 22204
703 979.5233

Cooley, Gary
2100 W Big Beaver Rd, Troy, MI 48084
313 643.6000

Cooley, Rick
Rt 1 Box 155, Check, VA 24072
703 651.4481

Cooper MD, James
A/25 W 45th St, NYC, NY 10036
212 398.9540

Cooper, Bob
1728 N Rock Spgs Rd, Atlanta, GA 30324
404 874.2014

Cooper, Cheryl
525 22nd Ave N, St Petersburg, FL 33704
813 822.5805

Cooper, Floyd
866 United Nations Plz, NYC, NY 10017
212 644.2020

Cooper, Gloria
5527 Malibu Dr, Mpls, MN 55436
612 822.5709

Cooper, PD
610 S Lincoln, Bloomington, IN 47401
812 334.1266

Cooper, Robert
302 N La Brea Ave, L.A., CA 90036
213 655.0998

Cooper, Sherrill
3804 Foxglove Ct, Finksburg, MD 21048
410 526.6985

Copeland, Greg
510 Marquette Ave, Mpls, MN 55402
612 339.0947

Copie
286 Oakwood Dr, Paramus, NJ 07652
201 265.2404

Coppin, Steve
101 Yesler Way, Seattle, WA 98104
206 447.1600

Coppock, Chuck
638 S Van Ness Ave, L.A., CA 90005
213 385.4585

Corkery, Eddie
152 N Myrtle, Villa Park, IL 60181
708 834.3039

Cormany, Tom Represents
7517 Manchester Ave, L.A., CA 90045
310 578.2191

Cormier, Wil
911 E Elizabeth St, Pasadena, CA 91104
818 797.7999

Cornelius, Ray-Mel
1526 Elmwood, Dallas, TX 75224
214 946.9405

Cornell, Laura
118 E 93rd St, NYC, NY 10128
212 534.0596

Cororan, Mark
185 W Houston St, NYC, NY 10014
212 691.8605

Corral, Ken
3614 Cerritos Ave, Long Beach, CA 90807
310.427.3507

Correll, Cory
11511 Sullnick Way, Gaithersburg, MD 20878
301 977.7254

Cosentino, Cira
1430 Bernardo Terr, Port St Lucie, FL 34952
407 335.2725

Cosgrove, Dan
405 N Wabash Ave, Chicago, IL 60611
312 527.0375

Cossette, Ann
7850 Chessire Ln N, Maple Grove, MN 55311
612 420.4249

Costantino, FM
13-B Pauline St, Winthrop, MA 02152
617 846.4766

Costanza, Stephen
25 W 45th St, NYC, NY 10036
212 398.9540

Cote, Barbara
40 Colonial Village Rd, Rochester, NY 14625
716 383.8338

Cote, Geneviève
187 St Catherine E, Montreal, QU,
Canada H2X 1K8
514 282.9399

Coto, Bob
13 Cloverhill Pl, Montclair, NJ 07042
201 509.8301

Couch, Greg
NYC, NY
212 581.8338
page 29

Couch, Greg
18 McKinley St, Rowayton, CT 06853
203 866.3734
fax 203 857.0842
page 29

Coulas, Mick
579 Richmond St W, Toronto, ON,
Canada M5V 1Y6
416 864.1182
fax 416 861.0294
page 160

Coulson, David
1107 Goodman St, Pittsburgh, PA 15218
412 243.7064

Cournoyer, Jacques
200 Aquetong Rd,
New Hope, PA 18938
215 862.2091
fax 215 862.2641
page 283

Cousineau, Normand
870 Avenue Oak, St Lambert, QU,
Canada J4P 1Z7
514 672.6940

Covert, Susan
40 Matthew Dr, Fairport, NY 14450
716 223.4765

Covington, Neverne
241 Central Ave,
St Petersburg, FL 33701
813 822.1267
fax 813 822.1267
page 47

Cowell, Lucinda
6422 Selma Ave, Hollywood, CA 90028
213 461.3696

Cox, Anthony
1861 W 96th St, L.A., CA 90047
213 755.7714

Cox, Bob
4701 Crystal Dr, Columbia, SC 29206
803 790.0208
page 467

Cox, Eddie
1510 Hewitt, Houston, TX 77018
713 681.9738

Cox, Paul
121 Madison Ave, NYC, NY 10016
212 683.1362

Cox, Teresa
7032 Montrose Rd, Woodbury, MN 55125
612 735.9029

Cox, Tracy
1666 Gough St, San Francisco, CA 94109
415 673.6461

Cozzolino, Paul
211 Glengariff Rd, Massapequa Park, NY 11762
516 795.2432

Crabtree, Joe
3616 E Second St, Long Beach, CA 90803
310 439.5206

Craft, Kinuko Y
83 Litchfield Rd, Norfolk, CT 06018
203 542.5018

Craig, Casey
PO Box 1841, Wimberley, TX 78767
512 847.7008

Craig, Daniel
118 E 26th St, Mpls, MN 55404
612 871.4539

Craig, John
Tower Rd Rte Two Box 224,
Soldiers Grove, WI 54655
608 872.2371

Crain, Charles Illustration
715 Montclaire Ave, Edwardsville, IL 62025
800 272.8814

Crandall, Jerry
PO Box 2606, Sedona, AZ 86339
602 284.1068

Crandall, Jim
5183 Overland Ave, Culver City, CA 90230
310 558.3325

Crane, Gary
1826 Asheville Pl, Charlotte, NC 28203
704 372.6007

Cranmer, Thomas
826 Bloomfield St, Hoboken, NJ 07030
201 795.9734

Crawford, Denise Chapman
2716 Albans, Houston, TX 77005
713 663.7377
fax 713 663.7377
page 457

Crawford, Duke
PO Box 2005, L.A., CA 90078
213 482.4889

Crawford, Jay Design
420 Country Club, Bensenville, IL 60106
708 595.8228

Crawford, Robert
123 Minortown Rd, Woodbury, CT 06798
203 266.0059

Crawford, Wilbur
1118 Market St, Phila, PA 19107
215 238.9000

Creative Capers
60 E 42nd St, NYC, NY 10165
212 682.1490

Creative Control
2831 Prospect Ave, La Crescenta, CA 91214
818 248.7663

The Creative Dept
118 1/2 N Main, Galena, IL 61036
815 777.3250

Creative Force Studio
1235-B Colorado Ln,
Arlington, TX 76015
817 467.1013
fax 817 274.4011
page 192

Creative Freelancers
25 W 45th St, NYC, NY 10036
212 398.9540

Creative Illustrations
44 Joseph St, Medford, MA 02155
617 391.7615

Creative Link
1721 Victory Blvd, Glendale, CA 91201
818 507.8733

Creative Network
12422 Whittington Drive, Houston, TX 77077
713 870.1102

Creative Network Illustration
100 Wyndham Cir W,
New Brighton, MN 55112
612 631.2353
page 361

The Creative Resource
12056 Summit Cir, Beverly Hills, CA 90210
310 276.5282

Creighton, Kathleen
295 Washington Ave, Brooklyn, NY 11205
718 857.9267

Crespo, George
14 E Second St, Mineola, NY 11501
212 227.1932

Cressy, Mike Illustration
3605 SW 112th St, Seattle, WA 98146
206 243.7338

Crews, Donald
653 Carroll St, Brooklyn, NY 11215
718 636.5773

Crisp Design
2811 Villa Way, Newport Beach, CA 92663
714 675.2737

Criss, Keith W Illustration
155 Filbert St, Oakland, CA 94607
510 444.4569

Criswell, Ron
900 W Jackson Blvd, Chicago, IL 60607
312 944.5680

Crittenden, Susan
5914 Lakecrest Dr, Garland, TX 75043
214 226.2196

Crnkovich, Tony
5706 S Narragansett, Chicago, IL 60638
312 586.9696

Crockett, David
Nine Harvard Ln,
Hastings-on-Hudson, NY 10706
914 478.3134

Crockett, Linda
23336 Williams Ave, Euclid, OH 44123
216 261.2505

Crockett, Peter
16460 Meadowlake Rd, Carlton, OR 97111
503 852.6002

Croll, Carolyn
666 Greenwich St, NYC, NY 10014
212 675.5719

Cronin, Brian
58 W 15th St, NYC, NY 10011
212 741.2539

Cronin, Brian
Mont Molin Royal Ter, Dublin, Ireland
011 35.31.280.7611

Crossgrove, Catherine Ann
1131 Oddstad Dr, Redwood City, CA 94063
415 599.9473

Crowell, James
218 Madison Ave, NYC, NY 10016
212 213.5333

Crowther, Will
2400 Suwanee Lakes Trl, Suwanee, GA 30174
404 513.0738

Cruse, Howard
88-11 34th Ave, Jackson Heights, NY 11372
718 639.4951

Cruz, Jose
6321 Bramble Dr, Fort Worth, TX 76133
817 292.2418

Cruz, Stephen
6339 Denny Ave, North Hollywood, CA 91606
818 753.2936

CSI
142-53 Sutter Ave, S Ozone Park, NY 11436
718 848.5532

Cuevas, Robert Designs
89-85 Hollis Ct Blvd,
Queens Village, NY 11427
718 479.5030

Cullum, Leo
2900 Valmere Dr, Malibu, CA 90265
310 456.9315

Cumming, Moira Illustration
9754 Parkford Dr, Dallas, TX 75238
214 343.8655

Cummings, Barbara
19261 Red Bluff Dr, Trbuco Canyon, CA 92679
714 858.4912

Cummings, Pat
28 Tiffany Pl, Brooklyn, NY 11231
718 834.8584

Cummings, Terrance
210 W 64th St, NYC, NY 10023
212 586.4193

Cuneo, John
1836 Blake St, Denver, CO 80202
303 296.7449

Cunningham, David
2328 Dewes, Glenview, IL 60025
708 .724.0344

Cunningham, Dennis
2405 NW Thurman St,
Portland, OR 97210
503 225.9687
fax 503 228.6030
page 235

Cunningham, Robert M
45 Cornwall Rd Box 1035, Warren, CT 06754
203 868.2702

Curcio, Jeffrey
1032 Valley Dr, Alexandria, VA 22302
703 820.3481

Curl, Steve Illustration
460 Everett Ave, Palo Alto, CA 94301
415 328.3499

Curran, Don
215 Parkland, St Louis, MO 63122
314 965.8672

Curry, Tom
901 W Sul Ross, Alpine, TX 79830
918 837.2311

Curtis Archives
1000 Waterway Blvd, Indpls, IN 46202
317 633.2070

Cusack, Margaret
124 Hoyt St, Brooklyn, NY 11217
718 237.0145

Cushman, Doug
30 Mansfield Dr, Northford, CT 06472
203 484.0809

Cusick, Shaun
530 E 89th St, NYC, NY 10128
212 472.7994

Custodio, Bernard
20103 Baltar St, Canoga Park, CA 91306
818 998.4242

Cutler, Dave
Seven Sunrise Rdg, Florida, NY 10921
914 651.1580

CWA Inc
4015 Ibis St, San Diego, CA 92113
619 299.0431

Cyr, Lisa L
PO Box 5754, Manchester, NH 03108
603 626.0043

Czebiniak, Gene
246 Main St, Johnson City, NY 13790
607 729.1984

Czeczot, Andrzej
117 1/2 Calyer St, Brooklyn, NY 11222
718 383.4150

D&B Group
386 Park Ave S, NYC, NY 10016
212 532.3884

D'Amato, Janet Potter
32 Bayberry St, Bronxville, NY 10708
914 779.6264

D'Angelo, Peter
338 Tappan St, Brookline, MA 02146
617 734.5330

D'Souza, Helen
487 Mortimer Ave, Toronto, ON,
Canada M4J 2G6
416 466.0630
page 418

Dabcovich, Lydia
29 Sargent-Beechwood St,
Brookline, MA 02146
617 232.7628

Dadds, Jerry
2221 Morton St, Baltimore, MD 21218
410 243.0211
fax 410 243.0215
page 42

Dagne, Gerd
18 Prospect Pl, Hillsdale, NJ 07642
201 666.9479

Dahlquist, Roland
13049 N 18th Dr, Phoenix, AZ 85029
602 993.9895

Daigle, Stéphan
501 Fifth Ave, NYC, NY 10017
212 490.2450
fax 212 697.6828
page 308

Dailey, Eileen
4929 Lisette Ave, St Louis, MO 63109
314 832.1335

Daily, Don
57 Academy Rd, Bala Cynwyd, PA 19004
610 664.5729

Daily, Renee Quintal
57 Academy Rd, Bala Cynwyd, PA 19004
610 664.5729

Dakini Designs
PO Box 13066, Burton, WA 98013
206 463.5412

Dale, Robert
41 Union Sq, NYC, NY 10003
212 206.0066

Daley, Joann
900 W Jackson Blvd, Chicago, IL 60607
312 944.5680

Daley, Tom
1320 Paseo San Luis, Sierra Vista, AZ 85635
602 458.0112

Dallas Society of Illustrators
PO Box 8263, Dallas, TX 75205
214 823.7573

Daly, Sean
85 South St, NYC, NY 10038
212 668.0031

Daly, Tom
47 E Edsel Ave, Palisades Park, NJ 07650
201 943.1837

Dameron, Ned
14 Manchester Pl, Silver Spring, MD 20901
301 585.8512

Damore, Georgan
200 E Delaware, Chicago, IL 60611
312 266.9451

Daniels, Sid
12 E 22nd St, NYC, NY 10010
212 673.6520

Dannenberg, Thomas
154 Crestwood Rd, Thornhill, ON,
Canada L4J 1A6
905 731.8038
fax 905 731.5689
page 391

Dano, Robert
129 Presidents Ln, Quincy, MA 02169
617 773.9087

Danz, David
4680 Demyhig Ln,
Placerville, CA 95667
916 622.3218
fax 916 622.4346
page 360

Danz, Sandy
4680 Demyhig Ln,
Placerville, CA 95667
916 622.3218
fax 916 622.4346
page 360

Darnell, Jim
PO Box 2193, Grapevine, TX 76099
817 481.2212
fax 817 481.2908
page 358

DaRold, Thierry
353 W 53rd St, NYC, NY 10019
212 682.2462

Darrow, David
8024 Jayseel St, Sunland, CA 91040
800 594.9132

Das Grüp
311 Ave H, Redondo Beach, CA 90277
310 540.5958
pages 346-347, 355

Daugavietis, Ruta
2241 N Leavitt St, Chicago, IL 60647
312 227.6225

Daugherty, John M
719 N County St, Waukegan, L 60612
708 244.6422

Davanti Media Inc
920 W Market St, Lima, OH 45805
419 227.4988

Davault, Elaine
326 N Coast Hwy, Laguna Beach, CA 91040
714 497.5339

Davidian, Anna
290 SW Second Ave, Boca Raton, FL 33432
407 395.2005

Davidson, Herb
406 Webster, Chicago, IL 60614
312 935.2545

Davidson, Jan
PO Box 365, Hermosa Beach, CA 90254
310 372.5540

Davies, Paul
1208 E 98th Ter, Kansas City, MO 64131
816 941.9313

Davis, David
737 SE Sandy Blvd, Portland, OR 97214
503 235.6878

Davis, Diane Kay
302 N La Brea Ave, L.A., CA 90036
213 655.0998

Davis, Gary
One Cedar Pl, Wakefield, MA 01880
617 245.2628

Davis, Harry
RR 1 Box 1738, Shohola, PA 18458
717 559.7919

Davis, Jack
108 E 35th St, NYC, NY 10016
212 889.3337

Davis, Jack E
121 Madison Ave, NYC, NY 10016
212 683.1362

Davis, Nelle
20 E 17th St, NYC, NY 10003
212 807.7737

Davis, Paul Studio
14 E Fourth St, NYC, NY 10012
212 420.8789

Davis, Susan
1107 Notley Rd, Silver Spring, MD 20904
301 384.9426

Davis, Will
353 W 53rd St, NYC, NY 10019
212 582.0023

Dawson, Henk
3519 170th Pl NE, Bellevue, WA 98008
206 882.3303

Dawson-Hearn, Diane
22 Spring St, Pawling, NY 12564
914 855.1152

Day, Brant
575 Station View Run,
Lawrenceville, GA 30243
404 963.0731

Day, Burnis C
15424 Lesure, Detroit, MI 48227
313 273.2329

Day, D Design
4769 Taranto Way, Agoura, CA 91301
818 879.1431

Day, Rob
6059 Ralston Ave, Indpls, IN 46220
317 253.9000

Dayal, Antar
1560 LasCanoas Rd, Santa Barbara, CA 93105
805 965.5988

dba Dula Gerrie Design
18401 Von Karman, Irvine, CA 92715
714 863.0330

De Amicis, John
35 S Durst Dr, Milltown, NJ 08850
908 249.4937

De Berardinis, Olivia
PO Box 4153 PT Dume Sta, Malibu, CA 90265
310 457.8065

De Cerchio, Joe
25 W 45th St, NYC, NY 10036
212 398.9450

de la Houssaye, Jeanne
400 N Peters, New Orleans, LA 70130
504 581.2167 800.524.4981
fax 504 581.1138
page 45

De Luz, Tony
Four Prospect St, Beverly, MA 01915
508 921.0887

De Mar, Charles David
7517 Manchester Ave, L.A., CA 90045
310 578.2191

De Marco, Susanne
45 Chardavoyne Rd, Warwick, NY 10990
914 258.1513

de Michiell, Robert
250 W 85th St, NYC, NY 10024
212 769.9192
fax 212 874.3747
page 171

de Moreta, Linda
1839 Ninth St, Alameda, CA 94501
510 769.1421

De Oro-Shayne, Marie
77-12 35th Ave, Jackson Heights, NY 11372
718 335.2603

De Palma, Mary Newell
45 Bradfield Ave, Boston, MA 02131
617 327.6241

De Santis, Laura
Four Prospect St, Beverly, MA 01915
508 921.0887

de Seve, Peter
25 Park Pl, Brooklyn, NY 11217
718 398.8099

De Souza, Joseph
221 Belmont Ave, Brockton, MA 02401
508 584.9545

De Vito, Grace
140 Hoyt St, Stamford, CT 06905
203 967.2198

Deal, Jim
3451 24th Ave W, Seattle, WA 98199
206 285.2986

Dean, Bruce
23211 Leonora Dr, Woodland Hills, CA 91367
818 716.5632

Dean, Glenn
RD Two Box 788, Sussex, NJ 07461
201 827.7350

Dean, Sandra
PO Box 19412, Seattle, WA 98109
206 634.1880

DeAnda, Ruben
890 Entrada Pl, Chula Vista, CA 91910
619 421.2845

DeanHouston Creative Group
2229 Gilbert Ave, Cincinnati, OH 45206
513 221.6622

Dearstyne, John
Ten La Purisima, Santa Margarita, CA 92688
714 589.6447

Dearth, Greg
68 E Franklin St, Dayton, OH 45459
513 433.8383

Dearwater Design
5650 Kirby, Houston, TX 77005
713 660.8513

Deas, Michael
528 Governor Nichols St,
New Orleans, LA 70116
504 581.7826

Deaver, Georgia
1045 Sansome St, San Francisco, CA 94111
415 362.8960

Deaver, Lucas
173 E 90th St, NYC, NY 10128
212 427.5642

Debusk, Robert
9783 Caminito Cuadro, San Diego, CA 92129
619 538.0729

DeCastro, Cesar
12121 Wilshire Blvd, L.A., CA 90025
310 826.9378

Decker, Rebecca
17543 Vacas Cir, Fountain Valley, CA 92708
714 964.9987

Dedell, Jacqueline Inc
58 W 15th St, NYC, NY 10011
212 741.2539

DeFelice, Ron
32A Akindale Rd, Pawling, NY 12564
914 855.5229

DeFord Fine Arts Studio
953 31st St, Richmond, CA 94804
510 237.5930

Degen, Paul
155 W 15th St, NYC, NY 10011
212 989.8770

DeGeus, Cynthia
2435 Pruett Dr, Vista, CA 92084
619 726.3487

deGroat, Diane
One Bristol Pl, Chappaqua, NY 10514
914 238.4115

Deichmann, Kim Grove
585 W Sierra Madra Blvd,
Sierra Madra, CA 91024
818 355.5015

Del Nero, Jeff
462 S Pine St, Orange, CA 92666
714 639.3740

Delaney, Debra
43 Virginia Ave, Monroe, NY 10950
914 774.7114

DeLapine, Jim
398 31st St, Lindenhurst, NY 11757
516 225.1247

Delessert, Etienne
Box 1689, Lakeville, CT 06039
203 435.0061

Dellorco, Chris
8278 Kirkwood Dr, L.A., CA 90046
213 650.1370

Delmonte, Steve
328 W Delavan Ave, Buffalo, NY 14213
716 883.6086

Delong, Faith
5960 Ave la Barranca NW,
Albuquerque, NM 87114
505 897.3457

DeLouise, Daniel
210 The Heights, Gloucester, MA 01930
508 282.1379

Demar, Charles David
7517 Manchester Ave, L.A., CA 90045
310 578.2191

DeMarco, Kim
Six E 12th St, NYC, NY 10003
212 675.2023

Dempsey, Paul
1863 S Pearl St, Denver, CO 80210
303 733.0128
fax 303 733.8154
page 152

DeMuth, Roger
4103 Chenago St, Cazenovia, NY 13035
315 655.8599

Denham, Karl
204 Park Ave, Hoboken, NJ 07030
201 792.6422

Denn, Walter
13332 Slope Crest Dr, Oakland, CA 94619
510 476.1152

Dervaux, Isabelle
543 Hudson St, NYC, NY 10014
212 929.1988

Deschamps, Bob
108 E 35th St, NYC, NY 10016
212 889.3337

DesignArts
2343 W Estrella Dr, Chandler, AZ 85224
602 786.9411

DesignTeam
2207 Palmer Dr, St Paul, MN 55112
612 631.2594

Desimini, Lisa
41 Morton St, NYC, NY 10014
212 645.2932

Detinger, Bill
7315 Fircrest Ave, Sebastopol, CA 95472
707 823.9807

Detrich, Susan
253 Baltic St, Brooklyn, NY 11201
718 237.9174

Detroit Digital Studios
895 N Lake Angeles Rd,
Lake Angeles, MI 48326
313 355.0241

Devarj, Silva
116 W Illinois St, Chicago, IL 60610
312 266.1358

Devaud, Jacques
1863 S Pearl St, Denver, CO 80210
303 733.0128
fax 303 733.8154
page 151

Dever, Eric
200 Aquetong Rd, New Hope, PA 18938
215 862.2091

Devita, Fred
5339 Randolph Rd, Rockville, MD 20852
301 770.2237

Devlin, Bill
108 E 35th St, NYC, NY 10016
212 889.3337

Dewey, Kenneth Francis
RD #1 Box Eight, S New Berlin, NY 13843
607 859.2580

Dewitt, Jim
1230 Brickyard Cove Rd,
Pt Richmond, CA 94801
510 232.4291

Dewitt, Kurt
2486 Hunter St, L.A., CA 90021
213 627.6118

Dey, Lorraine
45 Johnson Ln N, Jackson, NJ 08527
908 928.5510

DiComo, Charles
49 W 45th St, NYC, NY 10036
212 921.1199

Di Fabio, Jessica
301 E 75th St, NYC, NY 10021
212 988.9623

Di Fate, Vincent
12 Ritter Dr, Wappingers Falls, NY 12590
914 297.6842

Di Spigna, Tony
6633 Cameron Ct, Brooklyn, NY 11204
718 837.2204

Diamond Art Studio Ltd
11 E 36th St, NYC, NY 10016
212 685.6622

Diaz, David
6708 Corintia St, Rancho La Costa, CA 92009
619 438.0070

DiBlasio, Nicholas J
207 Commonwealth Ave,
Boston, MA 02116
617 266.2650
fax 617 226.2650
page 451

DiCesare, Joe
435A Ninth St, Brooklyn, NY 11215
718 499.9025

Dickens, Holly
612 N Michigan, Chicago, IL 60611
312 280.0777

Dickenson, John
430 Hill St, Laguna Beach, CA 92651
714 494.5046

Dickey, Burrell
4975 Elmwood Dr, San Jose, CA 95130
408 866.0820

Didion, Nancy
10884 Deliban Ave, Tujunga, CA 91042
818 353.4464

Diebel, John
4503 Pillsbury Ave S, Mpls, MN 55409
612 824.7337

Diefendorf, Cathy
420 Lexington Ave, NYC, NY 10170
212 986.5680
fax 212 818.1246
page 91

Dierksen, Jane
332 Shadylawn Dr, Duarte, CA 91010
818 359.7745

Dieterichs, Shelley
Five Plant Ave, St Louis, MO 63119
314 968.4515

Dietz, Mike
23962 Dovekie Cir, Laguna Niguel, CA 92677
714 448.0652

Diffenderfer, Ed
32 Cabernet Ct, Lafayette, CA 94549
510 254.8235

Digimata
36 Woodycrest Ave, Toronto, ON,
Canada M4J 3A7
416 462.3388

Digital Art
3166 E Palmdale Blvd, Palmdale, CA 93550
805 265.8092

Dill, Jane
123 Townsend, San Francisco, CA 94107
415 543.9152

Dillard, Elaine
PO Box 1171, Atlanta, GA 30655
404 267.8786

Dimarco, Anthony
2948 1/2 Grand Rt St John,
New Orleans, LA 70119
504 948.3128

Dimock Illustration
308 Prince St, St Paul, MN 55101
612 291.7718

Dinetz, Bob
818 Brannan St, San Francisco, CA 94103
415 621.0915

Dingler, Fred
1805 Raleigh Dr, Burnsville, MN 55337
612 890.3122

Dininno, Steve
553 E Fulton St, Long Beach, NY 11561
516 431.1495

Dinnerstein, Harvey
933 President St, Brooklyn, NY 11215
718 783.6879

Dinyer, Eric
5510 Holmes, Kansas City, MO 64110
816 363.4795

Dionisi, Sandra
859 King St W, Toronto, ON,
Canada M5V 1P2
416 867.1771

Dismukes, John Taylor
3408 W Burbank Blvd, Burbank, CA 91505
818 985.8181

Distinctive Calligraphic
30400 Wolf Rd, Bay Village, OH 44140
216 871.6590

Dixon, Don
2519 Cedar Ave, Long Beach, CA 90806
310 595.8487

Dodds, Glenn
392 Central Park W, NYC, NY 10025
212 866.7327

Dodge, Sharon Creative Services
1201 First Ave So, Seattle, WA 98134
206 622.7035

Dodge, Susan
One E St, Hull, MA 02045
617 925.0336

Dodson, David
24762 Masters Cup Way, Valencia, CA 91355
805 254.2096

Doghouse Studios
100 E Ohio, Chicago, IL 60610
312 988.7990

Doheny, Dennis
654 Pier Ave, Santa Monica, CA 90405
310 392.4877

Doherty & Associates
PO Box 4745, Woodland Park, CO 80866
719 687.9055

Doherty, John
Eight Pearl St, Beverly, MA 01915
508 927.5112

Doktor, Patricia
4118 Beck Ave, Studio City, CA 91604
818 769.7321
pages 10-11

Dolack, Monte
PO Box 8927, Missoula, MT 59807
406 549.3248

Dolan, Paul
4427 N Richmond, Chicago, IL 60625
312 539.9083

Dolby, Karen
307 N Michigan Ave, Chicago, IL 60601
312 855.9336

Domingo, Ray
108 E 35th St, NYC, NY 10016
212 889.3337

Doney, Todd
Pine Rd HCR, Neversink, NY 12765
914 985.2936

Donin, Judi
645 Westmount Dr, L.A., CA 90069
310 659.4344

Donna, Christina
25 Bridge Rd, Larkspur, CA 94939
415 924.7126

Donner, Carol
501 Fifth Ave, NYC, NY 10017
212 490.2450

Donovan's Dream Merchant
437 Engel Ave, Henderson, NV 89015
702 564.3598

Donovisions
791 Tremont St, Boston, MA 02118
617 247.3237

Doody, Jim
1010 S Robertson Blvd, L.A., CA 90035
310 652.7322

Dooley, James Design
595 May St, North Attleboro, MA 02760
508 761.9034

Dooling, Michael
161 Wyoming Ave, Audubon, NJ 08106
609 546.6507

Doret, Michael
6545 Cahuenga Ter, Hollywood, CA 90068
213 467.1900

Dorety, Joe
731 N 24th St, Phila, PA 19130
215 232.6666
fax 215 232.6585
page 337

Dorta, Alina
11013 SW Seventh Ter, Miami, FL 33174
305 554.6420

Doty, Curt
1825 Harmon Pl, Glendale, CA 91208
818 249.8737

Doty, Eldon
3435 260th Ave NE, Redmond, WA 98053
206 868.9540

Dougherty, Mervin
550 Battery St, San Francisco, CA 94111
415 391.1526

Dowd, Jason
9322 Olive St Rd, St Louis, MO 63132
314 997.2655

Dowdalls, James
12750 E Centralia St, Lakewood, CA 90715
310 865.9550

Dowlen, James
PO Box 15152, Santa Rosa, CA 95402
707 579.1535

Downes, Nicholas
PO Box 310107, Brooklyn, NY 11231
718 875.0086

Downs, Bob
11111 Main Range Trl, Littleton, CO 80127
303 971.0033

Downs, Richard
716 Sanchez St, San Francisco, CA 94114
415 285.8267

Doyle, Tom
16634 N 54th St, Scottsdale, AZ 85254
602 971.9068

Dragset, Erik
254 Cecil Pl, Costa Mesa, CA 92627
714 722.9707

Drake Art
3017 Heads Church Rd, Cedar Hill, TN 37032
615 746.3609

Drake, Bob
4052 Del Rey Ave, Venice, CA 90292
310 305.1998

Draper Studio
413 Tyler St, Dallas, TX 75208
214 526.4668

Draper, Tom Design
6032 Oberlin NE, Seattle, WA 98115
206 523.8639

Drawing Card
275 Market St, Mpls, MN 55405
612 339.7586

Drawson, Blair
14 Levty Ave, Toronto, ON, Canada M4E 2R3
416 693.7774

Drayton, Richard
PO Box 20053, Sedona, AZ 86341
602 284.9125

Drebelbis, Marsha
8150 Brookriver Dr, Dallas, TX 75247
214 951.0266

Drescher, Henrik
2434 California St, Berkeley, CA 94703
510 883.9616

Drescher, Joan
23 Cedar St, Hingham, MA 02043
617 749.5179

Dressel, Peggy
11 Rockaway Ave, Oakland, NJ 07436
201 337.2143

Drew, Kim
1617 Taylor Ave N,
Seattle, WA 98109
206 281.9298
page 137

Drexler, Sharon
110 W 40th St, NYC, NY 10018
212 768.8072

Drobek, Carol
1260 Broadway, S.F, CA 94109
415 776.6188

Drucker, Mort
42 Juneau Blvd, Woodbury, NY 11797
516 367.4920

Drugg, Martin
1820 Stearns St, La Habra, CA 90631
310 697.1890

Drummond, Allan
70 Rosaline Rd, London, England SW6 7QT
011 44.71.610.1801

Drury, Christian Potter
44 Spencer St, Litchfield, CT 06759
203 567.2075

DT 2
108 Montis Dr, Greenville, SC 29609
803 246.6407

du Bois, Gerard
211 E 89th St, NYC, NY 10128
212 289.5514
fax 212 987.2855
page 198

Duarte, Mary Young
350 First Ave, NYC, NY 10010
212 674.4513

Duarte, Pamela
1758 N Fairfax Ave, L.A., CA 90046
213 874.9509

DuBois, Tom
405 N Wabash, Chicago, IL 60611
312 527.3283
fax 312 527.9091
page 72

Dubrowski, Ken
49 Freeman St, Wollaston, MA 02170
617 328.1198
fax 617 328.1198
page 342

Ducak, Danilo
60 E 42nd St, NYC, NY 10017
212 867.8092

Duck Fountain Design
2733 N Fredric, Burbank, CA 91504
818 843.3430

Duckworth, Susie
2912 Kings Chapel Rd, Falls Church, VA 22042
703 698.8987

Duckworth, Tom
10109 Rain Drop Cir,
Granger, IN 46530
219 674.6226
page 176

Dudash, C Michael
RR 1, Moretown, VT 05660
802 496.6400

Dudley, Don
One Balboa, Inverness Park, CA 94937
415 663.1660

Dudzinski, Andrzej
54 E 81st St, NYC, NY 10028
212 772.3098

Duffy, Beverly
4120 Black Tail Dr, Sacramento, CA 95823
916 393.6133

Duffy, Daniel Mark
24 W 75th St, NYC, NY 10023
212 769.1510

Dugan, Brian
Six Candlewood Rd, Washington, NJ 08888
908 835.0101

Dugan, Louisa
5046 MacArthur Blvd NW, Wash, DC 20016
202 966.7549

Duggan, Lee
3780 Schooner Rdg, Alpharetta, GA 30202
404 664.1609

Duillo, Elaine I
146 Dartmouth Dr, Hicksville, NY 11801
516 681.8820

Duke, Bette
116 W 29th St, NYC, NY 10001
212 967.1393

Duke, Chris
E Maple Ave, Milbrook, NY 12545
914 677.9510

Duke, Lawrence W
PO Box 421443,
San Francisco, CA 94142
415 647.5660
fax 415 285.1102
page 378

Duke, William
90 Hillview Ave, Los Altos, CA 94022
415 949.1344

Dumville, Fritz
22 Edison Ave, Providence, RI 02906
401 861.7629

Dunakin, Ray
4665 Huggins St, San Diego, CA 92122
619 453.8613

Dunaway, Suzanne Shimek
10211 Chrysanthemum Ln, L.A., CA 90077
310 470.1914

Dunlavey, Rob
Eight Front St, Natick, MA 01760
508 651.7503

Dunn, Patricia
139 Richard St, Rochester, NY 14607
716 461.2279

Dunnahoe, Hugh
2720 S Harbor Blvd, Santa Ana, CA 92704
714 751.4846

Dunnick, Regan
41 Union Sq W, NYC, NY 10003
212 929.5590
page 251

DuPays, Nicky
353 W 53rd St, NYC, NY 10019
212 582.0023
fax 212 582.0090
page 147

DuPont, Lane
597 Riverside Ave,
Westport, CT 06880
203 226.4724
fax 203 454.9904
page 63

Dupont, Patrick
206 N First St, Mpls, MN 55401
612 332.2361

Dupre, Jone
415 Second St, Coronado, CA 92118
619 435.8369

Dupree, C Bruce
1867 S Ashe Ct, Auburn, AL 36830
205 887.3845

Duran, Nina
60 E 42nd St, NYC, NY 10165
212 682.1490

Duranceau, Suzanne
4899 Sherbrook W, Montreal, QU,
Canada H3Z 1H2
514 484.6229

Durand, Janice Lee
12144 Shadow Ridge Way,
Northridge, CA 91326
818 366.7654

Durden, Kirk
50 W 72nd St, NYC, NY 10023
212 877.2390

Dutko, Deborah
286 Mohegan Rd, Huntington, CT 06484
203 925.0878

Dverin, Anatoly
60 E 42nd St, NYC, NY 10165
212 682.1490

Dwyer, Yukari
861 N Fourth Ave, Covina, CA 91723
818 331.1797

Dye, Gregory
7952 W Quarto Dr,
Littleton, CO 80123
303 933.0340
page 312

Dyen, Don
410 Parkview Way, Newtown, PA 18940
215 968.9083

Dyess, John
703 Josephine Ave, Glendale, MO 63122
314 822.2893

Dykeman, James
738 Peekskill Hollow Rd,
Putnam Valley, NY 10579
914 528.6545

Dykes, John S
17 Morningside Dr S,
Westport, CT 06880
203 222.8150
fax 203 222.8155
page 179

The Dynamic Duo
95 Kings Hwy S, Westport, CT 06880
203 454.4518

Dypold, Pat
429 W Superior, Chicago, IL 60610
312 337 6919

Dyrud, Christine Wold
9500 Thomas Ave N,
Brooklyn Park, MN 55444
612 493.4170

E D Graphics
1196 Pleasant St, Weymouth, MA 02189
617 331.7979

Eade Creative Services
16 Russell Ave, Gaithersburg, MD 20877
301 963.7335

Eagle, Bruce
14713 Brasswood Blvd, Edmond, OK 73013
405 755.6228

Eagle, Cameron
1911 NW 290th St, Oklahoma City, OK 73106
405 525.6676

Eagle, Mike
Seven Captains Ln, Old Saybrook, CT 06475
203 388.5654

Eastman, Bryant
60 E 42nd St, NYC, NY 10017
212 867.8092

Eastman, Jody
1116 W Philadelphia St, Ontario, CA 91762
909 983.2515

Eastwood, Matthew
28 Shelton St, London,
England WC2H 9JN
011 44.71 240 2077
fax 011 44.71 836 0199
page 122

Eaves, Curtis
4869 Elmhurst Ave, Norfolk, VA 23513
804 853.0675

Ebel, Alex
30 Newport Rd, Yonkers, NY 10710
914 961.4058

Ebeling, Suzanne
282 Greenfield St, Fairfield, CT 06430
203 366.4905

Eberbach, Andrea
68 E Franklin St, Dayton, OH 45459
513 433.8383

Eberle, Linda Design
24470 S Snow Owl Ct, Worley, ID 83876
208 689.3799

Ebert, Len
408 Levengood Rd, Douglassville, PA 19518
610 689.9872

Ebube, Martin
3900 Hamilton St, Hyattsville, MD 20781
301 699.8528

Echevarria, Abe
119 W 23rd St, NYC, NY 10011
212 633.9880

Edens, John
2464 Turk Hill Rd, Victor, NY 14564
716 425.3441

Edgerton, Tom
911 Elizabethan Dr,
Greensboro, NC 27410
910 854.2816
fax 910 854.2816
page 260

Edgerton, Tom
1888 Century Park E, L.A., CA 90067
310 826.1332
fax 310 284.3290
page 260

Edholm, Michael
4201 Teri Ln, Lincoln, NE 68502
402 489.4314

Edinjinklian, Teddy
5652 Elmer Ave, N Hollywood, CA 91601
310 390.9595

Edison, Susan Illustration
12700 Hillcrest Rd, Dallas, TX 75230
214 233.8222

Edmonds, Laurie
PO Box 1592, Madison Sq Sta, NYC, NY 10159
212 477.5693

Edwards, Andrew
395 South End Ave, NYC, NY 10280
212 912.1344

Edwards, Glen
580 Canyon Rd, Smithfield, UT 84335
801 563.3553

Edwards, John
2356 E Broadway, Tuscon, AZ 85719
602 623.4325

Edwards, Karl
11126 Manhattan Mine Ln,
Nevada City, CA 95959
916 265.5666
fax 916 265.8118
pages 190-191

Edwards, Kate
11126 Manhattan Mine Ln,
Nevada City, CA 95959
916 265.4502
fax 916 265.8118
page 189

Edwards, Kathleen
Ten Lombard St, San Francisco, CA 94111
415 989.6501

Edwards, Mona Shafer
3143 Nichols Canyon Rd, L.A., CA 90046
213 876.6662

Edwards, Ron
13107 Strathern, North Hollywood, CA 91605
818 786.3162

Effler, Jim
203 E Seventh St, Cincinnati, OH 45202
513 721.1193

Egan, Roberta
Ten Myrtle St, White Plains, NY 10606
914 761.8650

Egan, Shawn
201 Country Creek,
Ballwin, MO 63011
314 227.7770
page 425

Egan, Timothy
7453 Jordan Ave, Canoga Park, CA 91303
818 347.1473

Eggleton, Bob
PO Box 5692, Providence, RI 02903
401 831.5030

Ehlers, Gary
3822 Bel Pre Rd, Silver Spring, MD 20906
301 460.3084

Ehlers, Lesley
244 Fifth Ave, NYC, NY 10001
212 683.2773

Ehlert, Lois
866 United Nations Plz, NYC, NY 10017
212 644.2020

Ehrenfeld, Jane
301 St George St, Farmville, VA 23901
804 392.6190

Eibner, Frederic
515 rue Osborne, St Lambert, QU,
Canada J4R 1C1
514 672.8636

Eidrigevicius, Stasys
211 E 89th St, NYC, NY 10128
212 289.5514

Ela, Erik
24 Northwest Rd, Westfield, MA 01085
413 568.4325

Eldredge, Ernie
2683 Vesclub Cir, Birmingham, AL 35216
205 822.3879

Eldridge, Gary
501 Fifth Ave, NYC, NY 10017
212 490.2450
fax 212 697.6828
page 299

Eldridge, Marion
47 Liberty Dr, North Billerica, MA 01862
508 667.5986

Eley, Charles
16656 Ventura Blvd, Encino, CA 91436
818 986.7660

Elgin, Mary Jane
1239 E Palm St, Altadena, CA 91001
818 798.1242

Ellefson, Dennis
1041 Edinburgh Ave, L.A., CA 90046
213 654.9141

Elliott, JoAnn
Ten Highland Pl, Richardson, TX 75081
214 231.5332

Elliott, Mark
20 Plymouth Rd, Massapeuqa, NY 11758
516 798.5083

Elliott/Oreman Artists' Rep
265 Westminster Rd, Rochester, NY 14607
716 244.6956

Ellis, Jon
1622 Brownsville Rd, Langhorne, PA 19047
215 750.6180

Ellis, Steve
730 S Pacific Coast Hwy,
Redondo Beach, CA 90277
310 792.1888
fax 310 792.1890
page 353

Ellis, Tim
PO Box 4567, Greensboro, NC 27404
910 288.6521

Ellison, Jake
2233 Kemper Ln, Cincinnati, OH 45206
513 861.1400

Ellison, Pauline
60 E 42nd St, NYC, NY 10165
212 682.1490

Ellithorpe, Chris
848 Greenwood Ave NE,
Atlanta, GA 30306
404 875.1363 800 347.0734
fax 404 875.9733
page 167

Ellithorpe, Chris
490 Dover Dr, Roselle, IL 60172
708.924.7938
fax 708 924.7950
page 167

Elmer, Richard
504 E 11th St, NYC, NY 10009
212 598.4024
page 344

Eloqui
100 G St, Mt Lake Park, MD 21550
301 334.4086
fax 301 334.4186
pages 112-113

Elsner, Rita
7406 Holly Ave, Takoma Park, MD 20912
301 585.4347

Elwell, Tristan
188 E 80th St, NYC, NY 10021
212 734.3353

Ely, Creston
279 Black Rock Tpke, Redding Ridge, CT 06876
203 938.8000

Ely, Paul
360 W Ocean Blvd, Long Beach, CA 90802
310 432.5932

Ember, Kathi
666 Greenwich St, NYC, NY 10014
212 675.5719

Emberley, Ed & Barbara
Six Water St, Ipswich, MA 01938
508 356.2805

Emerson, Carmela
217-11 54th Ave, Bayside, NY 11364
718 224.4251

Emmett, Bruce
509 Madison Ave, NYC, NY 10022
212 355.0910

Emmons, Barbara
756 Dalerose Ave, Decatur, GA 30030
404 377.8950

Endom, Charles
440 Railroad Ave, Pittsburgh, PA 94565
510 432.9397

Engel, Baron
812 Widget Dr, San Jose, CA 95117
408 243.3475

Engine House Studio
444 Weston Ave, Brighton, MA 02135
617 254.0428

England, David
129 Thomas St, Bel Air, MD 21014
410 838.5030

English, M John
4601 Rock Hill Rd, Kansas City, MO 64110
816 931.5648

English, Mark
512 Lakeside Ct, Liberty, MO 64068
816 781.0056

English, Sarah Jane
23 Hepworth Dr, Toronto, ON,
Canada M9R 3W1
416 247.7336
fax 416 247.5638
page 400

Engstrom, Michael
10333 Brookside Ln, Omaha, NE 68124
402 397.0393

Enik, Ted
24 Charles St, NYC, NY 10014
212 924.1076

Epstein, Len
230 Windsor Ave, Narberth, PA 19072
610 664.4700

Erdmann, Dan
3301 A S Jefferson Ave, St Louis, MO 63118
314 773.2600

Ericksen, Marc
1045 Sansome St, San Francisco, CA 94111
415 362.1214

Erickson, Kerne
26571 Oliva Pl, Mission Viejo, CA 92692
714 364.1141

Erickson, Richard
666 Greenwich St, NYC, NY 10014
212 675.5719

Erlacher, Bill
211 E 51st St, NYC, NY 10022
212 755.1365

Ernster, Scott
12832 Bloomfield St, Studio City, CA 91604
818 753.1504

Escher Illustrations
6630 Lyndale Ave S, Richfield, MN 55423
612 866.8732

Espinoza, Raul
3949 Clairemont Dr, San Diego, CA 92117
619 272.8070

Ettlinger, Doris
Ten Imlaydale Rd, Hampton, NJ 08827
908 537.6322

Eubank, Mary Grace
8615 Midway, Dallas, TX 75209
214 902.8778

Eucalyptus Tree Studio
2221 Morton St, Baltimore, MD 21218
410 243.0211
fax 410 243.0215
page 42

Evans, Bill
101 Yesler Way, Seattle, WA 98109
206 477.1600

Evans, Jan
23042 Park Sorrento, Calabasas, CA 91302
818 222.5040

Evans, Jonathan
3286 Ivanhoe, St Louis, MO 63139
314 781.7377
fax 314 781.8017
page 321

Evans, Leslie
17 Bay St, Watertown, MA 02172
617 924.3058

Evans, Michael
9457 Danbury, Cypress, CA 90630
714 761.1333

Evans, Richard
412 S Kenneth Rd, Burbank, CA 91501
818 954.9918

Evans, Robert
1045 Sansome St, San Francisco, CA 94111
415 433.1222

Evans, Sharron
Two Harold Ave, San Francisco, CA 94112
415 239.7024

Evcimen, Al
305 Lexington Ave, NYC, NY 10016
212 889.2995

Evenas, Allan
6025 Sepulveda Blvd, Van Nuys, CA 91411
818 997.3757

Evenson Design Group
4445 Overland Ave, Culver City, CA 90230
310 204.1995

Everitt, Betsy
582 Santa Rosa, Berkley, CA 94707
510 527.3239

Evers, June
125 Willow Ave, Hoboken, NJ 07030
201 216.9117

Eversz, Kim Wilson
368 Union St, Brooklyn, NY 11231
718 237.8546

Evolution Studio
1411 Grove Ave, Richmond, VA 23220
804 353.6470

Ewers, Joseph
220 Mill St, Holliston, MA 01746
508 429.6375

Fabbri, Miriam
134 Burnett St, Berkeley, CA 94702
510 849.1364

Fabricatore, Carol
1123 Broadway, NYC, NY 10010
212 463.8950

Fagan, Jeff
E Main St, Ware, MA 01082
413 967.9855

Faist, Rick
Box 257, Pleasantville, NY 10570
914 757.2220

Falcon Adv Art
1138 W Ninth St, Cleveland, OH 44113
216 621.4327

Falkenstern, Lisa
904 Ravine Rd, Califon, NJ 07830
908 832.5789

Famous Frames
5183 Overland Ave, Culver City, CA 90230
310 558.3325

Fancher, Lou
440 Sheridan Ave S, Mpls, MN 55405
612 377.8728

Faragher, Jill
11693 San Vicente Blvd, L.A., CA 90049
805 296.4989

Farago, Stephanie
6510 W Sixth St, L.A., CA 90048
503 223.8365

Faranak
11 Kings Ridge Rd,
Long Valley, NJ 07853
908 813.8718
fax 908 813.0076
page 35

Farber, Joan
1888 Century Park E, L.A., CA 90067
310 826.1332
fax 310 284.3290
page 264

Farber, Joan
12544 Sisar Rd, Ojai, CA 93023
805 933-3016
page 264

Farfalla Illustration & Design
12105 NE Sixth Ave, North Miami, FL 33161
305 891.1629

Faria, Jeff
937 Garden St, Hoboken, NJ 07030
201 656.3063

Faricy, Patrick
1110 Town Centre Dr, Eagan, MN 55123
612 687.9717

Farina, Mark Art Studio
227 Forest Ave, Pacific Grove, CA 93950
408 373.0886

Farley, Andrew
28 Shelton St, London,
England WC2H 9JN
011 44.71 240 2077
fax 011 44.71 836 0199
page 122

Farley, Malcolm
353 W 53rd St, NYC, NY 10019
212 582.0023
fax 212 582.0090
page 145

Farnham, Joe
Four Prospect St, Beverly, MA 01915
508 921.0887

Farnsworth, Bill
PO Box 959, Ridgefield, CT 06877
203 438.8386

Farquharson, Alexander
16 Adams St, Marlborough, MA 01752
508 485.5739

Farrell, Kevin
5183 Overland Ave, Culver City, CA 90230
310 558.3325

Farrell, Rick
3918 N Stevens St, Tacoma, WA 98407
206 752.8814

Farrell, Russ
353 W 53rd St, NYC, NY 10019
212 682.2462

Farrington, Susan
191 Middlesex Ave, Wilmington, MA 01887
508 988.0664

Fasolino, Peter
122 Second St, Brooklyn, NY 11231
718 834.6276

Fasolino, Teresa
233 E 21st St, NYC, NY 10010
212 533.5543

Fasolt, Natalie
165 Ave A, NYC, NY 10009
212 473.5909

Fastner & Larson
529 S Seventh St, Mpls, MN 55415
612 338.0959

Faulkner, David
6209 Academy Ridge Dr,
Albuquerque, NM 87111
505 296.5944

Faulkner, Sue
945 W Broadway St, Mesa, AZ 85210
602 964.1161

Faust, Clifford
322 W 57th St, NYC, NY 10019
212 581.9461

Fayas, Daron
1495 N Farwell Ave, Milwaukee, WI 53202
414 347.1181

FeBland, David
670 West End Ave, NYC, NY 10025
212 580.9299
fax 212 580.3030
page 93

Feinen, Jeff
4702 Sawmill Rd, Buffalo, NY 14031
716 759.8406

Feiza, Anne
25 W 45th St, NYC, NY 10036
212 398.9540

Feldman, Ken
333 E Ontario, Chicago, IL 60611
312 337.0447
page 464

Feldman, Steve
1402 W Jackman St, Lancaster, CA 93534
805 945.5966

Fell, Dan
420 Lexington Ave, NYC, NY 10170
212 986.5680
fax 212 818.1246
page 86

Fell, Dan/Studio Graphex
47 Thorncliffe Park Dr, Toronto, ON,
Canada M4H 1J5
416 867.9345
page 86

Fellman, Lynn
3026 Perry Ave N, Golden Valley, MN 55422
612 588.8572

Fellows, Kara
1785 Bryant Ave S, Mpls, MN 55403
612 377.6693

Fenn, Neil
2300 Avon St, Van Nuys, CA 91401
818 785.3239

Fenneman, Lynda
13007 Debby St, Van Nuys, CA 91401
818 785.3239

Fennimore, Linda
808 West End Ave, NYC, NY 10025
212 866.0279
pages 38-39

Ferentz, Nicole Illustration
1440 N Dayton St, Chicago, IL 60622
312 943.4864

Fernandes, Stanislaw
874 Broadway, NYC, NY 10003
212 533.2648

Ferris, Steve
15 W 72nd, NYC, NY 10023
212 799.2251

Ferryra, Enrique
926 Norton Ave, Glendale, CA 91202
818 242.4920

Ferster, Gary
57 West End Ave, Long Branch, NJ 07740
908 229.5774

Fickling, Phillip
1863 S Pearl St, Denver, CO 80210
303 733.0128

Fiedler, Joseph Daniel
41 Union Sq W, NYC, NY 10003
212 929.5590
page 241

Fiegenschue, Tina
1408 El Campo Dr, Dallas, TX 75218
214 327.7691

Field, Ann
2910 16th St, Santa Monica, CA 90405
310 450.6413

Field, Jillian
35093 Sunflower Ln, Squaw Valley, CA 93675
209 332.2832

Field, John Illustration
2226 NE Ridgewood Dr, Portland, OR 97212
503 335.0057

Field, Lori Nelson
3443 Wade St, L.A., CA 90066
310 390.9595

Fierro Graphics
4909 Townsend Ave, L.A., CA 90041
213 255.5322

Filippucci, Sandra
614-C Larchmont Acres E,
Larchmont, NY 10538
914 834.4282

Findley, John
729-G Edgewood Ave NE, Atlanta, GA 30317
404 255.1430

Finger, Ronald
60 E 42nd St, NYC, NY 10165
212 682.1490

Finished Art
708 Antone St NW, Atlanta, GA 30318
404 355.7902

Finn, Barbara
2521 N Burling St, Chicago, IL 60614
312 327.1398

Finnell, Jim
Box 9127, Santa Fe, NM 87504
505 982.2254

Fiore, Peter
PO Box 279, Matamoras, PA 18336
717 491.5002

Firehouse 101 Art & Design
492 Armstrong St,
Columbus, OH 43215
614 464.0928
page 277

Firestone, Bill
4810 Bradford Dr, Annandale, VA 22003
703 354.0247

Fisch, Paul
5111 Coffee Tree Ln,
North Syracuse, NY 13212
315 451.8147

Fischer, Judith
206 N Glenwood, Enid, OK 72703
404 242.6504

Fisher, Carolyn
473 Columbus Ave, NYC, NY 10024
212 877.8262

Fisher, Dawn
230 N Michigan Ave, Chicago, IL 60601
312 368.8777

Fisher, Jay
230 N M34 ichigan Ave, Chicago, IL 60601
312 368.8777

Fisher, Jeanne
60 Washington St, Nyack, NY 10960
914 353.4879

Fisher, Jeffrey
155 W 15th St, NYC, NY 10011
212 989.8770

Fisher, Leonard Everett
Seven Twin Bridge Acres Rd,
Westport, CT 06880
203 227.1632

Fisher, Mark
15 Colonial Dr, Westford, MA 01886
508 392.0303

Fisher, Mike
1620 Carol Sue Ave, Gretna, LA 70056
504 393.8947
fax 504 393.8947
page 417

Fisher, Randy
PO Box 2193, Grapevine, TX 76099
817 481.2212
fax 817 481.2908
page 358

Fisher, Shell
3395 San Luis Ave, Carmel, CA 93923
408 625.0130

Fissel, Sherry L
128 Beechtree Dr, Broomall, PA 19008
215 356.0362

Fitch, Tony
98A Church St, Rockville, MD 20850
301 294.6226

Fitting, Cynthia
2131 1/2 Pine St,
San Francisco, CA 94115
415 567.3353
fax 415 474.6935
page 319

Fitz-Maurice, Jeff
731 N 24th St, Phila, PA 19130
215 232.6666

Fitz-Maurice, Karen
731 N 24th St, Philadelphia, PA 19130
215 232.6666

Fitzgerald, Cathy
28 Tremlett St, Boston, MA 02124
617 288.7276

Fitzgerald, Frank
212 E 89th St, NYC, NY 10128
212 722.6793

Fitzgerald, Patrick
Two Milepost Pl, Toronto, ON,
Canada M4H 1C7
416 429.2512
fax 416 429.2512
page 398

Fitzhugh, Greg
407 Nancy Ave, Liathincum, MD 21090
410 636.5644

Flaherty, David
One Union Sq, NYC, NY 10003
212 274.9081

Flaming, Jon
4114 McMillan Ave, Dallas, TX 75206
214 823.8787

Flanders, Shelley
1596 Wright St, Santa Rosa, CA 95404
707 544.8103

Flat Lizard Graphics
HC 01 Box 125, Rockport, TX 78382
512 790.8102

Flat Tulip Studio
111 Small Valley Rd, Halifax, PA 17032
717 362.4443

Flatland
1128 Ocean Park Blvd,
Santa Monica, CA 90405
310 394.5204

Flea Ranch Graphics
2805 1/2 Greenwich St,
San Francisco, CA 94123
415 921.0266

Fleck, Tom
Two Piedmont Ctr, Atlanta, GA 30305
404 262.1209

Flecke, Richelle Garcia
10134 Maryvale Ln, St Louis, MO 63123
314 638.0835

Fleishman, Michael
247 Whitehall Dr, Yellow Springs, OH 45387
513 767.7955

Fleming Graphics
510 First Ave N, Great Falls, MT 59401
406 761.7887

Fleming, Dale
770 N Halsted Ste P102, Gary, IN 46403
219 938.3834

Fleming, Dean
3262 N Raymond Ave, Altadena, CA 91001
818 795.4636

Fleming, Joe
420 Lexington Ave, NYC, NY 10170
212 697.8525

Fleming, Margaret
65 W 55th St, NYC, NY 10019
212 767.0260

Fleming, Ron
60 E 42nd St, NYC, NY 10165
212 682.1490

Fleming, Stanley
559 Pacific Ave, San Francisco, CA 94133
415 397.4849

Flemming, Ron
2149 Lyon Ave, San Francisco, CA 94115
415 921.7140

Fletcher, Lawrence
PO Box 86332, L.A., CA 90086
213 227.8677

Flinn, Alan
2720 E Yampa, Colorado Springs, CO 80909
719 389.0182

Floeter, Nell
139 Grandville Ave SW,
Grand Rapids, MI 49503
616 451.8374

Flood, Dick
1603 Sheridan Rd,
Champaign, IL 61821
217 352.8356
page 389

Flory, Verdon
40 W 77th St, NYC, NY 10024
212 787.7265

Floyd, Sarah
6688 N Central Expy, Dallas, TX 75206
214 691.5200

Floyd, Walt
1118 Rosedale Dr, Atlanta, GA 30306
404 875.8061

Fluharty, Thomas L
420 Lexington Ave, NYC, NY 10017
212 687.3460

Flum, Kim
4820 Hollow Corner Rd,
Culver City, CA 90230
310 202.6528

Flynn Studio
L St, Newburyport, MA 01950
508 465.5971

Flynn, James
1930 W Newport, Chicago, IL 60657
312 871.4744

Fogle, James
53 Pearl St, Brooklyn, NY 11201
718 522.5724

Foley, Tim
139 Grandville Ave SW,
Grand Rapids, MI 49503
616 451.8374

Folio
318 Regency Rdg, Dayton, OH 45459
513 436.0911

Folon, Jean Michel
15 E 76th St, NYC, NY 10021
212 288.8010

Forbes, Bart
5323 Montrose Dr, Dallas, TX 75209
214 357.8077

Ford, Terri Illustration
401 N 17th St, San Jose, CA 95112
408 971.2662

Ford, Troy S
5650 Kirby Dr, Houston, TX 77005
713 660.8513

Forgus, Rick
8120 E Montebello Ave, Scottsdale, AZ 85250
602 483.7609

Fornalski, Michael
621 River Oaks Pkwy, San Jose, CA 95134
408 434.6434

Forsbach, Robert
1709 Tigris Trl, Mesquite, TX 75181
214 222.2332

Fortin, David
6365 Van Nuys Blvd, Van Nuys, CA 91401
818 997.0600

Fortin, Louise
3405 American Dr, Mississauga, ON,
Canada L4V 1T6
905 678.2500

Fortin, Pierre
3 Munroe St, Toronto, ON, Canada M4M 2B7
416 462.3679

Foster, Becky
3443 Wade St, L.A., CA 90066
310 390.9595

Foster, Dean
202 N La Brea, L.A., CA 90036
213 655.0998

**Foster, Matt
6766 Snowdon Ave,
El Cerrito, CA 94530
510 215.1251
fax 510 215.1257
pages 322-323**

Foster, Pat
22 E 36th St, NYC, NY 10016
212 685.4580

Foster, Phil
528 Independence Way,
Murfreesboro, TN 37129
615 895.1114

**Foster, Susan
853 Broadway, NYC, NY 10003
212 677.9100
fax 212 353.0954
page 383**

**Foster, Teenuh
840 Bricken Pl, St Louis, MO 63122
314 821.2278
page 108**

**Foster, Travis
1209 Shelton Ave,
Nashville, TN 37216
615 227.0895
fax 615 227.2996
pages 36-37**

Foty, Tom
3836 Shady Oak Rd, Minnetonka, MN 55343
612 933.5570

Fountain, Linda
34 Westwood Dr, East Rochester, NY 14445
716 385.8513

Fournier, Joe
151 N Elmwood, Oak Park, IL 60302
708 848.2756

Fournier, Walter
1358 Eagle Ridge Dr, Fort Myers, FL 33912
813 561.1066

Fowler, Eric
417 Beatty St, Trenton, NJ 08611
609 695.4305

Fox Art Inc
8350 Melrose, L.A., CA 90069
213 653.6484

Fox, Bill
2233 Kemper Ln, Cincinnati, OH 45206
513 861.1400

Fox, Mark
239 Marin St, San Rafael, CA 94901
415 258.9663

Fox, Rosemary
PO Box 186, Bearsville, NY 12409
914 657.8328

Foy Graphiis
243 Linwood Ave, Newton, MA 02160
617 244.3768

Frampton, Bill
200 W 15th St, NYC, NY 10011
212 243.4209

France Illustration
57 Fairview Ln, Pacific, MO 63069
314 938.3503

**Francis, John
1665 Logan St, Denver, CO 80203
303 894.8350
fax 303 894.8343
page 390**

Francis, Judy
110 W 96th St, NYC, NY 10025
212 866.7204

Franco Design
95-08 112th St, Richmond Hill, NY 11419
718 441.0919

Franco, Elizabeth
Box 257, Pleasantville, NY 10570
914 747.2220

Francuch, George
638 S Van Ness Ave, L.A., CA 90005
213 385.4585

Frank, Robert
Nine Babbling Brook Ln, Suffern, NY 10901
914 368.8606

Franke, Phil
Ten Nehring Ave, Babylon, NY 11702
516 661.5778

Franklin, Frederick
928 Ninth St, Richmond, CA 94801
510 234.6397

Franks, Bill
2300 Claremont Ave, L.A., CA 90027
213 666.3714

Fraser, Betty
240 Central Park S, NYC, NY 10019
212 247.1937

**Fraser, Douglas
41 Union Square W, NYC, NY 10003
212 929.5590
pages 254-255**

Fraze, Jon
14160 Red Hill Ave, Tustin, CA 92680
714 731.8493

Frazee, Marla
1199 N Holliston Ave, Pasadena, CA 91104
818 797.0612

Frazier, Craig
600 Townsend St, San Francisco, CA 94103
415 863.9613

Frazier, Jim
10465 Solta, Dallas, TX 75218
214 340.9972

Frazier, Orien
1705 Fernald Point Ln,
Santa Barbara, CA 93108
805 969.0769

Frazier, Rosanne
215 Sleepy Hollow Ct, Seabrook, TX 77586
713 326.2167

Freas, Kelly Studios
7713 Nita Ave, West Hills, CA 91304
818 992.1252

Fredericks Illustration Inc
9705 S 52nd Ave, Oak Lawn, IL 60453
708 857.8090

Frederking, Sarah
433 N Harvey Ave, Oak Park, IL 60302
708 386.6886

Fredrickson, Fred
853 S Pantano Pky, Tucson, AZ 85710
602 722.5777

Fredrickson, Mark
3286 Ivanhoe, St Louis, MO 63139
314 241.4014

Freelance Advantage
441 Lexington Ave, NYC, NY 10017
212 661.0900

Freelance Hotline
311 First Ave N, Mpls, MN 55401
612 341.4411

Freelance Solutions
31 E 28th St, NYC, NY 10016
212 213.0888

Freeman & Associates
2194 SW Temple, Salt Lake City, UT 84115
801 485.5721

Freeman, Lisa
770 E 73rd St, Indpls, IN 46240
317 255.1197
fax 317 254.9693
pages 222-223

Freeman, Robert
Box 257, Pleasantville, NY 10570
914 747.2220

French, Lisa
355 Molino Ave, Long Beach, CA 90814
310 434.5277

French, Martin
16004 NE 41st Ct, Redmond, WA 98052
206 936.3939

Frenett, Elaine
20600 Alder Croft Hts Rd,
Los Gatos, CA 95030
408 450.1630

Fresh Art by Dever Designs
9101 Cherry Ln, Laurel, MD 20708
301 776.2812

Fretz, John
500 Aurora, Seattle, WA 98109
206 623.1931
fax 206 623.1931
page 130

Frichtel, Linda
58 W 15th St, NYC, NY 10011
212 741.2539

Fricke, Bill
426 Adamston Rd, Brick, NJ 08723
908 477.5482

Fridell, Pat
PO Box 19412, Seattle, WA 98109
206 634.1880

Fried, Janice
459 Ninth St, Brooklyn, NY 11215
718 832.0881

Frieden, Sarajo
1910 N Serrano Ave, L.A., CA 90027
213 462.5045

Friedman, Barbara
29 Bank St, NYC, NY 10014
212 242.4951

Friedman, Marvin
128 Beectree Dr, Broomall, PA 19008
215 356.0362

Friel, Bryan
3914 E Second St, Long Beach, CA 90803
310 439.0107

Friend & Johnson
2811 McKinney, Dallas, TX 75204
214 559.0055
fax 214 559.0724
page 107

Frigell, Kersti
115 S 36th St, Boulder, CO 80303
303 494.6549

Frisari, Frank
78-11 161st Ave,
Howard Beach, NY 11414
718 848.5007
page 124

Frisino, Jim
6822 26th Ave NE, Seattle, WA 98115
206 523.9593
fax 206 523.9593
page 132

Froom, Georgia
62 W 39th St, NYC, NY 10018
212 944.0330

Frost, Robert
One Winsor Rd, Baldwin, NY 11510
516 623.4764

Fuchs, Bernie
Three Tanglewood Ln, Westport, CT 06880
203 227.4644

Fujimori, Brian
325 W Huron St, Chicago, IL 60610
312 787.6826

Fujisaki, Tuko
NYC, NY
718 789.7472
page 108

Fujisaki, Tuko
San Diego, CA
619 276.0566
page 108

Fuka, Ted
11421 S Brightway, Mokena, IL 60448
708 479.9442

Fuller, Glenn
408 N Main St, Lake Mills, WI 53551
800 944.2442

Fuller, Rocky
2540 Cleanview Ave, Cincinnati, OH 45206
513 281.5312

Fullmer, Scott
3348 Morgan St, West Lafayette, IN 47906
518 587.6732

Funkhouser, Kristen
716 Sanchez St, San Francisco, CA 94114
415 285.8267

Furukawa, Mel
116 Duane St, NYC, NY 10007
212 349.3225

Fussion
17845 Skypark Cir, Irvine, CA 92714
714 261.2207

Future Media
145 Natoma St, San Francisco, CA 94105
415 495.5966

Gaadt, David
211 E Ohio St, Chicago, IL 60611
312 704.0500

Gabbana, Marc
2453 Olive Ct, Windsor, ON,
Canada N8T 3N4
519 948.2418
fax 519 948.2418
page 396

Gaber, Brad
4946 Glenmeadow, Houston, TX 77096
713 723.0030

Gabor, Tim
229 Broadway E, Seattle, WA 98102
206 860.0089

Gadecki, Ted
900 W Jackson Blvd, Chicago, IL 60607
312 944.5680

Gadino, Victor
417 E 90th St, NYC, NY 10128
212 860.8066

Gaines, David
1497 Westerly Ter, L.A., CA 90026
213 663.8763

Gal, Susan
267 Cambridge Ave, Kensington, CA 94708
510 528.9343

Galchutt, David
2410 W Orangethorpe Ave,
Fullerton, CA 92633
714 447.1950

Gale, Cynthia
229 E 88th St, NYC, NY 10128
212 860.5429

Galindo, Felipe
509 Cathedral Pky, NYC, NY 10025
212 864.6648

Gall, Chris
853 Broadway, NYC, NY 10003
212 677.9100
fax 212 353.0954
page 382

Gallagher, Saelig
3624 Amaryllis Dr, San Diego, CA 92106
619 224.6313

Gallardo, Gervasio
217 E 86th St, NYC, NY 10028
212 355.0910

Galli, Stan
PO Box 66, Kentfield, CA 94914
415 461.5847

Galloway, Nixon
755 Marine Ave, Manhattan Beach, CA 90266
310 545.7709

Gallup, Tracy
313 E University, Royal Oak, MI 48067
810 398.2428

Gampert, John
PO Box 219, Kew Gardens, NY 11415
718 441.2321

Gans, Harry
63 Ardmore Rd, Berkeley, CA 94707
510 527.5459

Gar•th
1131 S Burnside Ave, L.A., CA 90019
213 857.0981
fax 213 857.0981
page 408

Garbot, Dave
8422 Westberry Ln,
Tinley Park, IL 60477
708 562.5210
page 416

Garcia, Art
2811 McKinney Ave, Dallas, TX 75204
214 922.9080

Garcia, Manuel
716 Sanchez St, San Francisco, CA 94114
415 285.8267

Garcia, Stephanie
85 Jefferson St, Hoboken, NJ 07030
201 963.8089

Gardiner, Dan
130 E Walnut, Green Bay, WI 54301
414 432.6336

Gardner Graphics
2453 East Billings, Mesa, AZ 85213
602 844.1956

Gardner, Bonnie
142 W 19th St, NYC, NY 10011
212 255.0863

Gardner, Steven Michael
4784 Andalusia Ave, San Diego, CA 92117
619 279.2326

Gargiulo, Frank
170 Edgewood St, Stratford, CT 06497
203 377.4259

Garland, Michael
19 Manor Rd, Patterson, NY 12563
914 878.4347

Garner, David
301 W 110th St, NYC, NY 10026
212 663.5625

Garner, H Grey
3400 Kyle Ave, Crystal, MN 55422
612 521.9577

Garnett, Joe
606 S Hobart Ave, L.A., CA 90005
213 387.2197

Garns, Allen
209 W First Ave, Mesa, AZ 85210
602 835.5769

Garramone, Rich
49 Ridgedale Ave, East Hanover, NJ 07936
201 887.7234

Garrett, Tom
817 Westwood Dr S, Mpls, MN 55416
612 374.3169

Garrison, Barbara
12 E 87th St, NYC, NY 10128
212 348.6382

Garrow, Dan
501 Fifth Ave, NYC, NY 10017
212 490.2450
fax 212 697.6828
page 304

Gartel, Laurence
501 Fifth Ave, NYC, NY 10017
212 490.2450

Garvie, Ben
9400 Cedarview Way, Elk Grove, CA 95758
916 683.1171

Gast, Joseph
68 E State St, Dayton, OH 45459
513 433.8383

Gaston, Jane
353 W 53rd St, NYC, NY 10019
212 582.0023
fax 212 582.0090
page 145

Gateway Arts
5799 Freebird Ln, Agoura, CA 91301
818 991.7925

Gatlin, Rita Represents
2350 Taylor St,
San Francisco, CA 94133
415 776.3833
fax 415 776.3824
page 276

Gauthier, Corbert
60 E 42nd St, NYC, NY 10165
212 682.1490

Gavin, Bill
268 Orchard St, Millis, MA 02054
508 376.5727

Gay, Patti
3443 Wade St, Pacifica, CA 90066
310 390.9595

Gayler, Anne
RR Six 187 Prospect Rd, Monroe, NY 10950
914 496.4425

Gazsi, Edward
7930 Sycamore Dr, New Port Richey, FL 34654
813 844.3482

Geary, Rick
701 Kettner Blvd, San Diego, CA 92101
619 234.0514

Gebert, Warren
Two Hunt Ct, Suffern, NY 10901
914 354.2536

Geehan, Wayne
118 Beech St, Belmont, MA 02178
617 484.0677

Gehm, Charles
420 Lexington Ave, NYC, NY 10170
212 697.8525

Geiger, Scott
529 S Seventh St, Mpls, MN 55405
612 672.9842

Gelb, Jacki
108 E 35th St, NYC, NY 10016
212 889.3337

Gellman, Sim
475 N Price Rd, St Louis, MO 63132
314 994.3045

Gellos, Nancy
3634 W Lawton St, Seattle, WA 98119
206 285.5838

Gem Studio
420 Lexington Ave, NYC, NY 10170
212 687.3460

Genova, Joe
60 E 42nd St, NYC, NY 10165
212 682.1490

Genovese, Janell
283 Market St, Brighton, MA 02135
617 782.3218

Genther, David
314 N 13th St, Phila, PA 19107
215 925.5177

Genzo, John Paul
802 Ravens Crest Dr, Plainsboro, NJ 08536
609 275.5601

Geographics
4178 Chestnut St, Riverside, CA 92501
909 369.1564

George, Jeff
11936 W Jefferson Blvd,
Culver City, CA 90230
310 390.8663

George, Nancy
302 N La Brea Ave, L.A., CA 90036
213 655.0998

George, William
2172 Sunset Crest Dr, L.A., CA 90046
213 654.2660

Georgevitch, Sasha
447 Woodbridge St,
San Luis Obispo, CA 93401
805 541.3155

Geras, Audras
501 Fifth Ave, NYC, NY 10017
212 490.2450

Gerber, Mark & Stephanie
18 Oak Grove Rd, Brookfield, CT 06804
203 775.3658

Gerdes, Darcy
5294 Roundup Rd, Norco, CA 91760
909 735.8142

Gergely, Peter
24 Roe Park,
Highland Falls, NY 10928
914 446.2367
page 177

Gerhard, Nik
27931 Paseo Nicole,
San Juan Capistrano, CA 92675
714 493.5596

Gerlach, Carmeron
25 W 45th St, NYC, NY 10036
212 398.9540

Germain, Frank
2870 Calle Geraldo, San Clemente, CA 92673
714 498.7234

Gersten, Gerry
177 Newtown Tpke, Weston, CT 06883
203 222.1608

Geter, Tyrone
866 UN Plz, NYC, NY 10017
212 644.2020

Geyer, Jackie
353 W 53rd St, NYC, NY 10019
212 682.2462

Geyer, Mark
2447 Ridgeway Dr, Atlanta, GA 30360
404 451.4778

Gharrity, Laura
1102 E Fourth Ave, Denver, CO 80218
303 733.2179

Ghelerter, Robin
1118 S Sherbourne Dr, L.A., CA 90035
310 659.1763

Giambarba, Paul
5851 Vine Hill Rd, Sebastopol, CA 95472
707 829.8921

Giannini Kabilyo Design
68 Harvard St, Crampton, RI 02920
401 781.3441

Giannotta, Tommaso
304 Hudson St, NYC, NY 10013
212 924.4422

Giardina, Laura
12 Buckingham Ct, Pomona, NY 10970
914 354.0871

Gibbs, Michael
Seven W Braddock Rd, Alexandria, VA 22301
703 684.7447

Gibson, Anica
2812 Minna Ave, Oakland, CA 94619
510 261.3144

Gibson, Clancy
Two Silver Ave, Toronto, ON,
Canada M6R 3A2
416 530.1500
fax 416 530.1401
page 460

Gibson, Michael
8527 F Burnet Ave, Sepulveda, CA 91343
818 894.0532

Gibson-Nash, Nancy
15 Alden Rd, Dedham, MA 02060
617 461.4574

Giddio, Tobie
203 E 89th St, NYC, NY 10128
212 534.4177

Giedd, Richard
101 Pierce Rd, Watertown, MA 02172
617 924.4350

Gieg, John Leonard
Seven Essex Rd, Sharon, MA 02067
617 784.3287

Giguere, Ralph
2220 Delancey Pl, Phila, PA 19103
215 545.6903

Gilbert, Jim
136 N Summit, Toledo, OH 43604
419 243.7600

Gilbert, Yvonne
666 Greenwich St, NYC, NY 10014
212 675.5719

Gilford, Darren
1400 N Hayworth Ave,
West Hollywood, CA 90046
213 851.7737

Gilfoy, Bruce
568 Washington St, Wellesley, MA 02181
617 235.8977

Gillot, Carol
67 E 11th St, NYC, NY 10003
212 353.1174

Gilmour, Joni
21 Holbrook St, Boston, MA 02130
617 524.6556

Gin, Byron
11936 W Jefferson Blvd,
Culver City, CA 90230
310 390.8663

Ginsburg, Max
40 W 77th St, NYC, NY 10024
212 787.0628

Ginzinger, Karla
20 W Hubbard, Chicago, IL 60610
312 222.1361

Giraud, Jean
6539 Jamieson Ave, Reseda, CA 91335
818 343.9922

Girden, Julie
2125 Cerrada Nopal, Tucson, AZ 85718
602 628.2740

Girvin, Tim Design
1601 Second Ave, Seattle, WA 98101
206 623.7808

Gitelman, Ellen
101 Tremont St, Boston, MA 02108
617 426.6668

Giurbino, Linda
3848 Los Feliz Blvd, L.A., CA 90027
213 662.9222

Giusti, Robert
340 Long Mountain Rd,
New Milford, CT 06776
203 354.6539

Glad, Deanna
PO Box 1962, San Pedro, CA 90733
310 831.6274

Gladney, Beckett
1131 Oddstad Dr, Redwood City, CA 94063
415 599.9473

Gladstone, Dale
32 Havemeyer St, Brooklyn, NY 11211
718 782.2250

Glasbergen, Randy
PO Box 797, Sherburne, NY 13460
607 674.9492

Glaser, Milton Inc
207 E 32nd St, NYC, NY 10016
212 889.3161

Glasgow, Dale
4493 Andy Ct, Woodbridge, VA 22193
703 590.1702
fax 703 590.8855
pages 54-55

Glass, Randy
108 E 35th St, NYC, NY 10016
212 889.3337

Glasser, Tracey
2431 1/2 Glencoe Ave, Venice, CA 90291
310 823.1364

Glassford, Carl
25361 Posada Ln, Mission Viejo, CA 92691
714 768.7288

Glattauer, Ned
343 E 30th St, NYC, NY 10016
212 686.6927

Glazer, Art
Two James Rd, Mt Kisco, NY 10549
914 666.4554

Glazer, Ted
28 Westview Rd, Spring Valley, NY 10977
914 354.1524

Glazier, Garth
353 W 53rd St, NYC, NY 10019
212 582.0023
fax 212 582.0090
page 145

Gleason, Bob
302 N La Brea Ave, L.A., CA 90036
213 655.0998

Gleeson, Tony
2525 Hyperion Ave, L.A., CA 90027
213 668.2704

Glick, Ivy & Associates
350 Townsend St,
San Francisco, CA 94107
415 543.6056
fax 415 543.6075
pages 40-43

Glisson, Steve
177 St Marks Ave, Brooklyn, NY 11238
718 398.2980

Gloeckner, Phoebe
PO Box 31682, San Francisco, CA 94131
415 905.9273

Glynn Graphics
Three Wildwood Rd, Plymouth, MA 02360
508 888.6086

Gnan, Patrick
731 N 24th St, Phila, PA 19130
215 232.6666
fax 215 232.6585
page 335

Go Design/Patty O'Friel
1112 Hoyne, Chicago, IL 60622
312 384.3496

Goddard, Douglas
3845 Inglewood, L.A., CA 90066
310 397.8739

Godfrey, Dennis
231 W 25th St, NYC, NY 10001
212 807.0840
page 355

Godts, Michel
4203 Montrose Blvd, Houston, TX 77006
713 522.1555

Goembel, Ponder
PO Box 762, Riegelsville, PA 18077
610 749.0337

Goethals, Raphaelle
724 Juniper Dr, Santa Fe, NM 87501
505 989.3467

Gogol, Darek
1400 N Hayworth Ave,
West Hollywood, CA 90046
213 851.7737

Gold, Albert
6814 McCallum St, Phila, PA 19119
215 848.5568

Gold, Marcy
5289 Cedar Lake Rd, Boynton Beach, FL 33437
407 737.2569

Gold, Marv
200 S Brentwood Blvd, St Louis, MO 63105
314 727.2807

Goldammer, Ken
116 W Illinios, Chicago, IL 60610
312 836.0143

Goldberg, Grace
PO Box 3093, Kennebunk, ME 04043
207 967.2065

Goldberg, Janice
77 Carlton St, Toronto, ON,
Canada M5B 2J7
416 410.0848
page 439

Goldberg, Michael
414 Riverdale Dr, Glendale, CA 91204
818 241.7455

Goldberg, Richard A
15 Cliff St, Arlington, MA 02174
617 646.1041
fax 617 646.0956
page 310

Golden, Harriet
170 E Second St, NYC, NY 10009
212 260.5081

Goldin, David
18 McKinley St, Rowayton, CT 06853
203 866.3734
fax 203 857.0842
pages 24-25

Goldin, David
NYC, NY
212 581.8338
pages 24-25

Goldin, David
111 Fourth Ave, NYC, NY 10003
212 529.5195
fax 212 674.3225
pages 24-25

Goldman, Bart
360 W 36th St, NYC, NY 10018
212 490.2450

Goldman, Dara
866 United Nations Plz, NYC, NY 10017
212 644.2020

Goldman, David Agency
41 Union Sq W, NYC, NY 10003
212 807.6627

Goldstein, Gwen Walters
50 Fuller Brook Rd,
Wellesley, MA 02181
617 235.8658
pages 110-111

Goldstein, Howard
7031 Aldea Ave, Van Nuys, CA 91406
818 987.2837

Goldstrom, Robert
471 Fifth Street, NYC, NY 11215
718 768.7367

Golson, Geoff
714 Washington Ave, Lake Bluff, IL 60044
708 615.2850

Gomberg, Susan
41 Union Sq W, NYC, NY 10003
212 206.0066

Gomez, Loretta
818 Bloomfield St, Hoboken, NJ 07030
201 656.5329

Gonnella, Rick
35 W Wacker, Chicago, IL 60601
312 472.6550

Gonsowski, Bill
341 Van Buren St, North Babylon, NY 11703
516 587.0623

Gonzales, Thomas
758 Brookridge Dr, Atlanta, GA 30306
404 872.7980

Gonzalez, Tomas
6300 Bannerhorn Run, Alpharetta, GA 30202
404 664.9379

Gonzo/Wolfstyle
272 E Seventh St, NYC, NY 10009
212 674.3237

Goode Graphics
One Prospect Park SW, Brooklyn, NY 11215
718 788.0989

Goode, Bob
567 Ellsworth, Memphis, TN 38111
901 452.7699

Goode, Harley
50 W 72nd St, NYC, NY 10023
212 877.2390

Goodfellow, Peter
11 Kings Ridge Rd, Long Valley, NY 07853
908 813.8718

Goodman, Jeremiah
300 E 59th St, NYC, NY 10022
212 750.9097

Goodman, Marlene K
625 Ivy Ct, Wheeling, IL 60090
708 255.5772

Goodman, Michael
1922 Windingridge Dr, Richmond, VA 23233
804 741.6577

Goodman-Willy, April
3301A S Jefferson Ave, St Louis, MO 63118
314 773.2600

Goodrich, Carter
1798 Main Rd,
Westport Pt, MA 02791
800 992.4552
pages 102-103

Goodwin
2021 Wine St, Ashland, OR 97520
617 482.6543

Gordon, Barbara
165 E 32nd St, NYC, NY 10016
212 686.3514

Gorman, Ron Automotive Ills
PO Box 2233, Eugene, OR 87402
503 343.3434

Gorton/Kirk Studio
85 South St, NYC, NY 10038
212 825.0190

Gosfield, Josh
682 Broadway, NYC, NY 10012
212 254.2582

Goslin, Charles
576 Fifth St, Brooklyn, NY 11215
718 499.6728

Goss, James
1606 N Sierra Bonita Ave, L.A., CA 90046
213 876.2205

Gothard, David
104 Creek Rd, Bangor, PA 18013
610 588.4937

Gottfried Renderings
12655 W Bayaud, Lakewood, CO 80228
303 988.1517

Gottfried, Max
82-60 116th St, Kew Gardens, NY 11418
718 441.9868

Gottlieb, Penelope
302 N La Brea Ave, L.A., CA 90036
213 655.0998

Goudey, Ray
1020 Cawston Ave, South Pasadena, CA 91030
818 799.4527

Goudreau, Darryl
E Main St, Ware, MA 01082
413 967.9855

Goudreau, Roc
Stone Mill Market Pl, E Main, Ware, MA 01082
413 967.9855

Graber, Jack
3443 Wade St, L.A., CA 90066
310 390.9595

Grace, Alexa
70 University Pl, NYC, NY 10003
212 254.4424

Grafica
7053 Owensmouth Ave,
Canoga Park, CA 91303
818 712.0071

Graham Studios
900 W Jackson Blvd, Chicago, IL 60607
312 944.5680
fax 312 421.5948
page 426

Graham, Corey Represents
Pier 33 N, San Francisco, CA 94111
415 956.4750

Graham, Jack
853 Broadway, NYC, NY 10003
212 677.9100
fax 212 353.0954
page 382

Graham, Mariah
PO Box 425, Jeffersonville, NY 12748
914 482.4036

Graham, Tom
408 77th St, Brooklyn, NY 11209
718 680.2975

Grajek, Tim
213 Webber Ave,
N Tarrytown, NY 10591
914 332.9704
page 100

Gran, Julia
3240 Henry Hudson Pky, Riverdale, NY 10463
718 601.8820

Grandpre, Mary
475 Cleveland Ave N, St Paul, MN 55104
612 645.3463

Grandstaff, Chris
12704 Harborview Ct, Woodbridge, VA 22192
703 494.0422

Graning, Ken
201 N Squirrel Rd, Auburn Hills, MI 48326
810 299.0677

Granner, Courtney
328 N Fifth St, Patterson, CA 95363
209 892.2973

Grant, Cynthia
536 Fifth St, Brooklyn, NY 11215
718 499.5938

Graphic Artist
Seven Park St, Lyndonville, VT 05851
802 626.5808

Graphic Artists Guild
3504 Wedgeworth Rd South,
Ft Worth, TX 76133
817 292.1855

Graphic Artists Guild
11 W 20th St, NYC, NY 10011
212 463.7730

Graphic Chart & Map Co Inc
236 W 26th St, NYC, NY 10001
212 463.0190

Graphic Factor
1487 E Washington Blvd, Pasadena, CA 91104
818 398.1222

Graphic Haus
1254 French Ave, Lakewood, OH 44107
216 221.0354

Graphic Ideas
39 Meadowbrook Rd, Bedford, MA 01730
617 275.2770

Graphic Key
4417 Pine St, Phila, PA 19104
215 222.3223

Graphique Design Studio
73-1270 Awakea St, Kailua-Kona, HI 96740
808 325.6678

Graphix
32 Guernsey St, West Roxbury, MA 02132
617 325.8953

Grashow, James
14 Diamond Hill Rd, West Redding, CT 06896
203 938.9195

Grasso, Mitch
731 N 24th St, Phila, PA 19130
215.232.6666

Graveline, Todd
770 E 73rd St, Indpls, IN 46240
317 255.1197

Graves, Angela
2507 Merribrook Rd, Wilmington, DE 19810
302 529.1942

Graves, David
84 Main St, Gloucester, MA 01930
508 283.2335

Graves, DB
160 W 24th St, NYC, NY 10011
212 463.9354

Graves, Keith
905 W 29th St, Austin, TX 78705
512 478.3338

Gray, Barbara
150 E 69th St, NYC, NY 10021
212 288.3938

Gray, Claudia
12520 Venice Blvd, L.A., CA 90066
310 391.5914

Gray, Elizabeth
3671 Bear St, Santa Ana, CA 92704
714 850.1964

Gray, Leonard
16409 Sunburst St, North Hills, CA 91343
818 894.7226

Gray, Mark
PO Box 15152, Santa Rosa, CA 95402
707 579.1535

Gray, Mike
870 Market St, San Francisco, CA 94102
415 989.2023

Gray, Steve
853 Broadway, NYC, NY 10003
212 677.9100

Gray, Steve
1437A 12th St, Manhattan Beach, CA 90266
310 546.2188

Gray, Susan
42 W 12th St, NYC, NY 10011
212 675.2243

Gray, Timothy E
662 Yates Ave, Calumet City, IL 60409
708 730.1667

Grayson, Rick
17 West St, Westboro, MA 01581
508 898.3943

Great Characters!
3802 E St Catherine, Phoenix, AZ 85040
602 437.2688

Greathead, Ian
1591 Sandpoint Dr, Roswell, GA 30075
404 640.6517

Grecke, Sue
4325 Byrd St, Flushing, NY 11355
718 539.7394

Green, Norman
119 W 23rd St, NYC, NY 10011
212 633.9880

Green, Patti
5222 N Clark St, Chicago, IL 60640
312 275.5895

Greenberg, Sheldon
200 Aquetong Rd,
New Hope, PA 18938
215 862.2091
fax 215 862.2641
page 278

Greene, Bryan
1576 Oakden Dr, San Diego, CA 92154
619 429.6655

Greene, Pauline
70 Village Pky, Santa Monica, CA 90405
310 450.4200

Greenwald, Jeff
650 Inca Ave, New Brighton, MN 55112
612 631.3355

Gregerson, Beth
35362A S Turtle Trl, Willoughby, OH 44094
216 975.0327

Gregoretti, Rob
41-07 56th St, Woodside, NY 11377
718 779.7913

Gregori, Lee
400 E 56th St, NYC, NY 10022
212 758.1662

Gregory, Fran
27 N Ashland Ave, La Grange, IL 60525
708 482.8452

Gregory, Lane
50 Fuller Brook Rd, Wellesley, MA 02181
617 235.8658

Greiner, Jerry
13831 NW Fwy, Houston, TX 77040
713 690.7878

Greisen, Bob
745 Alta Vista Blvd, L.A., CA 90046
213 935.6668

Gress, Ron
4036 Via Solano, Palos Verdes Est, CA 90274
310 378.5800

Grider, Richard
218 Madison Ave, NYC, NY 10016
212 213.5333

Grief, Gene
373 Broadway, NYC, NY 10013
212 941.8640

Grien, Anita
155 E 38th St, NYC, NY 10016
212 697.6170

Griesbach, Cheryl & Stanley
58 W 15th St, NYC, NY 10011
212 741.2539

Grieve, Judy Mayer
86 Cheryl Shepway, Toronto, ON,
Canada M2J 4R5
416 502.3874
fax 416 502.3874
page 401

Griffith, Linda Hill
13972 Hilo Ln, Santa Ana, CA 92705
714 832.8536

Grimes, Melissa
901 Cumberland Rd, Austin, TX 78704
512 445.2398

Grimes, Rebecca
936 Stone Rd, Westminster, MD 21158
410 857.1675

Grinnell, Derek
621A 42nd Ave,
San Francisco, CA 94121
415 221.2820
fax 415 221.2820
page 43

Groff, David
420 N Liberty St, Delaware, OH 43015
614 363.2131

Gross, Sam
115 E 89th St, NYC, NY 10128
212 534.0493

Gross, Susan-Illustration
696 Eighth Ave,
San Francisco, CA 94118
415 751.5879
fax 415 751.5876
page 309

Grossman Design Associates
4301 Hwy 7, Mpls, MN 55416
612 922.4343

Grossman, Marsha Polier
14509 Standing Oak Ct, Midlothian, VA 23219
804 644.8619

Grossman, Myron
12 S Fair Oaks Ave, Pasadena, CA 91105
818 795.6992

Grossman, Rhoda
216 Fourth St, Sausalito, CA 94965
415 331.0328

Grossman, Wendy
355 W 51st St, NYC, NY 10019
212 262.4497

Grote, Rich
21 Tyndale Rd, Hamilton Square, NJ 08690
609 586.5896

Grotsky
21-16 28th St, L.I.C., NY 11105
718 204.6184

Grove, David
382 Union St,
San Francisco, CA 94133
415 433.2100
page 365

Grove, Elaine
16 Waverly Pl, NYC, NY 10003
212 614.9815

Gruberger, Lois
7430 Stratford Ave, St Louis, MO 63130
314 725.4422

Gruhn, Elizabeth
2203 Willow Pt, Kingwood, TX 77339
713 358.1495

Gudynas, Peter
11 Kings Ridge Rd, Long Valley, NJ 07853
908 813.8718

Guell, Fernando
43 E 19th St, NYC, NY 10003
212 254.4996

Guenzi, Carol Agents
1863 S Pearl St, Denver, CO 80210
303 733.0128
fax 303 733.8154
pages 149-153

Gugerty, Steve
3519 E Second St, Long Beach, CA 90803
310 433.7372

Guida, Liisa Chauncy
420 Lexington Ave, NYC, NY 10170
212 986.5680
fax 212 818.1246
page 80

Guidice, Rick
Nine Park Ave, Los Gatos, CA 95030
408 354.7787

Guillory, Mike
13831 NW Fwy, Houston, TX 77040
713 690.7878

Guip, Amy
352 Bowery, NYC, NY 10012
212 674.8166

Guitteau, Jud
501 Fifth Ave, NYC, NY 10017
212 490.2450
fax 212 697.6828
page 295

Gulick, Dorothy
12056 Summit Cir, Beverly Hills, CA 90210
310 276.5282

Gullerud, Peter
5183 Overland Ave, Culver City, CA 90230
310 558.3325

Gullickson, Vicki
750 94th Ave N, St Petersburg, FL 33702
813 579.4499

Gully, Bethany
791 Tremont St, Boston, MA 02118
617 350.3089
page 75

Gumble, Gary
803 Elmwood Ave, Evanston, IL 60202
708 475.4712

Gumen, Murad
35-25 90th St, Jackson Heights, NY 11372
718 478.7267

Gundlach, Russell
51-11 72nd St, Woodside, NY 11377
718 424.1305

Gunion, Jefrey
8100 Harvard Dr,
Ben Lomond, CA 95005
408 336.3300
fax 408 336.3309
page 434

Gunn Associates
275 Newbury St, Boston, MA 02116
617 267.0618

Gunning, Kevin
37 Denison Rd, Middletown, CT 06457
203 347.0688

Gunsaullus, Marty
716 Sanchez St,
San Francisco, CA 94114
415 285.8267

Gunther, Ira
1214 Locust St, Phila, PA 19107
215 569.8890

Gurgul, Robert
606 Norwood Ct, Waukesha, WI 53188
414 521.1283

Gurney, John
261 Marlborough Rd, Brooklyn, NY 11226
718 462.5073

Gurvin, Abe
125 W 77th, NYC, NY 10024
212 799.6532
fax 212 724.4726
pages 180, 420

Gurvin, Abe
31341 Holly Dr,
Laguna Beach, CA 92677
714 499.2001
fax 714 499.2001
pages 180, 420

Gusay, Charlotte
10532 Blythe, L.A., CA 90064
310 559.0831

Gushock, Mike
217 E McKinley St, Phoenix, AZ 85004
602 258.0765
fax 602 258.0765
page 208

Gustafson, Dale
420 Lexington Ave, NYC, NY 10017
212 986.5680

Gustafson, Glenn
1300 Ivy Ct, Westmont, IL 60559
708 810.9527

Gustafson, Roger
One Allens Ave, Providence, RI 02903
401 521.0750

Gustafson, Scott
4045 N Kostner Ave, Chicago, IL 60641
312 725.8338

Guyer, Terry Illustration
1125 E Hillsdale Blvd, Foster City, CA 94404
415 570.5502

Guzman, Roy
8324 Penfield, Winnetka, CA 91306
818 700.9893

H.E.C.A.T.E. Productions
PO Box 17193, Phoenix, AZ 85011
602 954.8116

Haas, Ken
114 Split Rock Dr, Barryville, NY 12719
914 557.6664

Haber-Schaim, Tamar
1870 Beacon St, Brookline, MA 02146
617 738.8883

Haberstock, Christine
4211 Franklin Ave, L.A., CA 90027
213 662.3229

Hackett, Dave
14695 Lisbon Rd, Brookfield, WI 53005
414 783.6352

Hackett, Pat Artist Rep
101 Yesler Way, Seattle, WA 98104
206 447.1600

Hackney, Rick
559 Pacific Ave, San Francisco, CA 94133
415 982.1319

Hagen, David
5580 Village Ctr Dr, Centreville, VA 22020
703 830.4208

Hagio, Kunio
125 Table Top Rd, Sedona, AZ 86336
602 282.3574

Hahn, Marika
Box 670, Palisades, NY 10964
914 365.3317

Hahn, Moira
215 Park Ave S, NYC, NY 10017
212 674.8080

Haight, Sandy
223 Prospect, Seattle, WA 98109
206 282.8558

Haimes, Norma
PO Box 1330, Miami, FL 33243
305 665.2376

Halbert, Michael
420 Lexington Ave, NYC, NY 10170
212 986.5680
fax 212 818.1246
page 78

Halbsgut, Don
201 E Grove St, Westfield, NJ 07090
908 233.8488

Hall & Associates
1010 S Robertson Blvd,
L.A., CA 90035
310 652.7322
fax 310 652.3835
page 464

Hall, Bill
1235.B Colorado Ln,
Arlington, TX 76015
817 467.1013
fax 817 274.4011
page 192

Hall, H Tom
Warwick Furnace Rd, Pottstown, PA 19464
215 469.9744

Hall, Joan
155 Bank St, NYC, NY 10014
212 243.6059

Hall, Kate Brennan
301 DeArment Pkwy, Pittsburgh, PA 15241
412 833.9648

Hall, Stephen
11 Kings Ridge Rd, Long Valley, NJ 07853
908 813.8718

Hall, Susan T
3948 Buena Vista St, Dallas, TX 75204
214 522.5717

Hallenbeck, Pomona
3737 EGP Rd, Roswell, NM 88201
505 625.2643

Hallgren, Gary
98 Laurelton Dr, Mastic Beach, NY 11951
516 399.5531

Hallman Studio, Tom
2553 Mill House Rd, Macungie, PA 18062
610 395.5856

Halloran, Pat
2233 Kemper Ln, Cincinnati, OH 45206
513 861.1400

Hally, Greg
911 Victoria Dr, Arcadia, CA 91007
818 574.0288

Halstead, Virginia
4336 Gayle Dr, Tarzana, CA 91356
818 705.4353
page 455

Hamagami/Carroll & Associates
1316 Third St, Santa Monica, CA 90401
310 458.7600

Hamblin, Randy
731 N 24th St, Phila, PA 19130
215 232.6666
fax 215 232.6585
page 332

Hamill, Paul
1009 Empey Way, San Jose, CA 95128
408 280.0879

Hamilton, Ken
16 Helen Ave, West Orange, NJ 07052
201 736.6532

Hamilton, Meredith
55 W 11th St, NYC, NY 10022
212 243.9490

Hamilton, Neal
2020 Euclid Ave, Cleveland, OH 44115
216 694.2020

Hamilton, Pamela
4900 Overland Ave, Culver City, CA 90230
310 837.1784

Hamlin, Janet
47 St Marks Ave, Brooklyn, NY 11217
718 638.1735

Hamlin, Mary Jo
8024 Henry Clay Blvd, Liverpool, NY 13090
315 652.7236

Hammond, Gordon
2100 W Big Beaver Rd, Troy, MI 48084
810 643.6000

Hampshire, Michael
320 Bee Brook Rd, Washington, CT 06777
203 868.1011

Hampson, Denman & Tonia
172 N Salem Rd, Ridgefield, CT 06877
203 438.2419

Hampton, Blake
25 W 45th St, NYC, NY 10036
212 398.9540

Hampton, Gerry
4792 Tiara Dr, Huntington Beach, CA 92649
714 840.8239

Hampton, Stacie
1923 Chestnut St, Phila, PA 19103
215 563.1875

Hamrick, Chuck Illust Ltd
16 Sharp Hill Rd, Wilton, CT 06897
203 762.7775

Hancock Roberta
1506 W Lynwood St, Phoenix, AZ 85007
602 252.6368

Hand to Mouse Art
3700 E 34th St, Mpls, MN 55406
612 724.1172

Hand, Judy
2233 Kemper Ln, Cincinnati, OH 45206
513 861.1400

Haner, Bill
2311 Transcontinental, Metairie, LA 70001
504 837.6201

Hanes, Larry
6108 Faircrest Ct, Cincinnati, OH 45224
513 542.2473

Hanley, Debbie
500 Aurora, Seattle, WA 98109
206 621.0410
page 127

Hanna, B Scott
1140 N Columbus, Glendale, CA 91202
818 543.1715

Hanna, Gary
1002 NW 83rd St, Seattle, WA 98117
206 781.8927

Hannon, Holly
43 E 19th St, NYC, NY 10003
212 254.4996

Hansen, George
1925 W Bradley Pl, Chicago, IL 60613
312 929.5788

Hansen, Sue
5808 Holmes, Kansas City, MO 64110
816 363.8339

Hanson, Jim
777 N Michigan Ave, Chicago, IL 60611
312 337.7770

Hantel, Johanna
870 Market St, San Francisco, CA 94102
415 989.2023

Hanxleden, Rainer
1077-42 Santo Antonio Dr, Colton, CA 92324
909 824.8324

Hanzon-Kurrasch, Toni
1928 N Beverly Glen, L.A., CA 90077
310 474.1776

Harbort, Bill
3331 Sycamore Ln, Yorktown Hts, NY 10598
914 245.5369

Hardeback, George
2233 Kemper Ln, Cincinnati, OH 45206
513 861.1400

Harden, Laurie
121 Banta Ln, Boonton, NJ 07005
201 335.4578

Hardesty, Debra
1017 Vallejo Way, Sacramento, CA 95818
916 446.1824

Hardiman, Miles
6900 W Quincy Ave, Littleton, CO 80123
303 932.0688

Hardin, Will
210 W Jennings, Newburgh, IN 47630
812 853.5336

Hardy, Jill
1662-D Beekman Pl NW, Wash, DC 20009
202 667.4245

Hardy, Neil O
Two Woods Grove Rd, Westport, CT 06880
203 226.4446

Hargreaves, Greg
414 Cornwall Ave, Waterloo, IA 50702
319 233.7573

Hargreaves, Jon
301 N Water St, Milwaukee, WI 53202
414 347.1266

Hargreaves, Sean
1400 N Hayworth Ave,
West Hollywood, CA 90046
213 851.7737

Harlib, Joel Associates Inc
405 N Wabash Ave, Chicago, IL 60611
312 329.1370
fax 312 329.1397
pages 245, 318

Harmon, Mary
34057 Emily Way, Rancho Mirage, CA 92270
619 328.9554

Harper, Patrick
4755 Glenalbyn Dr, L.A., CA 90065
213 227.6088

Harper, Thomas
9192 Russell Ave, Garden Grove, CA 92644
714 530.5215

Harrelson, Pam-ela
2707 Beechmont Dr, Dallas, TX 75228
214 321.6061

Harrigan, Peggy
900 W Jackson Blvd, Chicago, IL 60607
312 944.5680

Harrington, Bobbi
4042 Thomas St, Oceanside, CA 92056
310 390.9595

Harrington, Glenn
329 Twin Lear Rd, Pipersville, PA 18947
610 294.8104

Harrington, Richard
87 N Clinton Ave, Rochester, NY 14604
716 262.4571

Harrington, Stephen
71 Aiken St, Norwalk, CT 06851
203 847.6430

Harris, Diane Teske
315 E 68th St, NYC, NY 10021
212 517.4919

Harris, Ellen
45 Marion St, Brookline, MA 02146
617 739.1867

Harris, Gretchen & Associates
5230 13th Ave S, Mpls, MN 55417
612 822.0650
fax 612 822.0358
pages 94-97

Harris, Leslie
1906 Wellbourne Dr NE, Atlanta, GA 30324
404 872.7163

Harris, Ralph
PO Box 1091, Sun Valley, ID 83353
208 726.8077

Harrison, Hugh
314 Pavonia Ave, Jersey City, NJ 07302
201 798.6086

Harrison, Mark
353 W 53rd St, NYC, NY 10019
212 682.2462

Harrison, Sean
1349 Lexington Ave, NYC, NY 10028
212 369.3831

Harrison, William
501 Fifth Ave, NYC, NY 10017
212 490.2450
fax 212 697.6828
page 302

Harritos, Pete
68 E Franklin St, Dayton, OH 45459
513 433.8383

Harston, Jerry
5732 Skyline Dr, Seven Hills, OH 44131
216 741.4722

Hart Graphics/Telemedia
12361 Harvey Ln, Garden Grove, CA 92641
714 539.8893

Hart, David
2972 Pacific Ave, San Francisco, CA 94115
415 931.1388

Hart, Debbie
6520 Adams Ave, Cincinnati, OH 45243
513 561.3593

Hart, John
494 State St, Brooklyn, NY 11217
718 852.6708

Hart, Thomas
108 E 35th St, NYC, NY 10016
212 889.3337

Hart, Vikki
780 Bryant St, San Francisco, CA 94107
415 495.4278

Harte, Thomas
88-07 151st Ave, Howard Beach, NY 11414
718 843.8559

Hartland, Jessie
165 William St, NYC, NY 10038
212 233.1413

Hartmann, Robin
1041 Delta Ave, Cincinnati, OH 45208
513 871.3560

Hartstock, Marcia
2233 Kemper Ln, Cincinnati, OH 45206
513 861.1400

Harvey, Ray
3037 Willow Creek Est Dr,
St Louis, MO 63031
314 837.2141

Harwood, John
60 E 42nd St, NYC, NY 10165
212 682.1490

Hasler, Gino
13630 Muscatine St, Arleta, CA 91331
818 782.1736

Hasselle, Bruce
8691 Heil Ave, Westminster, CA 92683
714 848.2924

Hastings, David
1809 Seventh Ave, Seattle, WA 98101
206 623.1044

Hatala, Dan
1225 W Fourth St, Waterloo, IA 50702
319 234.7055

Hatch, Wally
62 Mares Hill Rd, Ivoryton, CT 06442
203 767.1376

Hatcher, Lois
32 W 58th St, Kansas City, MO 64113
816 361.6230

Hatton, Enid
46 Parkway, Fairfield, CT 06430
203 259.3789

Hauser, Barb/Another Girl Rep
PO Box 421443,
San Francisco, CA 94142
415 647.5660
fax 415 285.1102
pages 378-381, 464

Havlicek, Karel
353 W 53rd St, NYC, NY 10019
212 582.0023
fax 212 582.0090
page 145

Hawk, Richard
7940 Silverton Ave, San Diego, CA 92126
619 549.8499

Hawkes, Kevin
30 Central Ave, Peaks Island, ME 04108
207 766.5153

Hayashi, Joyce
5122 NW 59th Ter, Kansas City, MO 64151
816 741.4918

Hayashida, Emma
3290 Primavera St, Pasadena, CA 91107
818 792.6069

Hayden, Charles
20 Church St, Montclair, NJ 07042
201 746.3456

Hayden, Chuck
65 W 55th St, NYC, NY 10019
212 767.0260

Hayes, Cliff
PO Box 1239, Chicago Heights, IL 60411
708 755.7115

Hayes, John
2145 N Dayton, Chicago, IL 60614
312 787.1333
fax 312 975.0956
page 232

Hayes, Kathy Associates
131 Spring St, NYC, NY 10012
212 925.4340
page 284

Hayes, Stephen
13400 SW Bay Meadows Ct, Beaverton,
OR 97005
503 524.6726
page 349

Haymans, Traci
88 Broad Reach Ct, Savannah, GA 31410
912 897.0902

Haynes, Bryan
4323 Bluffview Blvd, Dallas, TX 75209
214 352.9192

Haynes, Max
510 Marquette Ave, Mpls, MN 55402
612 339.0947

Haynes, Michael
19050 Fox Run, Pacific, MO 63069
314 458.6894

Hazlerig, Mark
3619 Washburn St, Columbus, OH 43213
614 239.9290

Head, Gary
6023 Wyandotte, Kansas City, MO 64113
816 363.3119

Head, Roger B
12419 Fairpoint Rd, Houston, TX 77099
713 575.7517

Head, Ron
1223 Danville, Richardson, TX 75080
214 644.7327

Healy, Deborah
72 Watchung Ave, Upper Montclair, NJ 07043
201 746.2549

Heater, James
283 Mott St, NYC, NY 10012
212 226.7844

Heath, Mark
3443 Wade St, L.A., CA 90066
310 390.9595

Heath, R Mark
1221 Berans Rd, Baltimore, MD 21117
410 752.2700

Heavner, Becky
202 E Raymond Ave, Alexandria, VA 22301
703 683.1544

Heavner, Obadinah
10310 Mary Ave NW, Seattle, WA 98177
206 789.0673

Hebert, Doug
2929 Briar Park, Houston, TX 77042
713 784.4141

HECHTECH
3871 Hatton St, San Diego, CA 92111
619 576.4140

Hecker, Jon
2048 E 106th St, Carmel, IN 46032
317 846.5039

Hedge, Joanne
1838 El Cerrito Pl, L.A., CA 90068
213 874.1661

Heer, Peter
500 Molino St, L.A., CA 90013
213 617.1282

Heffron, Joe
3825 E 26th St, Mpls, MN 55406
612 729.1774

Hegedus, James
11850 Otsego St, North Hollywood, CA 91607
818 985.9966

Heidel, Pat
2033 Walnut, Grand Prairie, TX 75050
214 262.5256

Heider, Lindsay
PO Box 19412, Seattle, WA 98109
206 634.1880

Heidrich, Tim
12128 Courser Ave, La Mirada, CA 90638
310 943.3239

Heimann, Jim
7517 Manchester Ave, L.A., CA 90045
310 578.2191

Heiner, Joe & Kathy
41 Union Sq W, NYC, NY 10003
212 929.5590
page 245

Heinz-Jenkins, Laurie
2405 NW Thurman St, Portland, OR 97210
503 225.9687

Heinze, Mitch
721 E Maxwell Ln, Lathrop, CA 95330
209 858.1131

Hejja, Attila
420 Lexington Ave, NYC, NY 10170
212 986.5680
fax 212 818.1246
page 87

Helder, Rudolf
PO Box 11510, Honolulu, HI 96828
808 949.2708

Hellman Associates Inc
1225 W Fourth St, Waterloo, IA 50702
319 234.7055

Hemingway, Ron
10825 Arnett Dr, St Louis, MO 63123
314 487.1409

Hempel, Marc
7844 St Thomas Dr, Baltimore, MD 21236
410 661.6897

Henderling, Lisa
232 Madison Ave, NYC, NY 10016
212 889.8777

Henderson, David
420 Lexington Ave, NYC, NY 10017
212 986.5680

Henderson, Garnet
820 Hudson St, Hoboken, NJ 07030
201 653.3948

Henderson, Hayes
1043 Miller St, Winston Salem, NC 27103
910 748.1364

Henderson, Meryl
225 Wayne Ave, West Easton, PA 18042
610 559.1953

Hendler, Sandra
1823 Spruce St, Phila, PA 19103
215 735.7380

Hendricks, Steve
353 W 53rd St, NYC, NY 10019
212 682.2462

Hendrickson, Kathy
128 Beechtree Dr, Broomall, PA 19008
215 356.0362

Hendrix, Bryan
777 Ponce de Leon Ter, Atlanta, GA 30306
404 875.4290

Hendrix, Gina Graphix
1966 California Rd,
Pomona, KS 66076
913 746.5465
fax 913 746.5465
page 440

Hennessy, Thomas Illustrations
210 Chapman Rd, Mill Valley, CA 94941
415 388.7959

Henrie, Cary
1659 E Maple Hills Dr, Bountiful, UT 84010
801 298.2044

Henry, Doug
353 W 53rd St, NYC, NY 10019
212 682.2462

Henry, James
29500 Heathercliff Rd, Malibu, CA 90265
310 457.1500

Henry, Mike
3400 Aurora Ave, Des Moines, IA 50310
515 279.9478

Henry, Paul
15 W 72nd St, NYC, NY 10023
212 799.2251

Henry, Steve
Seven Park Ave, NYC, NY 10016
212 532.2487

Henry-May, Rosemary
2625 Garfield St NW, Wash, DC 20008
202 667.0455

Henselmann, Caspar
21 Bond St, NYC, NY 10012
212 533.0430

Herbert, Jonathan
Computer Illustration
501 Fifth Ave, NYC, NY 10017
212 490.2450
fax 212 697.6828
page 289

Herder, Edwin
60 E 42nd St, NYC, NY 10017
212 867.8092

Hering, Al
16 Lown Ct, Poughkeepsie, NY 12603
914 471.7326

Herlihy, Jack
3126 Kelton Ave, L.A., CA 90034
310 474.0831

Herman, Mark
1400 Lincoln Ave, Mpls, MN 55403
612 374.5637

Herman, Terry
925 Elm Grove Rd,
Elm Grove, WI 53122
414 785.1940
fax 414 785.1611
page 216

Hernandez, Jorge
1200 83rd St, North Bergen, NJ 07047
201 869.9489

Hernandez, Leo
60 Monroe Ctr, Grand Rapids, MI 49503
616 451.2632

Herr, Mimi Representation
710 N Tucker, St Louis, MO 63101
314 621.7722
page 155

Herrera, Robert
252 Plainfield Ave, Floral Park, NY 11001
516 437.7187

Herrick, David
3350 N Orange Ave, Orlando, FL 32803
407 898.8921

Hersey, John Illustration
330 Sir Francis Drake Blvd,
San Anselmo, CA 94960
415 454.0771

Herzberg, Tom
4128 W Eddy, Chicago, IL 60641
312 736.1089

Hess, Lydia J
1246 SE 49th St, Portland, OR 97215
503 234.4757
page 351

Hess, Mark
88 Quicks Ln, Katonah, NY 10536
914 232.5870

Hess, Rob
63 Littlefield Rd, East Greenwich, RI 02818
401 885.0331

Hess, Viv Eisner
63 Littlefield Rd, East Greenwich, RI 02818
401 884.3424

Hewett, Daphne
420 Lexington Ave, NYC, NY 10170
212 986.5680
fax 212 818.1246
page 79

Hewgill, Jody
17 Bellwoods Pl, Toronto, ON,
Canada M6J 3V5
416 601.0301

Hewitson, Jennifer Ills
859 Sandcastle Dr, Cardiff, CA 92007
619 944.6154

Hewitt, Margaret
144 Soundview Rd,
Huntington, NY 11743
516 427.1404
fax 516 427.0419
pages 6-7

Heyer, Carol
925 E Ave De Los Arboles,
Thousand Oaks, CA 91360
805 492.3683

Hickey, Patrick
2831 Prospect Ave, La Crescenta, CA 91214
818 248.7663

Hicks, Brad
351 N Florence St, Burbank, CA 91505
818 558.6378

Hicks, Gail
580 Washington, San Francisco, CA 94111
415 362.8280

Hicks, Richard
127 Peachtree St, Atlanta, GA 30303
404 659.0919

Higa, James
272 Sylvan Rd, Glencoe, IL 60022
708 835.4887

High Impact Graphics
1494 Avocado Ave, Melbourne, FL 32935
407 255.7201

High, Richard
4500 Montrose, Houston, TX 77006
713 521.2772

Hildebrand, Sheryl
2115 Marywood Dr, Royal Oak, MI 48073
810 589.7916

Hildebrandt, Greg
120 American Rd, Morris Plains, NJ 07950
201 292.6857

Hildebrandt, Tim
217 E 86th St, NYC, NY 10022
212 355.0910

Hill, Michael
353 W 53rd St, NYC, NY 10019
212 682.2462

Hill, Norm
3511 N Hall, Dallas, TX 75219
214 520.2552

**Hill, Roger
501 Fifth Ave, NYC, NY 10017
212 490.2450
fax 212 697.6828
pages 290-291**

**Hill, Roger
63A Yorkville Ave, Toronto, ON,
Canada M5R 1B7
416 923.5933
fax 416 920.4546
pages 290-291**

Hill, Tina Lee
837 W Gregory Blvd, Kansas City, MO 64114
816 361.9827

Hillegass, Tony
3450 Adell Ct, Oakland, CA 94602
510 482.0767

Hillenbrand, William
808 Lexington Ave, Terrace Park, OH 45174
513 831.5830

**Hilliard, Fred
5425 Crystal Springs NE,
Bainbridge Is, WA 98110
206 842.6003
fax 206 842.7528
pages 379, 464**

**Hillman, Betsy
Pier 33 North,
San Francisco, CA 94111
415 391.1181
fax 415 391.6104
page 29**

Hilscher, Anthony
206 N First St, Mpls, MN 55401
612 332.2361

Himsworth, Jim
731 N 24th St, Phila, PA 19103
215 232.6666

Hines, Jordan
1844 Los Encantos Ct, Los Gatos, CA 95030
408 379.6444

Hines, Norman
719 Flint Way, Sacramento, CA 95818
916 444.6553

Hinkley, Mary
561 La Loma Rd, Pasadena, CA 91105
818 441.1944

Hinlicky, Gregg
PO Box 1521, Toms River, NJ 08754
908 270.4300

Hinton, Hank
302 N La Brea, L.A., CA 90036
213 655.0998

Hirashima, Jean
166 E 61st St, NYC, NY 10021
212 593.9778

Hirokawa, Masami
3144 W 26th Ave, Denver, CO 80211
303 458.1381

Hirschfeld, Al
699 Madison Ave, NYC, NY 10021
212 677.5330

Hitch, Jeffer
4500 Campus Dr, Newport Beach, CA 92660
714 250.8640

HK Portfolio
666 Greenwich St, NYC, NY 10014
212 675.5719

Hobbs, Bill
Four Pall Mall Pl, Greensboro, NC 27455
910 282.2377

Hobbs, David
734 15th St NW, Wash, DC 20005
202 347.0003

Hobbs, Pamela
1061 Valencia St, San Francisco, CA 94110
415 550.8899

Hobson, Ken
Three Pineburr Ct, Greensboro, NC 27455
919 282.7789

Hockerman, Dennis
6024 W Chapel Hill Rd, Mequon, WI 53092
414 242.4103

Hodgden, Bill
2106 Libbey, Houston, TX 77018
713 686.8482

Hodges, Ken
12401 Bellwood Rd, Los Alamitos, CA 90720
310 431.4343

Hodges, Mike
4323 Bluffview Blvd, Dallas, TX 75209
214 352.9192

Hoeffner, Deb
538 Cherry Tree Ln, Kinnelon, NJ 07405
201 838.5490

Hoff, Dana
1120 California, Corona, CA 91719
909 371.3025

Hoff, Terry
1525 Grand Ave, Pacifica, CA 94044
415 359.4081

Hofflund, Sylvia
909 Loma Ave, Long Beach, CA 90804
310 439.4175

Hoffman, Joanne
826 Kater St, Phila, PA 19147
215 928.9365

Hoffman, Martin
217 E 86th St, NYC, NY 10028
212 355.0910

Hoffmann, Nancy
115 W 23rd St, NYC, NY 10011
212 691.1445

**Hofkin, Bonnie
NYC, NY
212 581.8338
pages 26.27**

**Hofkin, Bonnie
18 Mckinley St, Rowayton, CT 06953
203 866.3734
fax 203 857.0842
pages 26-27**

**Hogan, Jamie
265 Pleasant Ave,
Peaks Island, ME 04108
207 766.9726
page 5**

Hogan, Shannon
715 Marco Pl, Culver City, CA 90291
310 821.8131

Hokanson, Lars
737 E Passyunk Ave, Phila, PA 19147
215 440.8280

**Holder, Jimmy
1507 Columbia Dr,
Glendale, CA 91205
818 244.6707
fax 818 244.6766
page 405**

Holewski, Jeff
PO Box 155, Passaic, NJ 07055
201 472.1225

Holladay, Reggie
7395 NW 51st St, Lauderhill, FL 33319
305 749.9031

Holland, Brad
96 Greene St, NYC, NY 10012
212 226.3675

**Holland, Mary & Co
6638 N 13th St, Phoenix, AZ 85014
602 263.8990
fax 602 277.0680
pages 154-157**

Hollenbeck, Phil
2833 Duval Dr, Dallas, TX 75211
214 331.8328

Hollobaugh, Greg
918 Seventh St, Santa Monica, CA 90403
310 394.0468

Holly, Cathy
301 N Water St, Milwaukee, WI 53202
414 272.2242

Holm, John
353 W 53rd St, NYC, NY 10019
212.582.0023
fax 212.582.0090
page 146

Holmberg, Irmeli
280 Madison Ave, NYC, NY 10016
212 545.9155

Holmes, Craig
737 SE Sandy Blvd, Portland, OR 97214
503 235.6878

Holmes, Matthew
8412 Gaylor Way,
Carmichael, CA 95608
916 944.7270
fax 916 944.3830
page 40

Holmgren, Jean
1348 Pidgeon Roost Rd, Byhalia, MS 38611
601 838.5501

Holt, Bruce
5833 Bonfair Ave, Lakewood, CA 90712
310 804.1196

Holtzman, Lisa
2249 Wellesley, L.A., CA 90064
310 820.5973

Holuze, John
1817 Rutger, St Louis, MO 63104
314 241.8614

Holz, Fred
8340 Greensboro Dr, McLean, VA 22102
703 442.9323

Hom & Hom
425 W 23rd St, NYC, NY 10011
212 242.6367

Hom, Check
65 W 55th St, NYC, NY 10019
212 767.0260

Hom, John
3197 W Black Hills Ct,
Westlake Vlg, CA 91362
805 374.9634

Hom, Phillip
3197 W Black Hills Ct,
Westlake Vlg, CA 91362
805 374.9634

Homad, Jewell Jan
716 Sanchez St, San Francisco, CA 94114
415 285.8267

Hong, Beverly
4860 Glencairn Rd, L.A., CA 90027
213 666.0635

Hong, Min Jae
54 Points of View, Warwick, NY 10990
914 986.8040
fax 914 987.1002
pages 174-175

Hooks, Mitchell
321 E 83rd St, NYC, NY 10012
212 226.3675

Hooper, Ward P
3000 N Lakeharbor Ln, Boise, ID 83703
208 853.4313

Hooten, Christopher
5050 Klump Ave, North Hollywood, CA 91601
818 508.9055

Hoover, Gary
302 N La Brea Ave, L.A., CA 90036
213 655.0998

Hoover, Jan
3443 Wade St, L.A., CA 90066
310 390.9595

Hoover, Sherry
12 Charles St, Hanover, PA 17331
717 637.5819

Hopkins, Chris
5018 Sound Ave, Everett, WA 98203
206 347.5613

Hoppa, Jeff
21-54 Crescent St, L.I.C., NY 11105
718 777.1292

Hopper, Jennifer
2225 Indigo Hills, Corona, CA 91719
909 279.9377

Hopper, Pegge
1164 Nuuanu Ave, Honolulu, HI 96817
808 524.1160

Hopson, Melissa
2416 1/2 McKinney, Dallas, TX 75201
214 747.3122

Hord, Bob
1760 Monrovia Ave, Costa Mesa, CA 92627
714 631.3890

Horn, Robert
1404 W Jarvis Ave, Chicago, IL 60626
312 262.0660

Horsting, Robert
709 Burchett St, Glendale, CA 91202
818 241.2024

Hosek, Brad
18553 Clymer St, Northridge, CA 91326
818 366.4804

Hossan, Carole
1122 N Ogden Dr,
West Hollywood, CA 90046
213 656.4804

Hostetler, David
4031 W Cochise Dr, Phoenix, AZ 85051
612 938.0108

Hoston, Jim
420 Clinton Ave, Brooklyn, NY 11238
718 230.7908

Hostovich, Michael
713 N 24th St, Phila, PA 19103
215 232.6666

Hot Art
10890 Gold Hill Dr, Grass Valley, CA 95945
916 477.5077

Hot Dog Studios
Six Jesmond Rd, Metuchen, NJ 08840
908 549.9819

Hot Wire Studios
PO Box 2156, Redwood City, CA 94064
415 599.9473

Hotchkiss, Robin
731 N 24th St, Phila, PA 19130
215 232.6666

Hovey, Bill
5730 Duluth St, Mpls, MN 55422
612 542.9970

Howa, Frank
4151 Via Marina, Marina del Rey, CA 90292
310 301.9794

Howard, John H
336 E 54th St, NYC, NY 10020
212 832.7980

Howard, Linda
4045 Lansdowne Ave, Cincinnati, OH 45236
513 891.1967

Howard, Victoria
1403 S Santa Fe Ave, L.A., CA 90021
213 629.2050

Howe, Philip
540 First Ave S, Seattle, WA 98104
206 682.3453

Howell, Van
Box 812, Huntington, NY 11743
516 424.6499

Hrabe, Curt
684 Pleasant Ave, Highland Park, IL 60035
708 432.4632

Hranilovich, Barbara
3422 Ridgefield Rd, Lansing, MI 48906
517 321.2917

Hubbard, Ann Morton
1420 E Berridge Ln, Phoenix, AZ 85014
602 274.6985

Hubbard, K Design
10 State St, Santa Barbara, CA 93101
805 966.1409

Hubbard, Roger
27520 Sierra Hwy, Canyon Country, CA 91351
805 251.2161

Huber Design
Two Hunter Dr, Derry, NH 03038
603 437.0214

Huerta, Catherine
337 W 20th St, NYC, NY 10011
212 627.0031

Huerta, Gerard
54 Old Post Rd, Southport, CT 06490
203 256.1625

Huerta, Ray Studio
5225 Blakeslee Ave,
North Hollywood, CA 91601
818 760.4343

Huey, Kenneth
460 N 39th St, Seattle, WA 98103
206 632.3759

Huffaker, Sandy
60 Laurel Ave, Kingston, NJ 08528
609 252.0267

Huffy Design Center
7701 Byers Rd, Miamisburg, OH 45342
513 866.6251

Hughes, Charlie Lettering
172 Eugenie St, Chicago, IL 60614
312 664.3184

Hughes, Kristin
5210 Maris Ave, Alexandria, VA 22304
703 379.0543

Hughes, Marianne
731 N 24th St, Phila, PA 19130
215 232.6666
fax 215 232.6585
page 327

Hughes, Mary Ellen
428 Espanola Way, Miami, FL 33139
305 531.0726

Hughes, Ralph
6003 Calhoun Dr, Fredericksbug, VA 22407
703 786.5420

Huhn, Tim
324 Acacia St, Altadena, CA 91001
818 791.1287

Hukill, Jeff
16 Parker Ave, L.A., CA 16323
310 826.1332

Hul, Jon Jr
5240 Whitsett, North Hollywood, CA 91607
818 508.8228

Huling, Jan
3443 Wade St, L.A., CA 90066
310 390.9595

Huling, Phil
938 Bloomfield St, Hoboken, NJ 07030
201 795.9366

Hull, Cathy
165 E 66th St, NYC, NY 10021
212 772.7743

Hull, John
353 W 53rd St, NYC, NY 10019
212 582.0023
fax 212 582.0090
page 147

Hull, Richard
Pine Rd HCR, Neversink, NY 12765
914 985.2936

Hull, Scott Associates
68 E Franklin St, Dayton, OH 45459
513 433.8383

Hulsey, Kevin
666 Bantry Ln, Stone Mtn, GA 30083
404 296.9666

Hume, Kelly
PO Box 10878, Bainbridge, WA 98110
206 780.9000

Hummel, Jim
3023 Delta Rd, San Jose, CA 95135
408 270.2349

Hummer, Donna
122 E Dexter St, Covina, CA 91723
818 339.2532

Humor Associates
21-16 28th St, L.I.C., NY 11105
718 204.6184

Humphries, Michael R
11241 Martha Ann Dr, Los Alamitos, CA 90720
310 493.3323

Hungry Dog Studio
1361 Markan Ct, Atlanta, GA 30306
404 872.7496

Hunt, Lynn
4247 Sea Pines Ct, Capitola, CA 95010
408 476.7775

Hunt, Robert
107 Crescent Rd, San Anselmo, CA 94960
415 459.6882

Hunt, Scott
Six Charles St, NYC, NY 10014
212 924.1105

Hunt, Walter
15 Callasaja Dr, Highland, NC 28741
704 526.4642

Hunter, Alan
1004 Oneonta Dr, L.A., CA 90065
213 254.4342

Hunter, David
56 Greek St, London, England W1V 5LR
011 44.71.439.6463

Hunter, Stan
Box 471 E Maple Ave, NYC, NY 12545
212 355.0910

Hurlin, Kristin
PO Box 452, Glen Arbor, MI 49636
616 334.3128

Hussar, Michael
147 North Chester Ave, Pasadena, CA 91106
818 444.0183

Huston, Lance
2958 Greenwich Rd, Glendale, CA 91206
818 956.7021

Huyssen, Roger
54 Olde Post Rd., Southport, CT 06490
203 256.9192

Hyatt, John
2217 Canyon Dr, L.A., CA 90068
213 463.0868

Hyatt, Mitch
353 W 53rd St, NYC, NY 10019
212 682.2462

Hyden, Karen
49 Warren St, NYC, NY 10007
212 766.5064

Hynes, Robert
5215 Muncaster Mill Rd, Rockville, MD 20855
301 926.7813

Iannaccone, Cynthia
Nine Sandcastle Dr, Rochester, NY 14622
716 288.0868

Ibusuki, James
13053 Beaver St, L.A., CA 91342
818 362.9899

Icard, Reid
1826 Asheville Pl, Charlotte, NC 28203
704 372.6007

Ickert, Tom
354 E 83rd St, NYC, NY 10028
212 794.9723

Icon Graphics Inc
34 Elton St, Rochester, NY 14607
716 271.7020
fax 716 271.7029
page 444

Idea Studio
129 S Washington St, Green Bay, WI 54301
414 435.4140

Ijichi, Kent
676 N St Clair, Chicago, IL 60611
312 951.2800

Illustrations by Cavette
22840 Jorgenson Ln, Red Bluff, CA 96080
916 529.0825

The Image Bank Northwest
101 Yesler Way, Seattle, WA 98104
206 343.9319

The Image Bank West
2400 Broadway, Santa Monica, CA 90404
310 264.4850

The Image Bank
444 N Wabash, Chicago, IL 60611
312 329.1817

ImagiNotion
3721 Cordero Dr, Santa Barbara, CA 93105
805 569.1335

Imperiale, Matthew
210 Thompson St, NYC, NY 10012
212 982.8731

In Graphics
PO Box 3761, Anaheim, CA 92803
714 991.3329

The Independent Pencil
76 State St, Newburyport, MA 01950
508 462.1948

Ingemanson, Donna
82 Central Ave, Braintree, MA 02184
617 848.2012

Ingle, Michael
2121 E Hickory Rd, Battle Creek, MI 49017
616 721.8385

Ingram, Fred
737 SE Sandy Blvd, Portland, OR 97214
503 235.6885

The Ink Tank
Two W 47th St, NYC, NY 10036
212 869.1630

Inkwell
1310 Ninth St NW, Wash, DC 20001
202 234.8480

Innes, Grant
Two Silver Ave, Toronto, ON,
Canada M6R 3A2
416 530.1500
fax 416 530.1401
page 462

Inouye, Carol
200 Aquetong Rd,
New Hope, PA 18938
215 862.2091
fax 215 862.2641
page 280

Insight Studios
7844 St Thomas Dr, Baltimore, MD 21236
410 661.6897

Integrity Creations
110 Inverness Ln, Valley Park, MO 63088
314 225.5989

Irwin, Dennis
164 Park Ave, Palo Alto, CA 94306
415 321.7959

Ishioka, Haruo
4202 W 133rd St, Hawthorne, CA 90250
310 644.1728

Isip, Jordin
44 Fourth Pl, Brooklyn, NY 11231
718 624.6538

Iskowitz, Joel
60 Vande Bogart Rd, Woodstock, NY 12498
914 679.6742

Isom, Randall
2321 San Francisco Dr, Dallas, TX 75228
214 327.1287

It's In The Works
381 Park Ave S, NYC, NY 10016
212 689.0371

Italiano, Joe G
9221 Wissinoming St, Phila, PA 19114
215 824.2808

Ito, Joel
505 NW 185th St, Beaverton, OR 97006
503 690.5378

Ivens, Rosalind
156 Prospect Park W,
Brooklyn, NY 11215
718 499.8285
page 376

Iversen, Erik E Illustration
459 San Benito Ave, Los Gatos, CA 95030
408 395.2062

Iwamoto, Jessica
301 E 75th St, NYC, NY 10021
212 988.9623

J Perry Illustration
630 Joann St, Costa Mesa, CA 92627
714 722.1364

Jaben, Seth
47 E Third St, NYC, NY 10003
212 675.5631

Jackson Did This
PO Box 19227, Austin, TX 78760
512 448.2336

Jackson, Barry
4118 Beck Ave, Studio City, CA 91604
818 769.7321
pages 10-11

Jackson, Lance
Berkeley, CA 94710
510 849.4313

Jackson, Tim
1171 Crispwood Ct, Apopica, FL 32703
407 880.2109

Jacobs, Jim
2525 McKinney, Dallas, TX 75201
214 720.7233

Jacobs-Koskie, Diane
4850 El Monte Ave, Temple City, CA 91780
818 579.2647

The Jacobsen Studio
97 Manzanita Dr, Solvang, CA 93463
805 688.4272

Jacobsen, Gary
101 Yesler Way, Seattle, WA 98104
206 447.1600

Jacobsen, Ken
1458 W 33rd St, Mpls, MN 55408
612 823.4662

Jaekel, Susan
409 Alberto Way, Los Gatos, CA 95032
408 354.1555

Jaffee, Al
140 E 56th St, NYC, NY 10022
212 371.5232

Jakesevic, Nenad
165 E 32nd St, NYC, NY 10016
212 686.3514

James, Dave
25885 Trabuco Rd, Lake Forest, CA 92630
714 837.5088

James, Derek
Six Fording Pl Rd, Lake Katrine, NY 12449
914 336.2629

James, Patrick
1452 W 37th St, San Pedro, CA 90731
310 519.1357

James, Richard
1668 E Bishopwood Blvd,
Harleysville, PA 19438
215 361.2644

Jamieson, Doug
41-08 43rd St, Sunnyside, NY 11104
718 392.0782

Janovitz, Marilyn
41 Union Sq W, NYC, NY 10003
212 727.8330

Janovsky Illustration
310 E Waltann Ln, Phoenix, AZ 85022
602 870.1227

Januz, Barbara
3443 Wade St, L.A., CA 90066
310 390.9595

Jareaux, Robin
28 Elliot St, Boston, MA 02130
617 524.3099

Jarecka, Danuta
114 E Seventh St, NYC, NY 10009
212 353.3298
page 77

Jarvis, David Studio
2533 Chattahoochee Cir, Roswell, GA 30075
404 993.0955

Jarvis, Nathan Young
13307 Park Hills Dr,
Grandview, MO 64030
800 765.0617
fax 816 765.8112
page 94

Jasin, Mark Design
3333 Blake St, Denver, CO 80205
303 295.2728

Jasinski, Terry
20 W Hubbard, Chicago, IL 60610
312 222.1361

Jasper, Jackie
165 E 32nd St, NYC, NY 10016
212 686.3514

Jaz & Jaz
223 Prospect, Seattle, WA 98109
206 282.8558
fax 206 285.4304
pages 125-141

JB Illustration
7726 Noland Rd, Lenexa, KS 66216
913 962.9595

Jeffers, Kathy
151 W 19th St, NYC, NY 10011
212 255.5196

Jeffries, Shannon
1905 Kalorama Road, Washington, DC 20009
202 234.0895

Jenkins, Steve
244 Fifth Ave, NYC, NY 10001
212 679.9430

Jenne, ER
210 N Higgins, Missoula, MT 59802
406 543.5535

Jenny Illustrations
25512 Via Inez Rd,
San Juan Capistrano, CA 92675
714 443.9603

Jensen Designs Inc
5715 Churchman Ave, Indpls, IN 46203
317 788.7700

Jensen, Andrea
3401 Aldrich Ave, South Mpls, MN 55408
612 822.8264

Jensen, Brian
420 N Fifth St, Mpls, MN 55401
612 339.7055
fax 612 339.8689
page 57

Jensen, Bruce
41-61 53rd St, Woodside, NY 11377
718 898.1887

Jerry, Alison
3443 Wade St, L.A., CA 90066
310 390.9595

Jessell, Tim
1906 Wedgewood Ct, Stillwater, OK 74075
405 377.3619

Jester, Thomas
4309 Belleview Ave, Kansas City, MO 64111
816 753.3134

Jette, Blaise
8402 SW Woods Creek Ct,
Portland, OR 97219
503 246.9511

Jetter, Frances
390 West End Ave, NYC, NY 10024
212 580.3720

Jezierski, Chet
25 W 45th St, NYC, NY 10036
212 398.9540

Jill Thayer Barton Associates
1626 19th St, Bakersfield, CA 93301
805 393.5138

Jimenez, Maria
3415 74th St, Jackson Heights, NY 11372
718 898.9044

Jinks, John
27 W 20th St, NYC, NY 10003
212 675.2961

Jobe, Jody
12 Hillside Ave, Nutley, NJ 07110
201 235.0461

Johannes, Greg
254 Southern W Wilson, Chicago, IL 60625
312 588.4828

John & Wendy
647 Myrle Ave, Brooklyn, NY 11205
718 643.3002

John, Shane
12056 Summit Cir, Beverly Hills, CA 90210
310 276.5282

Johnsen, Eric Peter
427 B St, Salt Lake City, UT 84103
801 532.6337

Johnson, Al
4170 S Arbor Cir, Marietta, GA 30066
404 924.4793

Johnson, Celia
108 E 35th St, NYC, NY 10016
212 889.3337

Johnson, Christine Adv Design
PO Box 507, Ranchos de Taos, NM 87557
505 751.1008

Johnson, David
299 South Ave, New Canaan, CT 06840
203 966.3269

Johnson, Donald H
1415 Carlton Ave W, Colquet, MN 55720
218 879.9788

Johnson, Doug
45 E 19th St, NYC, NY 10003
212 260.1880

Johnson, Evelyne
201 E 28th St, NYC, NY 10016
212 532.0928

Johnson, Gary Marketing Design
2548 S Pasadena St, Salt Lake City, UT 84109
801 972.2100

Johnson, Gloria
23 Via Lavendera, Rancho Santa Mar, CA 92688
714 858.1095

Johnson, Jack
206 N First St, Mpls, MN 55401
612 332.2361

Johnson, Joel Peter
PO Box 803, Buffalo, NY 14205
716 881.1757

Johnson, Julie
2512 State St, Dallas, TX 75209
214 969.1072

Johnson, Larry
50 Fuller Brook Rd, Wellesley, MA 02181
617 235.8658

Johnson, Layne Illustration
9618 Dapple Ln, Houston, TX 77065
713 469.1133

Johnson, Lonni Sue
357 West End Ave, NYC, NY 10024
212 873.7749

Johnson, Osie
2233 Kemper Ln, Cincinnati, OH 45206
513 861.1400

Johnson, Richard
610 Main St, Norwell, MA 02061
617 659.7222

Johnson, Rick
One S 608 Lambert Rd, Glen Ellyn, IL 60137
708 790.0084

Johnson, Rose
6638 N 13th St, Phoenix, AZ 85014
602 263.8990

Johnson, Scott
10 South Trail, Orinda, CA 94563
510 254.1635

Johnson, Stephen
81 Remsen St, Brooklyn, NY 11201
718 237.2352

Johnson, Steven
440 Sheridan Ave S, Mpls, MN 55405
612 377.8728

Johnson, Tani
927 27th St, Manhattan Beach, CA 90266
310 545.8981

Johnson/Fancher Illustration
440 Sheridan Ave S, Mpls, MN 55405
612 377.8728

Johnston, David McCall
30605 Inkster Rd, Franklin, MI 48025
313 626.9546

Johnston, Keith
One State Cir, Annapolis, MD 21401
410 269.5470

Johnston, Scott
244 Ninth St, San Francisco, CA 94103
415 621.2992

Johnston, WB
476 College Ave, Winnipeg, MB,
Canada R2W 1M8
204 582.1686
page 341

Johnstone, Anne
77 Liberty Ave,
Sommerville, MA 02144
617 666.8120
page 311

Joined At The Hip
859 Sandcastle Dr, Cardiff by Sea, CA 92007
619 432.6282

Joint Ethics Committee
PO Box 179 Grand Central Sta,
NYC, NY 10163
212 966.2492

Jolliffe, Carey
4000 Oran Gulf Rd, Manlius, NY 13104
315 682.6388

Jonas, Ann
653 Carroll St, Brooklyn, NY 11215
718 636.5773

Jones, Barry
4630 Timberline Dr, Walnutport, PA 18088
610 767.3696

Jones, Buck
4313 65th St, Des Moines, IA 50322
515 278.0379

Jones, Dan
716 Sanchez St, San Francisco, CA 94114
415 285.8267

Jones, Danielle
55 Charles St W, Toronto, ON,
Canada M5S 2W9
416 968.6277

Jones, Davy
7744 Garnett, Lenexa, KS 66214
913 962.1543

Jones, Jeff Design & Illustration
7011 N 22nd Way, Phoenix, AZ 85020
602 331.4599
page 155

Jones, John Michael
25 Mine St, Flemington, NJ 08822
908 735.4391

Jones, Judith
1220 Blair Mill Rd, Silver Spring, MD 20910
310 589.5675

Jones, Marilyn
77 Tower Mountain Dr,
Bernardsville, NJ 07924
908 953.0242

Jones, Mary
405 N Wabash, Chicago, IL 60611
312 527.3283
fax 312 527.9091
page 73

Jones, Michael
1944 N Wilmot, Chicago, IL 60647
312 278.4652

Jones, Michael Scott
400 W Erie, Chicago, IL 60610
312 787.7710

Jones, Randy
323 E Tenth St, NYC, NY 10009
212 677.5387

Jones, Reginald
2500 N Buttercup Dr, Tucson, AZ 85749
602 760.0811

Jones, Robert J
47 W Stewart Ave, Lansdowne, PA 19050
610 626.1245

Jones, Robin
1033 Miramar St, Laguna Beach, CA 92651
714 497.3525

Jones, Roger
34 Gorham St, Cambridge, MA 02138
617 661.8645

Jones, Russell
199 Eighth Ave, Brooklyn, NY 11215
718 965.3224

Jones, Rusty
3625 N Hall, Dallas, TX 75219
214 522.4132

Jones, Steve
654 Pier Ave, Santa Monica, CA 90405
310 392.4877

Jonke, Tim
88 Jefferson Ln, Chicago, IL 60107
708 670.0912

Jordan, Dick
3500 Joy Ln, Shingle Springs, CA 95682
916 677.2799

Jordan, Polly
29 Warren Ave, Somerville, MA 02143
617 776.0329

Jorg, Liz
121 Brompton Rd, Garden City, NY 11530
516 742.5068

Jorisch, Stephane
3569 rue Bordeaux, Montreal, QU,
Canada H2K 3Z3
514 527.6837

Jorgensen & Barrett
PO Box 19412, Seattle, WA 98109
206 634.1880
fax 206 632.2024
pages 182-185, 464

Jorgensen, Bruce
95 Youmans Ave, Washington, NJ 07882
908 689.7776

Jorgensen, Robert
1615 Berkeley Ave, St Paul, MN 55105
612 698.0213

Jorstad, Diane
194 Jones Rd, Cabot, PA 16023
412 352.2686

Jost, Larry
311 NW 77th St, Seattle, WA 98117
206 789.3979

Joy, Pat
1259 Oak Dr, Vista, CA 92084
619 726.2781

Joyce, William
3302 Centenary Blvd, Shreveport, LA 71104
318 868.6838

Joyner, Eric
227 Kentucky St, Petaluma, CA 94952
707 769.1344
page 388

Judd, Jeff
827 1/4 N McCadden Pl, L.A., CA 90038
213 469.0333

Juhasz, Victor
576 Westminster Ave, Elizabeth, NJ 07208
908 351.4227

Jung, Rodney
67-14 108th St, Forest Hills, NY 11375
718 544.4278

Juniper, David
Ten Gates St, London, England WC2 A3HP
011 44.71.242.9562

Just, Alan
520 SW Sixth, Portland, OR 97204
503 228.5853
fax 503 221.4296
page 352

Just, Hal
155 E 38th St, NYC, NY 10016
212 697.6170

Justinsen, Lars
420 Lexington Ave, NYC, NY 10170
212 697.8525

Jutton, Paul
226 Greeley St, Rochester, NY 14609
716 482.4761

K&K Art & Associates
510 Marquette Ave, Mpls, MN 55402
612 339.0947

K&K Kreations
19412 Pompano Ln,
Huntington Beach, CA 92648
714 969.0085

Kabak, Mark
4116 Clark Ave, Kansas City, MO 64111
816 753.0229

Kabaker, Gayle
18 McKinley St, Rowayton, CT 06853
203 866.3734
fax 203 857.0842
pages 18-19

Kabaker, Gayle
NYC, NY
212 581.8338
pages 18-19

Kabrin, Carole
1300 Porter St, Dearborn, MI 48124
313 561.7291

Kaczman, James
Seven Chester St,
Watertown, MA 02172
617 923.4605
fax 617 923.4739
pages 116-117

Kadiev, Petko
1400 N Hayworth Ave,
West Hollywood, CA 90046
213 851.7737

Kagansky, Eugene
515 Ave I, Brooklyn, NY 11230
718 253.0454

Kahl, David
85 Jefferson St, Hoboken, NJ 07030
201 963.7975

Kahn, Harvey
155 Millburn Ave, Millburn, NJ 07041
201 467.0223

Kahn, Jill
4317 Cornelia Cir, Mpls, MN 55435
612 925.1699

Kaji, Nobu
703 Market St/Tokyo Design Ctr,
San Francisco, CA 94103
415 543.4886
fax 415 543.4956
page 369

Kalafat, Loris
353 W 53rd St, NYC, NY 10019
212 582.0023

Kalish, Lionel
108 E 35th St, NYC, NY 10016
212 889.3337

Kalish, Renee
203 N Wabash, Chicago, IL 60601
312 704.0010
pages 10-11, 88

Kamel, Kathy
806 Hartzell St, Pacific Palisade, CA 90272
310 459.3341

Kammerer, Ann
925 Elm Grove Rd, Elm Grove, WI 53122
414 785.1940

Kane, John
Nine W Bridge St, New Hope, PA 18938
215 862.0392

Kane, Lehua
PO Box 82921, San Diego, CA 92138
619 268.8244

Kane, Thomas
2261 Fifth St, Berkeley, CA 94710
510 843.0701

Kanegawa, Doug
506 W 157th St, Gardena, CA 90248
310 329.5078

Kanelous, George
8020 Grenfell St, Kew Gardens, NY 11415
212 688.1080

Kann, Victoria
336 E 22nd St, NYC, NY 10010
212 979.0988
page 221

Kantra, Michele
306 W 93rd St, NYC, NY 10025
212 316.3176

Kanzler, John
30 Linden St, New Haven, CT 06511
203 782.6981

Kaplan, Mark
374 Fifth St, Brooklyn, NY 11215
718 832.2317

Kappes, Werner
73 Inverness Rd, Scarsdale, NY 10583
914 472.9056

Kapusta, Janusz
1060 Ocean Ave, Brooklyn, NY 11226
718 434.1859

Karaberis Design/Illustration
1200 Vine St, Denver, CO 80206
303 321.2225

Karapelou, John
731 N 24th St, Phila, PA 19130
215 232.6666

Karas, G Brian
4126 N 34th St, Phoenix, AZ 85018
602 956.5666

Karen, Adam
3810 Greystone Ave, Riverdale, NY 10463
718 543.1888

Kari, Morgan
22853 Mariano St, Woodland Hills, CA 91367
818 346.9167

Karl, Kevin
6730 Garner Ave, St Louis, MO 63139
314 781.9494

Karlin, Nurit
415 Central Park W, NYC, NY 10025
212 866.2130

Karn, George
6601 Fifth Ave, Richfield, MN 55423
612 798.5977

Karn, Murray
120 E 86th St, NYC, NY 10028
212 289.9124

Karpinski, John Eric
6259 N Hwy I, Fredonia, WI 53021
414 692.9354

Kars, Norman
13827 Olive St Rd, Chesterfield, MO 63017
314 878.1006

Kasahara, Margaret
2165 Vassar Dr, Boulder, CO 80303
719 520.1622

Kase, Ander
10829 Palms Blvd, L.A., CA 90034
310 204.1799

Kasinger/Mastel
8350 Melrose, L.A., CA 90069
213 653.6484

Kasnot, Keith
9228 N 29th St, Phoenix, AZ 85028
602 482.6501

Kasper, Robert
430 Ventura Pl, Vero Beach, FL 32963
617 236.1920

Kasperski, Tom
435 White Chapel Dr, O'Fallon, MO 63366
314 827.2752

Kastaris, Harriet & Associates
3301 A S Jefferson St, St Louis, MO 63118
314 773.2600

Kastner, John
158 Burwell Rd, Rochester, NY 14617
716 461.4701

Kasun, Mike
405 N Wabash Ave, Chicago, IL 60611
312 321.1336

Katayama, Mits
1904 Third Ave, Seattle, WA 98101
206 634.1880
fax 206 632.2024
page 184

Katsulis, Tom
43 E Ohio St, Chicago, IL 60611
312 527.2244

Katz, Karen
169 Mercer St, NYC, NY 10012
212 925.1279

Katz, Les
451 Westminster Rd, Brooklyn, NY 11218
718 284.4779

Kaufman, Donna
3044 Orange Ave, La Crescenta, CA 91214
818 248.7022

Kawabata, Tony
2047 Evergreen Ter, Arlington Hts, IL 60004
708 392.7195

Kawakami, Natsumi
1041-11 Tamado, Shimodate City, Japan
011 81.296.28.2920

KCP Caricatures
PO Box 540130, Millis, MA 02054
508 376.2649

Keating, Peggy
30 Horatio St, NYC, NY 10014
212 691.4654

Keats, Adrienne Calligraphy
980 Ashbury St, San Francisco, CA 94117
415 759.5678

Kecman, Milan
4736 S Hills Dr SW, Cleveland, OH 44109
216 741.8755

Keeter, Susan
666 Greenwich St, NYC, NY 10014
212 675.5719

Kehl, Richard
2227 Yale Avenue E,
Seattle, WA 98102
206 634.1880
fax 206 632.2024
page 182

Keith, Larry
3807 Drake St, Houston, TX 77005
713 664.3922

Keller, Jane
323 Sumner Rd, Annapolis, MD 21401
410 280.2832

Keller, Phil
1400 N Hayworth Ave,
West Hollywood, CA 90046
213 851.7737

Keller, Steve
108 E 35th St, NYC, NY 10016
212 889.3337

Kellerman, Bob
332 Congress St, Boston, MA 02210
617 542.2647

Kelley, Barbara
2022 Jones St, San Francisco, CA 94133
415 928.0457

Kelley, Gary
301 1/2 Main St, Cedar Falls, IA 50613
319 277.2330

Kelley, Patrick
1127 California St, Grand Rapids, MI 49504
616 949.0925

Kelley, Susan
4805 Colorado St, Long Beach, CA 90814
310 438.6413

Kellogg Creative Services
525 E Flower, Phoenix, AZ 85012
602 241.1828

Kemper, Bud
52 High Trl, Eureka, MO 63025
314 938.4122

Kendall, Brad
217 Slater Ave, Providence, RI 02906
401 351.8017

Kendig, Debi
1900 Crown Park Ct, Columbus, OH 43235
614 451.1744

Kennedy, Anne
666 Greenwich St, NYC, NY 10014
212 675.5719

Kennedy, Dean
Denver, CO 80210
303 733.0128

Kennedy, Veronica
8500 New Hampshire Ave,
Silver Spring, MD 20903
301 439.5922

Kennedy, Victor
514 Meadowfield Ct, Lawrenceville, GA 30243
404 339.0345

Kennemer, Linda
PO Box 140012, Irving, TX 75014
214 550.9073

Kennevan, Steve
2401 Thorndyke Ave,
Seattle, WA 98199
206 285.7758
fax 206 270.9225
page 350

Keogh, Johanna
2405 Clay Ave, Venice, CA 90291
310 578.6965

Kerns, Ron
15 W 72nd St, NYC, NY 10023
212 799.2231

Kessler, Leonard
Six Stoneham Ln, New City, NY 10956
914 354.2759

Ketler, Ruth Sofair
101 Bluff Ter,
Silver Springs, MD 20902
301 593.6059
fax 301 593.1236
page 284

Khachi, Ramina
693 S Second St, San Jose, CA 95112
408 298.9636

Kidd, Tom
59 Cross Brook Rd, New Milford, CT 06776
203 355.1781

Kiefer, Alfons
420 Lexington Ave, NYC, NY 10170
212 986.5680

Kihlstrom, Chris
890 Saratoga Rd, Berwyn, PA 19312
610 296.0353

Kilberg, James
8418 Naylor Ave, L.A., CA 90045
310 215.0092

Kileen, Tom
450 S Venice Blvd, Venice, CA 90291
310 306.7531

Kilfoy, Michael
3301A S Jefferson Ave, St Louis, MO 63118
314 773.2600

Kilroy, John
28 Fairmont Way, Hull, MA 02045
617 925.0582

Kimball, Tom
9300 Santa Fe Springs Rd,
Santa Fe Springs, CA 90670
310 903.3397

Kimche, Tania
425 W 23rd St, NYC, NY 10011
212 242.6367

King, Dale
7042 Sophia Ave, Van Nuys, CA 91406
818 786.1878

King, Ed
220 Ash St, Honesdale, PA 18431
717 253.4104

King, Greg
1805 Dawn Cir, Richardson, TX 75081
214 231.8473

King, Heather
76 Golden Gate Cir, Napa, CA 94558
707 226.1232

King, JD
158 Sixth Ave, Brooklyn, NY 11217
718 636.0768

King, Patty
1337 Honey Trl, Walnut Creek, CA 94596
510 938.7474

Kirchoff Wohlberg
866 United Nations Plz, NYC, NY 10017
212 644.2020

Kirk, Daniel
207 Baldwin St, Glen Ridge, NJ 07028
201 748.6997

Kirkland, James Ennis
234 Nimitz Ave, Redwood, CA 94061
415 366.2898

Kirkman, Rick
2432 W Peoria Ave, Phoenix, AZ 85061
602 997.6004

Kitchell, Joyce
2755 Eagle St, San Diego, CA 92103
619 291.1378

Kittelberger, Eric
2960 Stockton St, Akron, OH 44314
216 753.8334

Kitts, Thomas
1320 SE 28th, Portland, OR 97214
503 235.0606

Kitzerow, Scott
3505 N Pine Grove, Chicago, IL 60657
312 935.9234

Kiwak, Barbara
165 E 32nd St, NYC, NY 10016
212 686.3514

Klanderman, Leland
3286 Ivanhoe, St Louis, MO 63139
314 241.4014

Klare, Tom
PO Box 370561, San Diego, CA 92137
619 565.6167

Klassen, Tony
852 W Roscoe, Chicago, IL 60657
312 281.4663

Klauba, Douglas C
213 W Insitute Pl, Chicago, IL 60610
312 943.4676
fax 312 943.6946
page 194

Klavins, Uldis
60 E 42nd St, NYC, NY 10017
212 867.8092

Kleber, John
2301 N Tenth St, Phoenix, AZ 85006
312 464.0964

Klein, Hedy
111-56 76th Dr,
Forest Hills, NY 11375
718 793.0246
page 441

Klein, Jane
1635 E 22nd St, Oakland, CA 94606
510 535.0495
fax 510 535.0437
pages 108-109

Klein, Michael S
22 Edgewood Rd, Madison, NJ 07940
201 765.0623

Klein, Renee
164 Daniel Low Ter, Staten Island, NY 10301
718 727.0723

Kleman, Gary
811 S Florissant Rd, St Louis, MO 63135
314 521.5065

Klementz-Harte, Lauren
PO Box 4006, Meriden, CT 06450
203 235.6145

Klemm, Bill
2100 W Big Beaver Rd, Troy, MI 48084
810 643.6000

Klimt, Bill & Maurine
15 W 72nd St, NYC, NY 10023
212 799.2231

Klinko, Julia
Miami, FL 33133
305 445.5540

Klioze, Marcia
2409 Andorra Pl, Reston, VA 22091
703 620.4922

Kliros, Thea
313 E 18th St, NYC, NY 10003
212 254.2574

Klitsch, Libby Johnson
211 First Ave, Haddon Heights, NJ 08035
609 546.1202

Klobucar, Nancy
2226 Brier Ave, L.A., CA 90039
213 660.1454

Klopp, Karyl
5209 Eighth St, Charlestown, MA 02129
617 242.7463

Klug, David
2304 James St, McKeesport, PA 15132
412 754.5584

Kluglein, Karen
37 Cary Rd, Great Neck, NY 11021
212 684.2974

Kluskowski, Darryl
8300 W 30th 1/2 St, St Louis Park, MN 55426
612 931.3049

Knaack, Jennifer
733-A Franklin St, Oshkosh, WI 54901
414 231.6648

Knabel, Lonnie S
8506 Suburban Dr, Orlando, FL 32829
407 381.4226

Knable, Ellen & Associates
1233 S La Cienega Blvd, L.A., CA 90035
310 855.8855

Knaff, Jean-Christian
430 Ventura Pl, Vero Beach, MA 32963
617 236.1920

Knecht, Cliff
309 Walnut Rd, Pittsburgh, PA 15202
412 761.5666

Knight, Milton
PO Box 1262, Burbank, CA 91507
818 766.0685

Knoll, Kimberly
3443 Wade St, L.A., CA 90066
310 390.9595

Knotts, Steve
1679 Crofton Way, Pasadena, CA 91103
800 559.2643

Knowles, Philip
1633 Stearns Dr, L.A., CA 90035
213 934.7134

Knox, Berney
4110 Vasconia St, Tampa, FL 33629
813 831.8755

Knox, David Design
2424 N Rose, Mesa, AZ 85213
602 827.9339

Knutsen, Jan
10740 Toledo Ct, Bloomington, MN 55437
612 884.8083

Kocar, George
24213 Lake Rd, Bay Village, OH 44140
216 871.8325

Koeffler, Ann Represents
5015 Clinton St, L.A., CA 90004
213 957.2327

Koegel, Jeff
210 Eighth St, Huntington Beach, CA 92648
714 969.1775

Koehli, Urs
156 Fifth Ave, NYC, NY 10010
212 645.2686

Koelsch, Michael
232 Madison Ave, NYC, NY 10016
212 889.8777

Koerber, Nora
2408 Paloma St, Pasadena, CA 91104
818 791.1953

Kohl, Joe
522 Vine Ave, Toms River, NJ 08753
908 349.4149

Kohler Studios
3503 Stonewall Pl, Atlanta, GA 30339
404 436.8664

Kokinski, Marc
4393 rue de Bullion, Montreal, QU,
Canada H2W 2G2
514 281.0922

Kolacz, Jerzy
51 Camden St, Toronto, ON,
Canada M5V 1V2
416 362.1913
fax 416 362.6356
page 226

Kolosta, Darrel
PO Box 2715, Oakland, CA 94602
510 530.5917

Komisarow, Ralph
300 W 72nd St, NYC, NY 10023
212 873.2231

Kondo, Vala
230 W 79th St, NYC, NY 10024
212 517.4052

Kong, Emlie
11169 Weddington St,
North Hollywood, CA 91601
818 762.5471

Koni, Robin
28 Shelton St, London,
England WC2H 9JN
011 44 71 240 2077
fax 011 44 71 836 0199
page 122

Konz, Stephen
2837 NW 71st St, Seattle, WA 98117
206 783.4147
fax 206 783.4147
page 133

Kopp, Jim
566 Condor Ln, San Marcos, CA 92069
619 471.6983

Korab, Rick
475 Cleveland Ave N, St Paul, MN 55104
612 644.7770

Koralik Associates
900 W Jackson Blvd, Chicago, IL 60607
312 944.5680
fax 312 421.5948
pages 426-427

Koren, Edward
Pond Vlg, Brookfield, VT 05036
802 276.3103

Korn, Pamela
PO Box 521, Canadensis, PA 18325
717 595.9298

Kotik, Kenneth
Nine Last Chance Ct, St Peters, MO 63376
314 441.1091

Koury, Jennifer
512 Main St, El Segundo, CA 90245
310 640.8258

Kovalcik, Terry
80 Eighth Ave, NYC, NY 10011
212 620.7772

Kowalski, Mike
1515 Monroe St, Port Townsend, WA 98368
206 379.9691

Koz-Art
22214 Greekview Dr, Gaithersburg, MD 20882
301 921.6345

Kozlowski, Martin
141 Southside Ave, Hastings, NY 10706
914 478.7445

Kozmiuk, Michael
353 W 53rd St, NYC, NY 10019
212 682.2462

Krahulik, Dorie
17205 Avenida de la Herradura,
Pacific Palisade, CA 90272
310 459.4614

Kramer, Aaron
615 W Randolph, Chicago, IL 60606
312 454.1533

Krantz, Kathy
Pine Rd HCR, Neversink, NY 12765
914 985.2936

Kratter, Paul
PO Box 421443,
San Francisco, CA 94142
415 647.5660
fax 415 285.1102
pages 379-380

Kraus, James F/Art Guy Studios
195 W Canton St, Boston, MA 02116
617 437.1945
page 317

Krauss, Audrey
1129 S Bedford St, L.A., CA 90035
310 247.9347

Kray, Daniel
2175 Sampson Ave, Corona, CA 91719
714 278.2141

Kreidler, Bruce
3913 Paxton Rd, Cincinnati, OH 45209
513 351.6437

Kreiger, Salem
900 W Jackson Blvd, Chicago, IL 60607
312 944.5680

Krejca, Gary
520 N Michigan Ave, Chicago, IL 60611
312 527.0351

Kreloff, Marty
3443 Wade St, L.A., CA 90066
310 390.9595

Krenzke, Chris
2900 Ruby Ave, Racine, WI 53402
414 639.2802

Kress, Kurt
735 Pearl St, Laguna Beach, CA 92651
714 494.5101

Kressley, Michael
67 Brookside Ave, Boston, MA 02130
617 522.5132

Kretschmann, Karin
1052 Laura St, Casselberry, FL 32707
407 699.6919

Kretzchmar, Art
43 N Cherokee Ln, Bricktown, NJ 08724
908 295.5625

Kriebel, Nancy
411 Hermosa Dr NE, Albuquerque, NM 87108
505 268.5405

Kriegshauser, Shannon
3286 Ivanhoe, St Louis, MO 63139
314 781.7377

Krizmanic, Tatjana
250 Spinnaker Dr, Halifax, NS,
Canada B3N 3E4
902.477.2117

Krogle, Jim
12121 Wilshire Blvd, L.A., CA 90025
310 826.9378

Krogle, Robert
10835 W Cougar Gulch Rd, Coeurd'alene,
ID 83814
800 653.6536
page 88

Krogle, Robert
420 Lexington Ave, NYC, NY 10170
212 986.5680
fax 212 818.1246
page 88

Krommes, Beth
310 Old Street Rd, Peterborough, NH 03458
603 924.8790

Kroninger, Stephen
247 W. 10th St., NYC, NY 10014
212 691.8696

Kropp, Steve
153 Second Ave, Salt Lake City, UT 84103
801 364.7404

Krosnick, Paul
686 Undercliff Ave, Edgewater, NJ 07020
201 224.5495

Krovatin, Dan
Three Woodbury Rd, Trenton, NJ 08638
609 895.1634

Krueger, Brian
2233 Kemper Ln, Cincinnati, OH 45206
513 861.1400

Kubinyi, Laszlo
108 E 35th St, NYC, NY 10016
212 889.3337

Kuchar, Karen
900 W Jackson Blvd, Chicago, IL 60607
312 944.5680

Kuehnel, Peter & Associates
30 E Huron Plz, Chicago, IL 60611
312 642.6499

Kueker, Donald L
829 Ginger Wood Ct, Manchester, MO 63021
314 225.1566

Kuester, Robert
25 W 45th St, NYC, NY 10017
212 398.9540

Kuhn, Grant M
233 Bergen St, Brooklyn, NY 11217
718 596.7808

Kulczak, Frank
412 Diller Rd, Hanover, PA 17331
717 637.2580

Kung, Lingta
5317 Village Circle Dr, Temple City, CA 91780
818 448.2055

Kunstler, Mort
217 E 86th St, NYC, NY 10028
212 355.0910

Kunz, Anita
230 Ontario St, Toronto, ON,
Canada M5A 2V5
416 368.3947

Kunze, Helen
63 Woodlake Ct, Lake St Louis, MO 63367
314 332.3316

Kuper, Peter
250 W 99th St, NYC, NY 10025
212 864.5729

Kupper, Ketti
151 Southworth St, Milford, CT 06460
203 874.7082

Kyllo, James
PO Box 222946, Carmel, CA 93922
408 625.6176

L-Squared Studios
20 W 20th St, NYC, NY 10011
212 675.4681

La Fleur, Dave
9121 E 79th S, Derby, KS 67037
316 788.0253

La Galia, Linda
625 Main St, NYC, NY 10044
212 754.0350

Laager, Ken
304 N Elm St, Lititz, PA 17543
717 627.2085

Laan, Cor
414 Crest Dr, Redwood City, CA 94062
415 859.1754

Labadie, Ed
2309 Mountain View Dr, Boise, ID 83706
208 377.2447

LaBash, Michael
22 Douglas St, Brooklyn, NY 11231
718 625.7325

**Labbé, Jeff M
218 Princeton Ave,
Claremont, CA 91711
909 621.6678
page 347**

Labbe, John
97 Third Ave, NYC, NY 10003
212 529.2831

Lacamara Studio
22834 Burbank Blvd,
Woodland Hills, CA 91367
818 887.5211

Lacava, Vincent
1186 Broadway, NYC, NY 10001
212 725.8949

Lack, Don
216 Sunnyside Rd, Temple Terrace, FL 33617
813 989.0079

Lackner, Paul
976 Old Huntingdon Pike,
Huntingdon Vly, PA 19006
215 663.0587

Lackow, Andy
7004 Blvd E, Guttenburg, NJ 07093
201 854.2770

Ladden, Randee
7445 N Rockwell St, Chicago, IL 60645
312 761.6288

Laden, Nina
1517 McLendon Ave NE, Atlanta, GA 30307
404 371.0052

Lafrance, Laurie
53 Rowntree Ave, Toronto, ON,
Canada M6N 1R8
416 658.0263

Lagerstrom, Wendy
12056 Summit Cir, Beverly Hills, CA 90210
310 276.5282

Laird, Campbell
162 E 23rd St, NYC, NY 10010
212 505.5552

Laird, Thomas
706 Scott St, Philipsburg, PA 16866
814 342.2935

**Laish, James
55 Charles St W, Toronto, ON,
Canada M5S 2W9
416 921.1709
fax 416 968.6479
pages 30-31**

Lakota, Walter
2302 Columbia Dr, Costa Mesa, CA 92626
714 646.5231

Laliberte, Richard
198 Filbert Dr, Gaithersburg, MD 20879
301 330.6911

Lalingo, Don
5236 Bellaire Ave,
North Hollywood, CA 91607
818 763.8049

Lallky-Seibert, Bonnie
1675 NE 36th St, Ft Lauderdale, FL 33334
305 564.3259

**Lally, Michele
1001 S Alfred St, L.A., CA 90035
310 556.1439
fax 213 653.5696
page 385**

Lam, Nghia
832 Fifth Ave, San Diego, CA 92101
619 231.0207

LaMantia Studio
820 W Howe St, Bloomington, IN 47403
812 332.2667

Lambase, Barbara
5400 Calle De, Torrance, CA 90503
310 373.4993

Lambrenos, Jim
12 Salem Ct, Atco, NJ 08004
609 768.0580

Lamut, Sonja
165 E 32nd St, NYC, NY 10016
212 686.3514

Lancaster Design
1810 14th St, Santa Monica, CA 90404
310 450.2999

Lancelle, Gary
1234 Delray Ave, Green Bay, WI 54304
414 499.7697

Landerman Illustration
1800 Narberth Rd, Baltimore, MD 21228
410 788.7481

Landikusic, Katherine
4649 Stateline Rd, Kansas City, MO 64112
816 753.2247

Landis Studio
1372 50th Ave NE, St Petersburg, FL 33703
813 525.0757

Landon, Lucinda
26 Tucker Holmes Rd,
North Scituate, RI 02857
401 647.2253

Lane, Patricia
54 Preston Rd, Somerville, MA 02143
617 776.4150

Lane, Tammie
300 Pacific Ave, Aspen, CO 81611
303 925.9213

Laney, Ron
25 Madonna Ct, Highland, IL 62249
618 654.5142

Lang, Cecily
27923 Brndywine Rd,
Farmington Hills, MI 48334
810 489.1058

Lang, Donna Illustration
564 Madrone Ave, Sunnyvale, CA 94086
408 730.8511

Lang, Glenna
43 Stearns St, Cambridge, MA 02138
617 661.7591

Lang, Julie
27923 Brandywine, Farmington Hills, MI 48334
616 451.8374

Lange, Andrew
213 Fairmont Ave, Hackensack, NJ 07601
201 646.9210

Lange, Jim Design
750 94th Ave N, St Petersburg, FL 33702
813 579.4499

Langenbacher, Linda
824 Bonnie Brae St, L.A., CA 90057
213 388.3415

Langeneckert, Mark
3664 Bassett Woods, Pacific, MO 63069
314 451.5568

Langer, DC
32 Bradock Pk, Boston, MA 02116
617 536.6651

Langer, Jean-Claude
716 Sanchez St, San Francisco, CA 94114
415 285.8267

Langley Illustration
619 Maybell Ave, Palo Alto, CA 94306
415 857.9539

Langley, Stephanie
PO Box 19412, Seattle, WA 98109
206 634.1880
fax 206 632.2024
page 183

Langsdorf, Henrik
167 Ave A, NYC, NY 10009
212 505.8713

Languedoc, Patricia
850 Highlands Dr, Santa Barbara, CA 93109
805 962.4072

LaPine, Julia
Five Triad Ctr, Salt Lake City, UT 84180
801 350.9025

Lapinski, Joe
853 Broadway, NYC, NY 10003
212 677.9100

LaPointe, Camille
PO Box 2886, Castro Valley, CA 94546
510 581.4390

Lapsley, Bob Studio
2430 Glen Haven Blvd, Houston, TX 77030
713 667.4393

Lardy, Philippe
478 W Broadway, NYC, NY 10012
212 473.3057

Larkin, Bob
10 Bluebell Ln, Northport, NY 11768
516 261.4495

Larks, David
7917 Sale Ave, West Hills, CA 91304
818 888.8536

Larose, Lou
11768 Monte Leon Way, Northidge, CA 91326
818 360.1200

Larrain, Coco
95 Grand St, NYC, NY 10013
212 925.8747

Larsen, Tracy
920 SE Third Ter, Lees Summit, MO 64063
816 524.6949

Larson, Paul
1125 Sixth St, Santa Monica, CA 90403
310 458.9140

Larson, Seth
597 Riverside Ave,
Westport, CT 06880
203 226.4724
fax 203 454.9904
page 67

Latto, Sophia
723 President St, Brooklyn, NY 11215
718 789.1980

Lau, Bernadette
50 Perthshire St, Scarborough, ON,
Canada M1V 3A9
416 291.0524

Laub, Rolf
4101 Greenbriar, Houston, TX 77098
713 522.9873

Laughlin, David
220 S Norris Ave, Tucson, AZ 85719
602 624.7354

Laumann, Scott
402 Avenida Adobe,
Escondido, CA 92029
619 743.3910
page 181

Laurent, Richard Design
531 S Plymouth Ct, Chicago, IL 60605
312 472.6550

Laurie, Alan
527 Malden Ave E, Seattle, WA 98112
206 328.9325

Lauwers, Jeff
1105 Russell, Golden, CO 80401
303 279.0978

Lavaty, Frank & Jeff
217 E 86 St, NYC, NY 10022
212 355.0910

Lavern, Rod
PO Box 7093, Laguna Niguel, CA 92607
714 366.1120

LaVigne, Dan
11936 W Jefferson Blvd,
Culver City, CA 90230
310 390.8663

Lavy, Brian
10803 Magnolia Dr, Cleveland, OH 44106
216 791.7721

Lawson, Robert
900 W Jackson Blvd, Chicago, IL 60607
312 944.5680

Lazar, Brian
1200 SW 97th Ave, Miami, FL 33174
305 553.7736

Lazarus, Robin
814 Edgewood Dr, Westbury, NY 11590
516 338.0636

Lazure, Catherine
593 Riverside Dr, NYC, NY 10031
212 690.1867

Le Veque, Janet
2525 Laurel Pass, L.A., CA 90046
213 656.7868

Le-Tan, Pierre
155 W 15th St, NYC, NY 10011
212 989.8770

Leach, Ronald
5743 Howe St, Pittsburgh, PA 15232
412 361.6358

Leahy, Joe
4730 Latona Ave NE, Seattle, WA 98105
206 547.1001

Leary, Catherine
11936 W Jefferson Blvd,
Culver City, CA 90230
310 390.8663

Leary, T Pat
883 E 11150 S, Sandy, UT 84094
801 572.2753

Lebbad, James A
24 Independence Way, Titusville, NJ 08560
609 737.3458

Lebenson, Richard
253 Washington Ave, Brooklyn, NY 11205
718 857.9267

Lebold, Bruce
7118 Bobhird Dr, San Diego, CA 92119
619 463.5044

Lecons-Abdo, Lynda
22727 Schoolcraft St, West Hills, CA 91307
818 710.8108

Lederman, Marsha
107 N Columbus St, Arlington, VA 22203
703 243.5636

LeDuc, Bernard
4564 Chambord, Montreal, QU,
Canada H2J 3M7
514 844.0074

Lee & Lou Productions Inc
8522 National Blvd, L.A., CA 90232
310 287.1542

Lee, Bill
792 Columbus Ave, NYC, NY 10025
212 866.5664

Lee, Fran
1911 W Winona, Chicago, IL 60640
312 769.6566

Lee, Jim
5044 1/4 Colfax Ave,
North Hollywood, CA 91601
818 761.8546

Lee, Jody
PO Box 110, White Plains, NY 10603
914 686.5834

Lee, Lace
2233 Kemper Ln, Cincinnati, OH 45206
513 861.1400

Lee, Lilly
1021 University Ave, Berkeley, CA 94710
510 849.1900

Lee, Pamela
1005 2476 York Ave, Vancouver, BC,
Canada V6K 1E2
604 739.8034

Lee, Victor
1633 California St, San Francisco, CA 94109
415 775.3613

Lee, Victoria
7810 Clark Rd, Jessup, MD 20794
301 596.3532

Leech, Jean
18 Belmont Ave, Canonsburg, PA 15317
412 746.9138

Leedy, Jeff
480 Gate Five Rd, Sausalito, CA 94965
415 331.1354

Leer, Rebecca
440 West End Ave, NYC, NY 10024
212 595.5865

Lefebvre, Renae
206 N First St, Mpls, MN 55401
612 332.2361

Leff, Jerry Associates
420 Lexington Ave, NYC, NY 10170
212 697.8525
fax 212 949.1843
pages 435, 457, 464

Lefkowitz, Mark
132 Oakhill Dr, Sharon, MA 02067
617 784.5293

Lehman, Connie
218 S Banner St, Elizabeth, CO 80107
303 646.4638

Lehner & Whyte Inc
8-10 S Fullerton Ave, Montclair, NJ 07042
201 746.1335

Leib, Vikki
101 Yesler Way, Seattle, WA 98109
206 447.1600

Leigh, LeeAnn
2304 Rosemary, Simi Valley, CA 93065
805 527.8955

Leigh, Thomas
205 Rote Hill, Sheffield, MA 01257
413 229.8258

Leighton & Co
Four Prospect St, Beverly, MA 01915
508 921.0887
fax 508 921.0223
pages 115-117

Leiner, Alan
353 W 53rd St, NYC, NY 10019
212 582.0023

Leister, Bryan
202 E Raymond Ave, Alexandria, VA 22301
703 683.1544

Lejnar, Steve
12627 Wisteria Dr, Germantown, MD 20874
301 540.3954

Lemelman, Martin
1286 Country Club Rd, Allentown, PA 18106
610 395.4536

Lempa, Mary Flock
194 Olmsted, Riverside, IL 60546
708. 447.4454

Lence, Edward
1126 Pebble Hill Cir, Sandy, UT 84094
801 565.8893

Lendway, Andy
731 N 24th St, Phila, PA 19130
215 232.6666
fax 215 232.6585
page 330

Lengyel, Kathy
1224 Fairway Dr, Atlanta, GA 34698
404 875.1363

Lenz, Herbert
4915 N Winchester Ave, Chicago, IL 60640
312 334.2011

Leon, Karen
154-01 Barclay Ave, Flushing, NY 11355
718 461.2050

Leonard, Richard
212 W 17th St, NYC, NY 10011
212 243.6613

Leong, Shelton
580 Washington, San Francisco, CA 94111
415 362.8280

Lesh, David
NYC, NY
212 581.8338
pages 22-23

Lesh, David
18 McKinley St, Rowayton, CT 06853
203 866.3734
fax 203 857.0842
pages 22-23

Lesh, David
5693 N Meridian St, Indpls, IN 46208
317 253.3141
fax 317 255.8462
pages 22-23

Lessard, Marie
5155 rue Bordeaux, Montreal, QU, Canada H4C
2C7
514 524.5383

Lesser, Ron
420 Lexington Ave, NYC, NY 10170
212 697.8525

Lester, Michelle
15 W 17th St, NYC, NY 10011
212 989.1411

Lester, Mike
17 E Third Ave, Rome, GA 30161
706 234.7733

Letostak, John
7801 Fernhill Ave, Parma, OH 44129
216 885.1753

Letter Perfect
PO Box 785, Gig Harbor, WA 98335
206 851.5158

Letterform Design
501 N Orange Dr, L.A., CA 90036
213 932.1875

Letzig, Michael
3318 Gillham Rd, Kansas City, MO 64109
816 931.7138

Levee, Gayle
51 Century St, Medford, MA 02155
617 396.9656

Levin, Arnie
23 Glenlawn Avenue, Sea Cliff, NY 11579
516 676.1228

Levin, Sergio
PO Box 155, Passaic, NJ 07055
201 472.1225

Levine, Andy
23-30 24th St, L.I.C., NY 11105
718 956.8539

Levine, Bette
639 S Highland Ave, L.A., CA 90036
213 935.9199

Levine, John
2921 Bentan St, Denver, CO 80214
303 233.3348

Levine, Laura
444 Broome St, NYC, NY 10013
212 431.4787

Levine, Lucinda
2604 Connecticut Ave NW, Wash, DC 20008
202 667.5365

Levine, Marsha
PO Box 456, Lincolndale, NY 10540
914 248.4639

Levinson, David
86 Parson Rd, Clifton, NJ 07012
201 614.1627

Levinson, Jason
11625 Sun Cir Way, Columbia, MD 21044
410 720.1004

Levirne, Joel
Two Penn Plz, NYC, NY 10121
212 727.9277

Lewczak, Scott
1600 E Jefferson Ct, Sterling, VA 20164
718 622.3882

Lewis, HB
119 Benefit St, Providence, RI 02903
401 272.6922

Lewis, Keith
319 Franklin St, Richmond, VA 23219
804 644.8619

Lewis, Maribeth
441 Myrtle Ave, Albany, NY 12208
518 433.9403

Lewis, Maurice
353 W 53rd St, NYC, NY 10019
212 582.0023
fax 212 582.0090
page 146

Lewis, Ray
4575 Murat Ct, San Diego, CA 92117
619 270.9680

Lewis, Stacey
225 S 18th St, Phila, PA 19103
215 545.5614

Lewis, Tim
184 St Johns Pl, Brooklyn, NY 11217
718 857.3406

Leyonmark, Roger
265 Westminster Rd, Rochester, NY 14607
716 244.6956

Li, Philip
8326 Geary Blvd, San Francisco, CA 94121
415 221.0692

Liao, Sharmen
314 N Mission Dr, San Gabriel, CA 91775
818 458.7699

Liaw, Anson
64 Fraser Ave, Toronto, ON, Canada M6K 1Y6
416 536.1080

Liberman, Joni Levy
14 Hill Park Ter, Randolph, MA 02368
617 986.4657

Licea, Alfred
443 Park Ave S, NYC, NY 10016
212 545.7549

Lickona, Cheryl
210 E 63rd St, NYC, NY 10021
212 688.2562

Liedahl, Bryan
15628 S Eden Dr, Eden Prairie, CA 94122
415 753.5113

Liepke, Skip
30 W 72nd St, NYC, NY 10023
212 724.5593

Lieppman, Jeffrey
1250 23rd Ave, San Francisco, CA 94122
415 753.5113

Lies, Brian
Nine Humboldt St, Cambridge, MA 02140
617 876.0678

Ligasan, Darryl
151 E 31st St, NYC, NY 10016
212 889.5020

Lightburn, Ron
232 Madison Ave, NYC, NY 10016
212 889.8777

Lilie, Jim
110 Sutter St, San Francisco, CA 94104
415 441.4384
fax 415 395.9809
page 275

Lillard, Jill
2930 Lombardy Rd, Pasadena, CA 91107
818 792.5921

Lilly, Don
2031 N Maple St, Burbank, CA 91505
818 843.2565

Lim, Paul
109-20 71st Rd, Forest Hills, NY 11375
718 793.8350

Lindberg, Dean
5205 Woodlawn Blvd, Mpls, MN 55417
612 721.4993

Lindberg, Jeffrey
449 50th St, Brooklyn, NY 11220
718 492.1114

Lindgren & Smith
Chicago, IL
312 819.0880
pages 237-255

Lindgren & Smith
41 Union Sq W, NYC, NY 10003
212 929.5590
fax 212 989.8588
pages 237-255

Lindgren & Smith
San Francisco, CA
415 788.8552
pages 237-255

Lindgren, Cindy
4957 Oliver Ave S, Mpls, MN 55409
612 929.0657

Lindlof, Ed
PO Box 421443,
San Francisco, CA 94142
415 647.5660
fax 415 285.1102
page 379

Lindner, Verne Title Design
1011 Castro St, San Francisco, CA 94114
415 206.0275

Lindstrom, Jack
6300 Shingle Creek Pky, Mpls, MN 55430
612 561.6543

Line Art Services Inc
1268 Easthill Dr, Columbus, OH 43213
614 866.4165

Link
Two Silver Ave, Toronto, ON,
Canada M6R 3A2
416 530.1500
fax 416 530.1401
pages 460-463

Linley Illustration & Design
1504 W First Ave, Columbus, OH 43212
614 486.2921

Linn, Warren
4915 Broadway, NYC, NY 10034
212 942.6383

Linnett Studios
99 High St, Canton, MA 02021
617 828.4972

Lins, Rico
215 Park Ave S, NYC, NY 10017
212 674.8080

Linse, Pat
2059 N Maiden Ln, Altadena, CA 91001
818 797.2869

Lipelt Art Services
3050 Raleigh Ave, St Louis Park, MN 55416
612 922.4150

Lipshutz, Ellen
Buckhill Farm Rd, Arlington, VT 05250
802 375.6316

Lipton, Richard
26 Mather St, Boston, MA 02124
617 288.1953

Litman, Bruce
1514 Magee Ave, Phila, PA 19149
215 744.7442

Little Apple Art
409 Sixth Ave, Brooklyn, NY 11215
718 499.7045

Littmann, Barry
57 Overlook Dr, Hackettstown, NJ 07840
908 850.4405

Liu, Diana
83 Corte Placida, Greenbrae, CA 94904
415 461.2792

Liu, Hui Han
2735 Calpine Pl, Concord, CA 94518
510 827.2893

Live Wire Studios
2020 Euclid Ave, Cleveland, OH 44115
216 694.2020

Livingston, Eric
189 Brittany Dr, Freehold, NJ 07728
609 476.2047

Livingston, Francis
19 Brookmont Cir, San Anselmo, CA 94960
415 456.7103

Livingston, Lourdes
240 Scott St, San Francisco, CA 94117
415 252.7449

Lizardo, Jose
332 Congress St, Boston, MA 02210
617 542.2647

Lloreda, Ricardo
35 S Wilson Ave, Pasadena, CA 91106
818 577.3906

Lloyd, Bill
520 N Michigan Ave, Chicago, IL 60611
312 222.1771

Lloyd, Mary Anne
147 Wolcott St, Portland, ME 04102
207 773.4987

Loader, Dick
750 94th Ave N, St Petersburg, FL 33702
813 579.4499

LoBianco, Peter
135 E 56th St, NYC, NY 10022
212 935.0661

Loch, Lindsey
833 Richmond St, Boise, ID 83706
208 386.9074

Lochray, Tom
3225 Oakland Ave S, Mpls, MN 55407
612 823.7630

Locke, Gary
1005 Woodruff Bldg, Springfield, MO 65806
417 866.2885

Locke, John Studios
15 E 76th St, NYC, NY 10021
212 288.8010

Lockwood, Chris
2472 Bolsover, Houston, TX 77005
713 523.8444
fax 713 523.8485
page 443

Lockwood, Todd
1863 S Pearl St, Denver, CO 80210
303 733.0128
fax 303 733.8154
page 153

Loehle, Richard
2608 River Oak Dr, Decatur, GA 30033
404 633.5639

Loew, David
232 Madison Ave, NYC, NY 10016
212 889.8777

LoFaro, Jerry
353 W 53rd St, NYC, NY 10019
212 582.0023
fax 212 582.0090
page 147

Loftus, David
70 Rosaline Rd, London, England SW6 7QT
011 44.71.610.1801

LoGrippo, Robert
217 E 86th St, NYC, NY 10028
212 355.0910

Lohstoeter, Lori
41 Union Sq W, NYC, NY 10003
212 929.5590
page 242

Lonestar Studio
4916 Kelvin Dr, Houston, TX 77005
713 520.1298

Long, Cheryl
PO Box 430, Bastrop, TX 78602
512 321.5472

Long, Jim
4415 Briarwood Ct N, Annandale, VA 22003
703 354.8052

Long, Loren
3208 Sherman Ave, Middletown, IN 45044
317 424.7466

Long, Suzanne M
1430 Pacific Ave, San Francisco, CA 94109
415 776.3487

Longcore, Bill
258 Riley Rd, New Windsor, NY 12553
914 564.6972

Longtemps, Kenneth
362 Clinton St, Brooklyn, NY 11231
718 852.2178

The Looneybin
3912 E Second St, Long Beach, CA 90803
310 434.1016

Lopez, Paul
320 Bee Brook Rd, Washington, CT 06777
203 868.1011

Lord, David
2100 Cord St, Speedway, IN 46224
317 248.1992

Lord, Tim
2814 NW 72nd St, Seattle, WA 98117
206 784.1136

Lorenz, Al
49 Pine Ave, Floral Park, NY 11001
516 354.5530

Lorenz, Lee
108 E 35th St, NYC, NY 10016
212 889.3337

Lorenz, Stefan
Mozartstrasse 26, Freiburg, Germany 79104
011 07.61.35265

Lorusso, Joseph
4600 JC Nichols Pky, Kansas City, MO 64112
816 756.5723

Loschiavo, Doree
2714 S Marvine St, Phila, PA 19148
215 336.1724

Lott, Michele
345 S Cochran Ave, L.A., CA 90036
213 938.6500

Lott, Peter & George
60 E 42nd St, NYC, NY 10165
212 953.7088
page 368

Lotta, Tom
100 Rockwood St, Rochester, NY 14610
716 461.1390

Loudon, Greg
1804 Pine Rd, Homewood, IL 60430
708 799.4339

Love, Judy
68 Agassiz Ave, Belmont, MA 02178
617 484.8023

Love, Sara
770 E 73rs St, Indpls, IN 46240
317 255.1197

Lovejoy, Lois
646 Georgia Ave, Palo Alto, CA 94306
415 424.0636

Loveless, Roger
1199 S Main St, Centerville, UT 84014
801 292.0943

Lovell, Rick
2860 Lakewind Ct, Alpharetta, GA 30202
404 442.3943

Low, William
194 Third Ave, NYC, NY 10003
212 475.0440

Lowe, Paul
2850 N Beverly Dr, Beverly Hills, CA 90210
310 550.0499

Lowe, Tanya
2112 Century Park Ln, L.A., CA 90067
310 551.2822

Lowery, David
4283 Murietta Ave, Sherman Oaks, CA 91423
818 907.1873

Lowry, Janice
1116 N French St, Santa Ana, CA 92701
714 569.0476

Lowry, Rose Marie
119 Little Michigan Rd, Jaffrey, NJ 03452
603 532.8433

Loyd, Barbara
1912 Stoney Brook Dr, Houston, TX 77063
713 782.4739

Loza, Rebecca
731 E Palm Ave, Burbank, CA 91501
818 843.8225

Lozner, Ruth
9253 Three Oaks Dr, Silver Spring, MD 20901
301 587.3125

Lubofsky, T Page
28925 Golden Meadow Dr,
Rancho Palos Verdes, CA 90274
310 541.2656

Lucas, Sheila
2405 NW Thurman St,
Portland, OR 97210
503 225.9687
fax 503 228.6030
page 234

Luce, Ben
Five E 17th St, NYC, NY 10003
212 255.8193

Lucey Studio & Gallery
84 Crestwood Dr, San Rafael, CA 94901
415 453.3172

Ludeke, Chuck
900 W Jackson Blvd, Chicago, IL 60607
312 944.5680
fax 312 421.5948
page 427

Ludtke, Jim
Ten Ford St, San Francisco, CA 94114
415 863.6187

Luebke Studios
988 Oaks Ln, Omaha, NE 68137
402 895.4742

Lulu
4645 Colfax Ave S, Mpls, MN 55409
612 825.7564
pages 99, 109

Lund, David
14721 Bear Creek Ln NE,
Woodinville, WA 98072
206 881.3609
page 185

Lund, Gary
302 N La Brea Ave, L.A., CA 90036
213 655.0998

Lundeen, Cathy
Mpls, MO 55415
612 343.0432

Lundgren, Alvalyn
5530 Tanoak Ln, Agoura, CA 91301
818 707.0635

Lundquist, Roger
217 E 86th St, NYC, NY 10022
212 355.0910

Lunia Blue Graphics
4625 Ravenwood Ave, Sacramento, CA 95821
916 488.3425

Lunsford, Annie
515 N Hudson St, Arlington, VA 22201
703 527.7696

Luscombe, Mark
667 Crater Camp Dr, Calabasas, CA 91302
818 591.0333

Lustig, Ellen
2046-A N Racine Ave, Chicago, IL 60614
312 787.8852

Lustig, Loretta
330 Clinton Ave, Brooklyn, NY 11205
718 789.2496

Lutzow, Jack A
2350 Taylor St, San Francisco, CA 94133
415 776.3833

Lux, Frank & Associates Inc
20 W Hubbard, Chicago, IL 60610
312 222.1361
fax 312 222.0753
pages 421-423

Luzuriaga, Denis
1123 Broadway, NYC, NY 10010
212 243.1600

Lyall, Dennis
Five Highview Ave, Norwalk, CT 06851
212 986.5680

Lyhus, Randy
4853 Cordell Ave, Bethesda, MD 20814
301 986.0036

Lyles, L Kelly
5029 26th Ave SW, Seattle, WA 98106
206 937.2058

Lynch, Alan Artists
11 Kings Ridge Rd,
Long Valley, NJ 07853
908 813.8718
fax 908 813.0076
pages 34-35

Lynch, Bob
138 W 25th St, Baltimore, MD 21218
410 366.6535
fax 410 366.6535
page 207

Lynch, Fred
22 Muzzey St, Lexingtone, MA 02173
617 861.6258

Lynch, Jeff
420 Lexington Ave, NYC, NY 10017
212 986.5680

Lynch, Larry & Andrea
5521 Greenville, Dallas, TX 75206
214 369.6990
fax 214 369.6938
pages 362, 457

Lynch, Michael
3134 Halliday Ave, St Louis, MO 63118
314 772.5255

Lynn, Chellie
PO Box 63741, Phoenix, AZ 85082
602 890.8719

Lyons, Claudia
39 Starbuck Dr, Sausalito, CA 94965
415 383.6171

Lyons, Steven
136 Scenic Rd, Fairfax, CA 94930
415 459.7560

Lytle, John
PO Box 10, Standard, CA 95373
209 928.4849

Lyubner, Boris
559 Pacific Ave,
San Francisco, CA 94133
415 291.0963
fax 415 291.0726
pages 32-33

Macanga, Steve
20 Morgantine Rd, Roseland, NJ 07068
201 403.8967

MacDonald, Greg
PO Box 19412, Seattle, WA 98109
206 634.1880

MacDonald, Ross
189 Franklin St, NYC, NY 10013
212 966.2446

MacDougall, Brian
1565 Oak St, San Francisco, CA 94117
415 558.8214

MacDougall, Rob
420 Lexington Ave, NYC, NY 10170
212 986.5680
fax 212 818.1246
page 84

Maceren, Jude
92 Kossuth St, Piscataway, NJ 08854
908 752.5931

MacEwan, Debra
E Main St, Wade, MA 01082
413 967.9855

Machalek, Jan
3355 Queen Mary Rd, Montreal, QU,
Canada H3B 1A5
514 341.1592

Machamer, Gene
PO Box 747, Mechanicsburg, PA 17055
717 697.1642

Machincuepa Producciones
50 Fuller Brook Rd,
Wellesley, MA 02181
617 235.8658
pages 110-111

MacKall, Debbie
2133 Ginger Cir, Palatine, IL 60074
708 359.0289

Mackie, Bob
842 Russell Pl, Pomona, CA 91767
909 629.7124

MacLeod, Ainslie
332 E 15th St, NYC, NY 10003
917 851.2215

MacLeod, Lee
826 Camino Ranchitos, Sante Fe, NM 87501
505 982.8744

MacNair, Greg
3286 Ivanhoe, St Louis, MO 63139
314 241.4014

MacNeill, Scott
74 York St, Lambertville, NJ 08530
609 397.4631

MacNicol, Gregory
732 Chestnut St, Santa Cruz, CA 95060
408 459.0880

Madan, Dev
2814 NW Golden Dr,
Seattle, WA 98117
206 789.2601
page 138

Madcap Creations
777 Silver Spur Rd,
Rolling Hills Estates, CA 90274
310 544.4825

Maddox, Kelly
328 Greenwood Ave, Decatur, GA 30030
404 377.0519

Madill, Warren
28 Shelton St, London,
England WC2H 9JN
011 44.71 240 2077
fax 011 44.71 836 0199
page 123

Madson, Steven
4129 Hampstead Ln, Woodbridge, VA 22192
703 590.4341

Maffia, Daniel
236 S Dwight Pl, Englewood, NJ 07631
201 871.0435

Magadan, Frank
320 Locust Rd, Harwinton, CT 06791
203 485.0871

Magadia, Farley
13984 Hubbard St, Sylmar, CA 91342
818 365.5794

Magee, Alan & Monika
Rte 68 Box 132, Cushing, ME 04563
207 354.8838

Magee, Charlie
2679 University St, Eugene, OR 97401
503 344.1711

Maggard III, John P
102 Marian, Terrace Park, OH 45174
513 248.1550

Maglio, Mark
PO Box 872, Plainville, CT 06062
203 793.0771

Magnus, Libby
PO Box 2761, Beverly Hills, CA 90213
310 441.1458

Magovern, Peg
Pier 33 N, San Francisco, CA 94111
415 956.4750

Magsig, Steve
2100 W Big Beaver Rd, Troy, MI 48084
313 643.6000

Mahan, Benton
PO Box 66, Chesterville, OH 43317
419 768.2204

Mahler, Joseph
770 E 73rd St, Indpls, IN 46240
317 255.1197

Mahon, Rich
1522 Macadamia Dr,
FallBrook, CA 92028
619 728.5670
page 1

Mahoney, John
61 Dartmouth St, Boston, MA 02116
617 267.8791

Mahoney, Katherine
60 Hurd Rd, Belmont, MA 02178
617 868.7877

Mahoney, Patricia
Pier 33 N, San Francisco, CA 94111
415 956.4750

Mahoney, Ron
353 W 53rd St, NYC, NY 10019
212 582.0023
fax 212 582.0090
page 146

Mahurin, Matt
666 Greenwich St, NYC, NY 10014
212 691.5115

Maile, Bob/Letterforms
901 Abbot Kinney Blvd, Venice, CA 90291
310 450.2488

Main Street Design
573 Mission St, San Francisco, CA 94105
415 543.5760

Maisner, Bernard
108 E 35th St, NYC, NY 10016
212 889.3337

Majlessi, Heda
1616 Summit Ave, Seattle, WA 98122
206 323.2694

Major Designs
15070 Perlite Dr, Reno, NV 89511
702 853.8683

Mak, Kam
45 Henry St, NYC, NY 10002
212 964.6054

Mallous, Christine
4206 Franklin Ave, L.A., CA 90027
213 664.4674

Maloney, David
PO Box 720731, Houston, TX 77272
713 530.2587

Maloney, Tom
307 N Michigan Ave,
Chicago, IL 60601
312 704.0500
fax 312 236.5752
pages 45, 52, 312, 409, 424

Mamrose, Sharon
9598 Leatherwood Ln, Douglasville, GA 30135
404 949.6349

Manahan, Daniel
3253 Cabo Blanco Dr,
Hacienda Hts, CA 91745
818 333.1326

Manasse, Michele
200 Aquetong Rd,
New Hope, PA 18938
215 862.2091
fax 215 862.2091
pages 278-283

Manchess, Greg
233 E Wacker, Chicago, IL 60601
312 565.2701

Manchester, Paul
1345 Havenhurst Dr, W Hollywood, CA 90046
213 656.6483

Mandel, Bette
265 E 66th St, NYC, NY 10021
212 737.5062

Manders, John
6058 Stanton Ave, Pittsburgh, PA 15206
412 362.6580

Mandrachio, Richard
2275 Sutter, San Francisco, CA 94115
415 921.5938

Mangiat, Jeff
420 Lexington Ave, NYC, NY 10017
312 861.0016

Mannes, Don
345 E 76th St, NYC, NY 10021
212 288.1392

Manning, Lisa
12 Ledge Ln, Gloucester, MA 01930
508 281.3983
page 212

Manning, Michele
1250 Addison St, Berkeley, CA 94702
510 644.2240

Manson, Christopher
2205 42nd St NW, Wash, DC 20007
202 965.5117

Mantel, Richard
114 E 32nd St, NYC, NY 10016
212 889.2254

Mantha, Nancy
3101 Shoreline Dr, Austin, TX 78728
512 388.0229

Manton, Helen
99 Pleasant St, Plainville, MA 02762
508 695.5862

Manwaring, Kerry
PO Box 7621, Alhambra, CA 91802
818 309.9790

Manzelman, Judy
Nine 1/2 Murray Ln, Larkspur, CA 94939
415 461.9685

Marcellino, Fred
432 Park Ave S, NYC, NY 10016
212 532.0150

Marchese, Carol
9800 Mill Hill Rd, Southport, CT 06490
203 254.3162

Marci, Anita
23-C Hillside Ter, White Plains, NY 10601
914 328.7897

Marciuliano, Frank
420 Lexington Ave, NYC, NY 10170
212 697.8525

Marconi, Gloria
2525 Musgrove Rd, Silver Spring, MD 20904
301 890.4615

Marden, Phil
28 E 21st St, NYC, NY 10010
212 260.7646

Marderosian, Mark
E Main St, Ware, MA 01082
413 967.9855

Mardon, Allan
108 E 35th St, NYC, NY 10016
212 889.3337

Marek, Mark
199 Owatonna St, Haworth, NJ 07641
201 384.1791

Marelich, Jeffrey Illustrator
3251 Countryside Dr, San Mateo, CA 94403
415 578.8635

Margeson, John
1030 Aoloa Pl, Kailua, HI 96734
800 893.3393

Margolis, Don
4300 N Narragansett, Chicago, IL 60634
708 670.0912

Marguerita
40 E 19th St, NYC, NY 10003
212 677.6100

Margulies, Robert
561 Broadway, NYC, NY 10012
212 219.9621

Marin Associates
60 Belvedere St, San Rafael, CA 94901
415 459.2561

Marinelli, Jeff
74 S Main St, Canandaigua, NY 14424
716 394.2856

Marlon, Bruce
507 Highland Ave, Half Moon Bay, CA 94019
415 726.0595

Marion, Gerald
Rte Four Box 263, Advance, NC 27006
910 998.0185

Mariuzza, Peter
146 Hardscrabble Rd, Briarcliff, NY 10510
914 769.3310

Mark, Jamie
4170 S Arbor Cir, Marietta, GA 30066
404 924.4793

Mark, Mona
155 E 38th St, NYC, NY 10016
212 697.6170

Mark, Roger Illustration
353 W. 53rd St., NYC, NY 10019
212 582.0023

Mark, Steve
3516 Arbor Ln, Minnetonka, MN 55305
612 938.4255

Marks, David
726 Hillpine Dr, Atlanta, GA 30306
404 872.1824

Marks, Steven
168 Fifth Ave, NYC, NY 10010
212 924.7800

Marr, Dan
26 Juanita Way, San Francisco, CA 94127
415 564.2096

Marrero, Carlos A
4900 N Marine Dr, Chicago, IL 60640
312 769.1147

Marsh, Dilleen
Pine Rd HCR, Neversink, NY 12765
914 985.2936

Marsh, Don
4303 Erie Ave, Cincinnati, OH 45227
513 561.3267

Marshall, Craig
425 Hugo St, San Francisco, CA 94122
415 661.5550

Marshall, Fred
420 E 70th St, NYC, NY 10021
212 944.7771

Martha Productions
4445 Overland Ave, L.A., CA 90230
310 204.1771
page 245

Martin, Anthony
38 Gramercy Park, NYC, NY 10010
212 677.1060

Martin, David P
11242 Peachgrove St, N Hollywood, CA 91601
818 763.3704

Martin, Don
PO Box 1330, Miami, FL 33243
305 665.2376

Martin, Gregory S
1307 Greenlake Dr, Cardiff, CA 92007
619 753.4073

Martin, James
7517 Manchester Ave, L.A., CA 90045
310 578.2191

Martin, John
20 Castle Ct, Albany, NY 12211
518 489.1436

Martin, John
501 Fifth Ave, NYC, NY 10017
212 490.2450
fax 212 697.6828
page 298

Martin, Judie
7019 Ethel Ave, N Hollywood, CA 91605
818 764.3969

Martin, Karen
265 Westminster Rd, Rochester, NY 14607
716 244.6956

Martin, Lyn
PO Box 51972, Knoxville, TN 37950
615 588.1760

Martin, Mary Cobb
115 N Clay Ave, St Louis, MO 63135
314 524.7248

Martin, Roger A
605 Hillview Pl, Rockford, MI 49341
616 866.3289

Martinelli, Robert
Box 257, Pleasantville, NY 10570
914 747.2220

Martinez, Ed
420 Lexington Ave, NYC, NY 10170
212 986.5680

Martinez, Phyllis
5522 Norwich Ave, L.A., CA 90032
213 223.8809

Martinot, Claude
1133 Broadway, NYC, NY 10010
212 473.3137

Martis, Michael W
612 SE Spring, Des Moines, IA 50315
515 285.8122
fax 515 287.6483
page 340

Marton, Charles
PO Box 328, Hannawa Falls, NY 13647
315 268.8667

Martylewski, M Chandler
140 Harborview Ave, Bridgeport, CT 06605
203 367.6636

Maruyama, Sen T
1307 Scott Rd, Burbank, CA 91504
818 559.6554

Marwood Studios
18707 Parthenia St, Northridge, CA 91324
818 886.6325

Mary Anne Bellis/MAB Graphics
1115 Canyon Trl, Topanga, CA 90290
310 455.2627

Maryatt, Kitty
22137 Ave San Luis, Woodland Hills, CA 91364
818 703.0257

Marzan, Jose
325 E 104th St, NYC, NY 10029
212 348.7974

Marzano, Arthur
305 N Nassau Ave, Margate City, NJ 08402
609 822.6018

Maschietto, Romano
4534 N Springfield Ave, Chicago, IL 60625
312 478.6044

Maschler, Lorraine
1310 Brenda Ct, Upland, CA 91786
909 949.2458

Masciovecchio, Marie
90 Gold St, NYC, NY 10038
212 233.3672

Masiello, Ralph Peter
571 Linden St, Boyleston, MA 01505
508 869.6540

Maslen, Barbara
216 Suffolk St, Sag Harbor, NY 11963
516 725.3121

Mason, Hatley Norton
2630 L St, Sacramento, CA 95816
916 321.1038

Mason, Marietta & Jerry
3825 E 26th St, Mpls, MN 55406
612 729.1774
fax 612 729.0133
pages 162, 432

Mason, Susan
Nine Marble Ter,
Hastings-on-Hudson, NY 10706
914 478.4508

Mass, Rhonda
3301A S Jefferson, St Louis, MO 63118
314 773.2600

Massaroni, Dino
529 E Cuyahoga Falls, Akron, OH 44310
216 929.0431

Massicotte, Alain
1121 W St Catherine, Montreal, QU,
Canada H3B 4J5
514 843.4169
fax 514 849.5955
page 204

Mast, Tris
1814 Westcliff Dr, Newport Beach, CA 92660
714 650.0519

Master Design L.A.
7504 Vantage Ave, N Hollywood, CA 91605
818 717.8555

Mastopietro, Amy
655 Rosemary Ln, Burbank, CA 91505
818 842.2371

Mastrorocco, Diane
200 W 90th St, NYC, NY 10024
212 362.0103

Masuda, Coco
300 E 51st St, NYC, NY 10022
212 753.9331
pages 2-3

Match Frame
8531 Fairhaven, San Antonio, TX 78229
210 614.5678

Mate, Michael
1863 S Pearl, Denver, CO 80210
303 733.0128

Mateu, Franc
5205 Cottage Ave, North Bergen, NJ 07047
201 330.1378

Mathews, Adam
142 Bickley Rd, Glenside, PA 19038
215 884.9247

Mathewuse, Jimmy
15 W 72nd St, NYC, NY 10023
212 799.2231

Mathieu, Joseph
64 Pheasant Ln, Brooklyn, CT 06234
203 774.5550

Matsick, Anni
345 Oakley Dr, State College, PA 16803
814 234.4752

Matson, Marla Represents
341 W Vernon, Phoenix, AZ 85003
602 252.5072
fax 602 252.5073
pages 142-143, 205-209

Matsuki, Jiro
6234 Crestwood Way, L.A., CA 90042
213 257.6110

Matsuoka, Julie
342 Loma Ave, Long Beach, CA 90814
310 438.5667

Mattelson, Marvin & Judy
37 Cary Rd, Great Neck, NY 11021
212 684.2974

Matthews, Adam
1214 Locust St, Phila, PA 19107
215 569.8890

Matthews, Scott
7528 Ethel Ave, St Louis, MO 63117
314 647.9899

Matthews, William
1617 Wazee St, Denver, CO 80202
303 534.1300

Mattingly, David B
1112 Bloomfield St, Hoboken, NJ 07030
201 659.7404

Mattioli, Angela
10655 Rochester Ave, L.A., CA 90024
310 475.9883

Maughan, William
3182 Penview Dr, Vista, CA 92084
619 941.2938

Maurer, Seda
2100 Cedarcrest Dr, Carrollton, TX 75007
214 242.6643

Max, Adam
211-16 28th St, L.I.C., NY 11105
718 204.6184

Maxey, Betty
520 N Michigan, Chicago, IL 60611
312 527.0351

May, Darcy
201 E 28th St, NYC, NY 10016
212 532.0928

May, Jeff
7368 Ahern Ave, St Louis, MO 63130
314 727.1476

May, Melinda
3443 Wade St, L.A., CA 90066
310 390.9595

Mayabb, Darrell D
10180 W 73 Pl, Arvada, CO 80005
303 420.7200

Maydak, Michael
7310 Joshua Cir, Pleasanton, CA 94566
510 484.4461

Mayer, Bill
240 Forkner Dr, Decatur, GA 30030
404 378.0686
fax 404 373.1759
pages 12-13

Mayes, Christopher
5615 Kirby Dr, Houston, TX 77005
713 520.5654

Mayes, Kevin Illustration
3002 Timberlane Cir, Wichita, KS 67216
316 683.4504

Mayforth, Hal
121 Rockingham Rd, Londonderry, NH 03053
603 432.2873

Mayo, Frank
265 Briar Brae Rd, Stamford, CT 06903
203 322.3650

Mayor, Barbara
12916 Greenwood Rd, Minnetonka, MN 55343
612 938.8061

Mayor, Philip
655 Kelton Ave, L.A., CA 90024
310 824.1120

Mayse, Steve
7515 Allman, Lenexa, KS 66217
913 962.2285

Mazzetti, Alan
834 Moultrie St, San Francisco, CA 94110
415 647.7677

McAdams, Barbara
2339 Third St, San Francisco, CA 94107
415 255.0222

McAfee, Steve
451 N Highland Ave, Atlanta, GA 30307
404 659.8227

McAlevey, Yolande
735 Sir George Ct, Moorpark, CA 93021
805 529.1210

McAllen, Bob
3268 Military Ave, L.A., CA 90034
310 477.8374

McAllister, Chris
716 Sanchez St, San Francisco, CA 94114
415 285.8267

McBee, John
23 Lakin St, Pepperell, MA 01463
508 433.9232

McBride, Mary
35-B Windle Park, Tarrytown, NY 10591
914 631.1989

McCall, Paul
5801 W Henry St, Indpls, IN 46241
317 273.8703

McCants, Sol Studios
PO Box 28282, Queens Village, NY 11428
917 458.0215

McCarthy, Errol
3918 Pacific, Long Beach, CA 90807
310 424.9014

McCarthy, Kevin
4052 Del Rey Ave, Venice, CA 90292
310 305.1998

McCarthy, Mitzi
3918 Pacific Ave, Long Beach, CA 90807
310 424.9014

McCarthy, Ron
4530 W Chicago St, Chandler, AZ 85226
602 961.0321

McCash, Beth
1350 Chemical St, Dallas, TX 75207
214 05.9037

McCauley, Ad
2410 Eighth Ave, Oakland, CA 94606
510 832.0860

McClure, Beth
4052 Del Rey Ave, Venice, CA 90292
310 305.1998

McClure, Tim
1350 Chemical St, Dallas, TX 75207
214 748.8663

McCollum, Rick
1838 El Cerrito Pl, L.A., CA 90068
213 874.1661

McCollum, Sudi
3244 Cornwall Dr, Glendale, CA 91206
818 243.1345

McConnell, Jack
182 Broad St, Wethersfield, CT 06109
203 563.6154

McConnell, James
Four Sunrise Hill Rd, Bangor, CA 95914
800 672.2282

McCormack, Daphne
150 Longboat Ave, Toronto, ON,
Canada M5A 464
416 868.0190
fax 416 868.0190
page 393

McCormack, Geoffrey
420 Columbia St, Santa Cruz, CA 95060
408 426.0933

McCracken, Bev
757 Cricket Ln, Perrysburg, OH 43551
419 874.2751

McCraken, Steven
410 Fourth St SE, Wash, DC 20003
202 332.5857

McCraney, Marianne
2240 Hillside Ct, Walnut Creek, CA 94596
510 930.7197

McCue, Karri
3443 Wade St, L.A., CA 90066
310 390.9595

McDaniel, Jerry
155 E 38th St, NYC, NY 10016
212 697.6170

McDermott, Joe
900 W Jackson Blvd, Chicago, IL 60607
312 944.5680

McDermott, Teri
38 W 563 Koshare Trl, Elgin, IL 60123
708 888.2206

McDonald, Jerry
180 Clipper St, San Francisco, CA 94114
415 824.1377

McDonald, Jim Design
5703 E Evans Dr, Scottsdale, AZ 85254
602 494.0747

McDonald, Mercedes
1459 Athenour Ct,
San Jose, CA 95120
408 268.0662
page 107

McDonnell, Patrick
11 Laureldale Ave, Metuchen, NJ 08840
908 549.9341

McDonnell, Pete
111 New Montgomery St,
San Francisco, CA 94105
415 957.1290

McDougall, Scott
712 N 62nd St, Seattle, WA 98103
206 783.1403

McElhaney, Gary L
8104 Peaceful Hill Ln, Austin, TX 78748
512 282.5743

McElroy, Darlene
3723 Birch,
Newport Beach, CA 92660
714 252.1147
page 354

McElwain, Dianne
770 E 73rd St, Indpls, IN 46240
317 255.1197

McGar, Michael
526 Shirley Ct, Richardson, TX 75081
214 235.8320

McGee, William Jr
1104 West Oak Ave, Lompoc, CA 93436
805 735.4250

McGinness, Jim
3822 Jancie Rd, Fairfax, VA 22030
703 691.0758

McGinnis, Robert
13 Arcadia Rd, Old Greenwich, CT 06870
203 637.5055

McGovern, Walt
114 E 40th St, NYC, NY 10016
212 661.3131

McGowan, Daniel
6318 15th Ave NE, Seattle, WA 98115
206 526.8927

McGowan, David
1648-A Chimney House Rd, Reston, VA 22090
703 787.4685

McGuinness, Jim
1122 Golden Way, Los Altos, CA 94024
415 967.3811

McGurl, Michael
501 Fifth Ave, NYC, NY 10017
212 490.2450
fax 212 697.6828
page 293

McGurl, Michael
14 Garbosa Rd, Santa Fe, NM 87505
505 986.5889
fax 505 982.8253
page 293

McIndoe, Vince
41 Union Sq W, NYC, NY 10003
212 929.5590
page 249

McIntire, Larry
515 Madison Ave, NYC, NY 10022
212 486.9644

McIntire, Leo
6537 Meridian St, L.A., CA 90042
213 255.5495

McIntosh, Guy
2233 Kemper Ln, Cincinnati, OH 45206
513 861.1400

McIntosh, Jon
430 Ventura Pl, Vero Beach, FL 32963
617 236.1920

McIntosh, Mark
391 Broadway, Costa Mesa, CA 92627
714 642.7445

McInturff, Steve
25 Prospect St, Mechanicsburg, OH 43044
513 834.3539

McIntyre, Jill
2075 S University Blvd, Denver, CO 80210
303 871.9166

McKay, Craig
15 Parkway, Cincinnati, OH 45216
513 821.8052

McKee, Tom
405 N Racine, Chicago, IL 60622
312 829.6464

McKeever, Michael
3475 Southwood Ct, Davie, FL 33328
305 476.6884

McKelvey, David
125 W 77th St, NYC, NY 10024
212 799.6532

McKelvey, Shawn
4421 E Fifth St, Long Beach, CA 90814
310 434.4402

McKenzie, Norma
43 Mandalay Rd, South Weymouth, MA 02190
617 335.1603

McKie, Roy
165 E 32nd St, NYC, NY 10016
212 686.3514

McKinley, John
231 Lake Dr, Aptos, CA 95003
408 662.0880

McKinnon, Gary
638 1/2 N Alta Vista Blvd, L.A., CA 90036
213 934.4267

McKowen, Scott
211 E 89th St, NYC, NY 10128
212 289.5514
fax 212 987.2855
page 195

McLain, Warren Clay
600 N Bishop Ave, Dallas, TX 75208
214 946.6569

McLaren, Chesley
116 E 27th St, NYC, NY 10016
212 725.3806

McLary, Jeff
34 Tyler Ave, W Sayville, NY 11796
516 563.8508

McLaughlin, Cynthia
4628 Conwell Dr, Annandale, VA 22003
703 256.4924

McLaughlin, Paul
11 Kings Ridge Rd, Long Valley, NJ 07853
908 813.8718

McLean, Wilson
902 Broadway, NYC, NY 10010
212 473.5554

McLennan, Constance
3908 Baltic Cir, Rocklin, CA 95677
916 624.1957

McLoughlin, Wayne
501 Fifth Ave, NYC, NY 10017
212 490.2450
fax 212 697.6828
page 301

McMacken, David B
19481 Franquelin Pl, Sonoma, CA 95476
707 996.5239

McMahon, Bob
7260 Apperson St, Tujunga, CA 91042
818 352.9990

McMahon, Brad
1949 S Manchester Ave, Anaheim, CA 92802
714 733.0489

McMahon, Brian
1535 N Western Ave, Chicago, IL 60622
312 227.6755

McMahon, Mike
1826 Asheville Pl, Charlotte, NC 28203
704 372.6007

McMahon, Ozzie
3545 N Lincoln Ave, Chicago, IL 60657
312 883.0125

McMillan, Ken
425 W 23rd St, NYC, NY 10011
212 242.6367

McMillen, Mike
4317 Cornelia Cir, Edina, MN 55435
612 925.1699

McNally, Kathleen
21 North St, Saco, ME 04072
207 282.2713

McNamara, Tim
9400 Mission Rd, Prairie Village, KS 66206
913 341.8988

McNeel, Richard
140 Hepburn Rd, Clifton, NJ 07012
201 779.0802

McNeff, Tom
1216 Hawthorne, Houston, TX 77006
713 493.3060

McPheeters, Neal
16 W 71st St, NYC, NY 10023
212 799.7021

McVicker, Charles
PO Box 183, Rocky Hill, NJ 08553
609 924.2660

Meacham, PJ
685 Stratford Green,
Avondale Estates, GA 30002
404 299.5842

Meachen, Craig
111 Hicks St, Brooklyn, NY 11201
718 852.6551

Mead, Kimble Pendleton
125 Prospect Park W, Brooklyn, NY 11215
718 768.3632

Meadows, Laura
1863 S Pearl, Denver, CO 80210
303 733.0128

Meaker, Mike
3443 Wade St, L.A., CA 90066
310 390.9595

Medbery, Sherrell
6409 Lone Oak Dr, Bethesda, MD 20817
202 223.2127

Medici, Raymond
16 Hawthorne St, Boston, MA 02131
617 323.0842

Medivisuals
1221 Riverbend Dr, Dallas, TX 75247
214 634.3996

Medlock, Scott
716 Sanchez St,
San Francisco, CA 94114
415 285.8267
fax 415 285.8268
page 186

Medoff, Jack
14 Hillside Rd S, Weston, CT 06883
203 454.3199

Meek, Steve Inc
743 W Buena, Chicago, IL 60613
312 477.8055
page 454

Meganck, Robert
9117 Harmad Dr, Richmond, VA 23235
804 644.9200

Mehalko, Donna
404 E 83rd St, NYC, NY 10028
212 794.6297

Mehosh
1016 Olive St, Santa Barbara, CA 93101
805 966.2232

Meier, David Scott
PO Box 353, Laguna Beach, CA 92652
714 494.4206

Meier, Melissa
85 S Washington, Seattle, WA 98104
206 621.0450

Meiklejohn
28 Shelton St, London,
England WC2H 9JN
011 44.71 240 2077
fax 011 44.71 836 0199
pages 120.123

Meisel, Paul
666 Greenwich St, NYC, NY 10014
212 675.5719

Melia, Paul
3121 Atherton Rd, Dayton, OH 45409
513 294.0669

Mellett Illustration
1480 McFarland Rd, Pittsburgh, PA 15216
412 563.4131

Mellon, David
5500 Village Green, L.A., CA 90016
310 458.2793

Melmon, Deborah
580 Washington, San Francisco, CA 94111
415 362.8280

Melodia, Barbara
1141 Bernal Ave,
Burlingame, CA 94010
415 343.7331
fax 415 347.2352
page 370

Melrath, Susan Illustration
3100 Jackson Ridge Ct,
Phoenix, MD 21131
410 785.0797
fax 410 785.1196
page 268

Menchin, Scott
640 Broadway, NYC, NY 10012
212 673.5363

Mendillo, Jim
347 W Third St, Moorestown, NJ 08057
609 596.6990

Mendola Ltd
Chicago, IL
312 861.0016
pages 78-91

Mendola Ltd
420 Lexington Ave, NYC, NY 10170
212 986.5680
fax 212 818.1246
pages 78-91

Menk, France
16 Cedar Ridge Rd, New Paltz, NY 12561
914 255.3755

Mentrax, Susan
5653 Shannon Ln, Dublin, OH 43017
614 791.1479

Merewether, Patrick C
1836 Blake St, Denver, CO 80202
303 296.8857

Merrell, Patrick
80 Eighth Ave, NYC, NY 10011
212 620.7777

Merrilees, Rebecca
57 Vine St, Northfield, VT 05663
802 485.8591

Merrill, Abby
400 E 70th St, NYC, NY 10021
212 772.6853

Merrill, Karen
18551 Cocqui Rd, Apple Valley, CA 92307
619 242.4635

Merrill, Laurance
18551 Cocqui Rd, Apple Valley, CA 92307
619 242.4635

Merritt, Norman
621 Paseo de los Reyes,
Redondo Beach, CA 90277
310 378.4689

Messi, Enzo
41 Union Sq W, NYC, NY 10003
212 206.0066

Metcalf, Ben
1767 Locust St, Pasadena, CA 91106
818 449.3789

Metz, Kathy
127 N Doheny Dr, L.A., CA 90048
310 276.4588

Meyer, Gary
21725 Ybarra Rd,
Woodland Hills, CA 91364
818 992.6974
fax 818 992.4538
page 59

Meyer, Jeff
3825 E 26th St, Mpls, MN 55406
612 729.1774

Meyer, Jim
1010 Lake St NE, Hopkins, MN 55343
612 938.0058
page 224

Meyer, Karen
PO Box 191, Saratoga Springs, NY 12866
518 581.0310

Meyerholtz, Steve
520 N Michigan Ave, Chicago, IL 60611
312 527.0351

Meyerowitz, Rick
Six Jane St, NYC, NY 10014
212 989.7074

Meyers, Kristine
5262 Butterwood Cir, Orangevale, CA 95662
916 989.2450

Meyers, Mike
5319 Ramsdell Ave, La Crescenta, CA 91214
818 248.6386

Michaels, Serge
123 N Madison Ave, Monrovia, CA 91016
818 544.2586

Michaud, Caroline
1361 St Joseph Est, Montreal, QU,
Canada H2J 1M4
514 598.9509

Michel, Jean Claude
353 W 53rd St, NYC, NY 10019
212 682.2462

Micich, Paul
1228 42nd St, Des Moines, IA 50311
515 255.4531

Mickelsen, Ken
2200 N Lamar, Dallas, TX 75202
214 871.7667

MicroColor Inc
2345 Broadway, NYC, NY 10024
212 787.0500

Middendorf, Frances
337 E 22nd St, NYC, NY 10010
212 473.3586
800 536.8287
page 51

Mikec, Larry
925 Elm Grove Rd,
Elm Grove, WI 53122
414 785.1940
fax 414 785.1611
page 220

Milam, Larry
3530 SE Hawthorne,
Portland, OR 97214
503 236.9121
fax 503 236.9121
page 140

Milbourn, Patrick
270 Park Ave S, NYC, NY 10010
212 260.4153

Miles, Chris
160 Garfield Pl, Brooklyn, NY 11215
718 499.1656

Milgrim, David
Eight Gramercy Park S,
NYC, NY 10003
212 673.1432
page 71

Mille, Mark
133 W Pittsburgh Ave, Milwaukee, WI 53204
414 278.8400

Miller, AJ
2207 Bay Blvd, Indian Rks Beach, FL 34635
813 596.6384

Miller, Andy
900 W Jackson Blvd, Chicago, IL 60607
312 944.5680
fax 312 421.5948
page 426

Miller, Blake
3701 Travis St, Houston, TX 77002
713 520.1096

Miller, Cliff
60 E 42nd St, NYC, NY 10165
212 867.8092

Miller, Dave
353 W 53rd St, NYC, NY 10019
212 582.0023
fax 212 582.0090
page 146

Miller, Edward
11 Kings Ridge Rd,
Long Valley, NJ 07853
908 813.8718
fax 908 813.0076
page 35

Miller, Jane
35 Stillman, San Francisco, CA 94107
415 543.6881

Miller, Kristen
1540 Creek Run Trl,
Excelsior, MN 55331
612 470.2284
fax 612 470.2269
page 97

Miller, Lyle
3100 Carlisle St, Dallas, TX 75204
214 871.1195

Miller, Russell
1618 Idylwild Dr, Prescott, AZ 86301
602 778.6527

Miller, Steve
2586 Majella Rd, Vista, CA 92084
619 758.0804

Miller, Verlin
731 N 24th St, Phila, PA 19130
215 232.6666

Mills, Chris
PO Box 1336, Suquamish, WA 98392
206 697.2384

Mills, Joan Scott Design
4400 Chippewa Dr, Boulder, CO 80303
303 494.2109

Milman, Caren Calligraphy
14317 Bauer Dr, Rockville, MD 20853
301 871.6714

Milne, Jonathan
420 Lexington Ave, NYC, NY 10170
212 986.5680

Milner, Ty
2200 N Lamar, Dallas, TX 75202
214 871.7667

Milot, René
501 Fifth Ave, NYC, NY 10017
212 490.2450
fax 212 697.6828
page 300

Minisci-Appleton, Diana
15 Warrenton Ave, Hartford, CT 06105
203 523.4562

Minor, Wendell
15 Old North Rd,
Washington, CT 06793
203 868.9101
fax 203 868.9512
page 465

Mintz, Margery
Nine Cottage Ave, Sommerville, MA 02144
617 623.2291

Minuto, Doreen
60 E 42nd St, NYC, NY 10165
212 867.8092

Mion, Tina
4521 Campus Dr, Irvine, CA 45214
714 856.0200

Miralles, Jose
43 E 19th St, NYC, NY 10003
212 254.4996

Mirocha, Paul
2774 W Calle Morado, Tuscon, AZ 85745
602 623.1515

Misconish, David
175 D Peachtree Hills Ave, Atlanta, GA 30305
404 231.9711

Mission House Artworks
RR 1, Moretown, VT 05660
802 496.6400

Mitchell, Hetty
2105 E 123rd St, Burnsville, MN 55337
612 894.4589

Mitchell, Ken
21 Regent Ter, Milford, CT 06460
203 877.4138

Mitchell, Mary Jane
3443 Wade St, L.A., CA 90066
310 390.9595

Mitgang, Esther
2088 Union St, San Francisco, CA 94123
415 346.7032

MKG Graphics
625 Ivy Court, Wheeling, IL 60090
708 255.5772

MLR Computer Illustration
219 Glenwood Dr, Houston, TX 77007
713 864.9041

Moeller, Christopher
RD One Box 295, Bentleyville, PA 15314
412 239.5432

Moiré Studio/Bill Dobbs
3152 Elliot Ave S, Mpls, MN 55407
612 827.6407

Molayem, Rebecca
10317 Ashton Ave, L.A., CA 90024
310 247.1550

Molinello, Alexander
314 N Rock Isl St, Angelton, TX 77515
713 523.5328

Molloy, Jack
817 Westwood Dr S, Mpls, MN 55416
312 321.1336

Monahan, Leo
1912 Hilton Dr, Burbank, CA 91504
818 843.6115

Mond, Gary & Associates
6524 Ventura Canyon Ave,
Van Nuys, CA 91401
818 786.6085

Mones, Isidre
43 E 19th St, NYC, NY 10003
212 254.4996

Mongeau, Marc
211 E 89th St, NYC, NY 10128
212 289.5514
fax 212 987.2855
pages 200–201

Monko, Kevin
211 N 13th St, Phila, PA 19107
215 751.1114

Monley, Jerry
2100 W Big Beaver Rd, Troy, MI 48084
313 643.6000

Monlux Illustration
7622 S Yakima Ave, Tacoma, WA 98408
206 471.0820

Montagano, David
405 N Wabash Ave, Chicago, IL 60611
312 527.3283
fax 312 527.9091
pages 72–73

Montana, Leslie
35 Montclair Ave, Montclair, NJ 07042
201 744.3407

Montecalvo, Bruce
815 SW 11th St, Ft Lauderdale, FL 33315
305 763.3923

Monteiro, Marcos
731 N 24th St, Phila, PA 19130
215 232.6666

Monteiro, Mary
32 Lyng St, North Dartmouth, MA 02747
508 999.2880

Monteleone, John
305 Lattingtown Rd, Lattingtown, NY 11560
516 674.8834

Montgomery, Donna Mae
1325 47th Ave, San Francisco, CA 94122
415 681.7582

Montgomery, Linda
20 D'Arcy St, Toronto, ON, Canada M5T 1J7
416 77.4002

Montgomery, MK
1150 Pine Tree Ln,
Sebastopol, CA 95472
707 829.2135
fax 707 829.8606
page 366

Monti, Ron
27 Ruxview Ct, Baltimore, MD 21204
410 823.8451

Montiel, David
453 Fourth St, Brooklyn, NY 11215
212 929.3659

Montoliu, Raphael
223 S Francisca Ave,
Redondo Beach, CA 90277
310 798.2516

Montoya, Priscilla
1863 S Pearl St, Denver, CO 80210
303 733.0128

Moody, Skye
501 Burgandy, New Orleans, LA 70112
504 522.8985

Mook, Tony
4307 Alabama, Houston, TX 77027
713 622.6119

Moonlightpress Studio
362 Cromwell Ave, Ocean Breeze, NY 10305
718 979.9695

Moonstruck Pictures
229 Berkely St, Boston, MA 02116
617 266.3858

Moore Moscowitz
99 Chauncy St, Boston, MA 02111
617 482.8180

Moore, Chris
60 E 42nd St, NYC, NY 10165
212 682.1490

Moore, Garret M
PO Box 7912, Fremont, CA 94537
510 796.1599

Moore, Helene
9011 Skyline Blvd, Oakland, CA 94611
510 530.4366

Moore, Jack
131 Cedar Lake W, Denville, NJ 07834
201 627.6931

Moore, Jay
12407 W Second Pl, Lakewood, CO 80228
303 989.5224

Moore, Larry
1635 Delaney St, Orlando, FL 32806
407 648.0832

Moore, Lois
55 Plover Hill Rd, Ipswich, MA 01938
508 356.2796

Moore, Stephen
1077 Country Creek Dr, Lebanon, OH 45036
513 932.4295

Moore, Susan
5265 Crystal Vista Ln, Reno, NV 85923
702 746.3073

Moores, Jeff
PO Box 521, Canadensis, PA 18325
717 595.9298

Mora, Francisco
45 N Allen Ave, Pasadena, CA 91106
818 449.0183

Moraes, Greg Studio
7536 Ogelsby Ave, L.A., CA 90045
310 641.8556

Morales Studio
PO Box 1763, Bloomfield, NJ 07003
201 676.8187

Morales, Manuel
520 N Michigan Ave, Chicago, IL 60611
312 527.0351

Morales, Roberta C
130 Sycamore Ln, Louisville, CO 80027
303 666.6048

Morales, Rosemary
5775 Foothill Dr, L.A., CA 90068
213 467.4674
pages 1, 10-11, 447

Morales, Rosemary
L.A., CA
310 396.1213
pages 1, 10-11, 447

Morales, Suzanne
4143 Hatfield Pl, L.A., CA 90032
213 221.6065

Moran, John
711 W 17th St, Costa Mesa, CA 92627
714 722.0992

Moran, Michael
39 Elmwood Rd, Florham, NJ 07932
201 966.6229

Mordan, CB
5317 W 201st Ter, Stilwell, KS 66085
913 897.1141

Moreau, Alain
1844 Sweet Briar, Thousand Oaks, CA 91362
805 493.0650

Moreton, Daniel
866 UN Plz, NYC, NY 10017
212 644.2020

Morgan, Jacqui
692 Greenwich St, NYC, NY 10014
212 463.8488

Morgan, Len
PO Box 155, Passaic, NJ 07055
201 472.1225

Morgan, Leonard E
730 Victoria Ct, Bolingbrook, IL 60440
708 739.7705

Morgan, Mary
200 51st Ter, Kansas City, MO 64112
816 561.0590

Morgan, Michele
2646 DuPont Dr, Irvine, CA 92715
714 722.1026

Morin, Josee
211 E 89th St, NYC, NY 10128
212 289.5514
fax 212 987.2855
page 203

Morin, Paul
RR Four, Rockwood, ON, Canada NOB 2KO
519 833.9906

Moritsugu, Alison
504 West 111th St, NY, NY 10025
212 219.8435

Moroney, Christopher
12107 Magnolia Blossom,
San Antonio, TX 78247
512 494.3674

Morris, Alex
25 W 39th St, NYC, NY 10018
212 921.1550

Morris, Brian T
2419 Mayhew Dr, Indpls, IN 46227
317 881.9657

Morris, Burton
400 Noble St, Pittsburgh, PA 15232
412 682.7963
fax 412 682.7964
page 16

Morris, Frank
15 W 72nd St, NYC, NY 10023
212 799.2231

Morris, Pat
1712 E Butler Cir, Chandler, AZ 85225
602 899.0600

Morris, Rick
5013 Hartwick St, L.A., CA 90041
213 255.6615

Morris, Thomas
PO Box 1007, Orinda, CA 94567
510 253.0917

Morrison, Bill
68 Glandore Rd, Westwood, MA 02090
617 329.5288

Morrison, Don
155 E 38th St, NYC, NY 10016
212 697.6170

Morrison, Jeff
20300 W 12 Mile Rd, Southfield, MI 48076
810 799.9080

Morrison, Pat
1512 Crittenden St NW, Wash, DC 20011
202 723.1824

Morrow, JT
220 Kavanaugh Way, Pacifica, CA 94044
415 355.7899

Morrow, Michael
5508 Dorsett Shoals Rd,
Douglasville, GA 30135
404 949.2745

Morrow, Skip
123 Ware St, Wilmington, VT 05363
802 464.5523

Morse, Bill
731 N 24th St, Phila, PA 19130
215 232.6666
fax 215 232.6585
page 334

Morse, Tony
5624 Kales Ave, Oakland, CA 94618
510 658.5899
fax 510 658.5899
page 41

Morser, C Bruce
108 E 35th St, NYC, NY 10016
212 889.3337

Mortensen, Cristine
514 Bryant St, Palo Alto, CA 94301
415 321.4787
page 106

Moscato Communications
7319 Giddings, Burr Ridge, IL 60521
708 655.1453

Moses, David
3410 Renault, Memphis, TN 38118
901 684.1449

Moses, Duff
5183 Overland Ave, Culver City, CA 90230
310 558.3325

Mosley, Mark
509 W 37th St, Wilmington, DE 19802
302 761.9847

Mosonyi, Nicholas
4140 Workman Mill Rd, Whittier, CA 90601
310 695.5565

Moss, Geoffrey
2909 Cole Ave, Dallas, TX 75204
214 871.1316

Mosser, Tom
131 Spring St, NYC, NY 10012
212 925.4340

Mossman Associates
1388 NW Second Ave, Boca Raton, FL 33432
407 368.5668

Motion Artists Inc
1400 N Hayworth Ave,
West Hollywood, CA 90046
213 851.7737

Motta, Wm A
1499 Monrovia Ave, Newport Beach, CA 92663
714 720.5300

Motzkus, Roger
889 W Huntington Dr, Arcadia, CA 91006
818 447.8293

Moutra, Sidney
3950 Hillcrest Dr, L.A., CA 90008
213 293.7634

Mowry, Ken
2621 Iman Dr, Raleigh, NC 27615
919 829.4747

Mowry, Scott
32 Chestnut St, Charlestown, MA 02129
617 242.2419

Moyers, David
131 Spring St, NYC, NY 10012
212 925.4340

Mozley, Peggy
17914 Hillcrest Rd, Dallas, TX 75252
214 248.2704

Mrak, Michael
354 W 110th St, NYC, NY 10025
212 865.9447

Mroz, Mark
11439-A Ptarmigan, Auston, TX 78758
512 339.2920

Mueller, Derek
920 Galvin Dr, El Cerrito, CA 94530
510 527.7971

Mueller, Kate
3504 11th Ave S, Mpls, MN 55407
612 724.6230

Mull, Christy
3182 Holly Mill Run, Atlanta, GA 30062
404 255.1430

Mulligan, Donald
418 Central Park W, NYC, NY 10025
212 666.6079

Munck, Paula
58 W 15th St, NYC, NY 10011
212 741.2539

Muncy Graphics
5862 Ludlow Ave, Garden Grove, CA 92645
714 892.2242

Munro Goodman
405 N Wabash, Chicago, IL 60611
312 321.1336
fax 312 321.1350
page 194

Munro Goodman
NYC, NY
212 691.2667
fax 212 633.1844
page 194

Muns, Marjorie
501 Obispo Ave, Long Beach, CA 90814
310 438.2165

Munson, Donald
235 W 76th St, NYC, NY 10023
212 595.1014

Murakami, Tak
230 N Michigan, Chicago, IL 60601
312 368.8777

Murawski, Alex
108 E 35th St, NYC, NY 10016
212 889.3337

Murdock, John
1028 S Wilson St, Tempe, AZ 85281
602 966.8212

Murdock, Richard
225 Maple Rd, Easton, CT 06612
203 261.3042

Murphy's Art
9708 Robert Jay Way, Ellicott City, MD 21042
410 750.7222

Murphy, Charley Network
4146 Pillsbury Ave S, Mpls, MN 55409
612 827.8166

Murphy, Chris
156 Fifth Ave, NYC, NY 10010
212 243.1333

Murray, Barbara
23 Oakdale Ct, Sterling, VA 20165
703 450.9634

Murray, John
770 Boylston St, Boston, MA 02199
617 424.0024

Murray, Robert
11228 E Laurel Ln, Scottsdale, AZ 85259
602 860.0535

Murray, Tom
153 Henry St, San Francisco, CA 94114
415 863.8292

Murtha, Karen
155 Hedgerow Dr, Warwick, RI 02886
401 885.6036

Murtishaw, Jessica
2028 Cherry Dr, Dickinson, TX 77539
713 337.5998

Murton, Simon
1400 N Hayworth Ave,
West Hollywood, CA 90046
213 851.7737

Muse, Pete Illustration
2334 Highland Hts, Carrollton, TX 75007
214 307.8975

Muslusky, Kim
9420 Activity Rd, San Diego, CA 92126
619 693.7380

Musselman, Christian
520 N Michigan Ave, Chicago, IL 60611
312 527.0351

Musso, Joseph
1400 N Hayworth Ave,
West Hollywood, CA 90046
213 851.7737

Muzick, Terra
1805 Pine St, San Francisco, CA 94109
415 346.6141

Myer, Andy
731 N 24th St, Phila, PA 19130
215 232.6666
fax 215 232.6585
page 333

Myers, Glenn
5935 N Belt W, Belleville, IL 62223
618 277.6288

Myers, Lisa L
1724 Dunwoody Trl, Atlanta, GA 30324
404 262.3073

Myers, Lou
108 E 35th St, NYC, NY 10016
212 889.3337

Myers, Matt
Rte One Box 163, Rocky Comfort, MO 64861
417 628.3392

Mytar, M Randall
3925 Sepulveda Blvd, Sherman Oaks, CA 91403
818 789.7719

Naas, Paul
PO Box 2203, Sunnyvale, CA 94087
408 720.1508

Nachreiner Boie Art Factory
925 Elm Grove Rd,
Elm Grove, WI 53122
414 785.1940
fax 414 785.1611
pages 213-220

Nachreiner, Tom
925 Elm Grove Rd,
Elm Grove, WI 53122
414 785.1940
fax 414 785.1611
page 214

Nacht, Merle
374 Main St, Wethersfield, CT 06109
203 563.7993

Nadine Represents
80 Wellington Ave, PO Box 307,
Ross, CA 94957
415 456.7711
fax 415 454.9162
pages 104-107

Nagaoka, Shusei
15 W 72nd St, NYC, NY 10023
212 799.2231

Nagata, Mark
1948 Leavenworth St,
San Francisco, CA 94133
415 922.6612
fax 415 776.1230
page 368

Nagy, Daniel D Graphix
1384 Bembridge Dr, Rochester Hills, MI 48307
313 650.8567

Nahigian, Alan
33-08 31st Ave, L.I.C., NY 11106
718 274.4042

Najaka, Marlies Merk
241 Central Park W, NYC, NY 10024
212 580.0058

Nakamura, Carl
135 S La Brea, L.A., CA 90036
213 936.2620

Nakamura, Joel
221 W Maple Ave, Monrovia, CA 91016
818 301.0177

Nakamura, Tak
411 N Benton Way, L.A., CA 90026
213 383.6991

Nakanishi/Kato Inc
11759 San Vicente Blvd, L.A., CA 90049
310 820.0902

Napoli, Augie
74 Perkiomen Ave, Staten Island, NY 10312
718 356.0513

Nascimbene, Yan
41 Union Sq W, NYC, NY 10003
212 929.5590
page 247

Nash, Scott
Nine Galen St, Waterton, MA 02172
617 923.2583
page 115

Nass, Rhonda
3301A S Jefferson Ave, St Louis, MO 63118
314 773.2600

Nasser, Christine
253-A 26th St, Santa Monica, CA 90402
805 499.9718

Natchev, Alexi
666 Greenwich St, NYC, NY 10014
212 675.5719

Nation, Tate
719 Bradburn Dr, Mt Pleasant, SC 29464
803 884.9911

National Creative Network
1220 Cole Pl, L.A., CA 90038
213 463.9474

Nau, Steven
731 N 24th St, Phila, PA 19130
215 232.6666
fax 215 232.6585
page 339

Naugle, Diane
3665 Thousand Oaks Blvd,
Thousand Oaks, CA 91362
805 374.1174

Navratil Art Studios
1305 Clark Bldg, Pittsburgh, PA 15222
412 471.4322

Nayduch, John
65 W 55th St, NYC, NY 10019
212 767.0260

Neeper, William L
370 Degraw St, Brooklyn, NY 11231
718 858.2925

Nees, Susan
Eight Water St, Watkinsville, GA 30677
706 769.8393

Neff, Glynda
76 Clifton Pl, Jersey City, NJ 07304
201 333.4716

Negron, David
16313 Clark Ave, Bellflower, CA 90706
310 920.7004

Neider, Alan
597 Riverside Ave,
Westport, CT 06880
203 226.4724
fax 203 454.9904
page 64

Neidigh, Sherry
1712 E Butler Cir, Chandler, AZ 85225
602 899.0600

Neilson, Anne
24722 Newhall Ave, Newhall, CA 91321
805 298.3104

The Neis Group
11440 Oak Dr, Shelbyville, MI 43944
616 672.5756

Nelsen, Randy
1863 S Pearl St, Denver, CO 80210
303 733.0128
fax 303 733.8154
page 150

Nelson & Associates
1024 W Lincoln Ave, Milwaukee, WI 53215
414 671.6191

Nelson, Bill
107 E Cary St, Richmond, VA 23219
804 783.2602

Nelson, Craig
11943 Nugent Dr, Granada Hills, CA 91344
818 363.4494

Nelson, Hilber
2410 Rostron Cir, Twin Falls, ID 83301
208 733.5447

Nelson, Janise
824 S Marine Hills Way,
Federal Way, WA 98003
206 292.9186

Nelson, Jerry
500 Aurora Ave N, Seattle, WA 98109
206 292.9186

Nelson, John
Pier 33 N, San Francisco, CA 94111
415 956.4750

Nelson, Kenton
11936 W Jefferson Blvd,
Culver City, CA 90230
310 390.8663

Nelson, Lynne Graphic Design
4140 Evans Dr, Boulder, CO 80303
303 499.5313

Nelson, R Kenton
12 S Fair Oaks, Pasadena, CA 91105
818 792.5252

Nelson, Susan
2363 N Fitch Mtn Rd, Healdsburg, CA 95448
707 431.7166

Nelson, Will
10535 Saranac, Boise, ID 83709
208 375.2901

Nenzione, Gabriele
320 Bee Brook Dr, Washington, CT 06777
203 868.1011

Neski, Peter
315 E 68th St, NYC, NY 10021
212 737.2521

Nessim, Barbara & Associates
63 Greene St, NYC, NY 10012
212 219.1111

Nethery, Susan
1336 N Harper Ave, L.A., CA 90232
213 656.2735

Network Studios
Five Logan Hill Rd, Northport, NY 11768
516 757.5609

Neubecker, Robert
395 Broadway, NYC, NY 10013
212 219.8435

Neumann, Ann
78 Franklin St, Jersey City, NJ 07307
201 420.1137

Newbury, Claire
123 Fifth St NE, Atlanta, GA 30308
404 872.8811

Newell, Chris & Associates
11139 117th Way N, Largo, FL 34648
813 398.7809

Newell, Claudia
151 First Ave, NYC, NY 10003
718 384.5916

Newman Design Illustration
1904 Third Ave, Seattle, WA 98101
206 622.3025

Newman, Andrew Graphic Design
54 Winding Cove Rd,
Marstons Mills, MA 02648
508 420.1161

Newman, B Johansen
45 South St, Needham, MA 02192
617 449.2767

Newman, Carole
1119 Colorado Ave, Santa Monica, CA 90401
310 394.5031

Newman, Ken Studio
66 Bodle Rd, Carverton, PA 18644
717 333.4019

Newsom Illustration
7713 Red Rock Cir, Larkspur, CO 80118
303 681.2472

Newstart Art
8166 Jellison St, Orlando, FL 32825
407 273.8365

Newton, Richard
501 Fifth Ave, NYC, NY 10017
212 490.2450

Newton-King, Laurie
5910 Grand, Kansas City, MO 64113
816 444.8159

Nez, John
320 Bee Brook Dr, Washington, CT 06777
203 868.1011

Ng, Michael
25 W 45th St, NYC, NY 10036
212 398.9540

Ng, Simon
51 Camden St, Toronto, ON,
Canada M5V 1W2
416 362.1913

Nguyen, Quan
1903 Edgefort Ct, San Jose, CA 95122
408 274.2585

Nicholas, Jess
566 Seventh Ave, NYC, NY 10018
212 221.8090

Nicholls, Calvin
48 Bond St, Lindsay, ON,
Canada K9V 3R2
705 878.1640
page 403

Nichols, James
18 Old Creek Rd, San Francisco, CA 94952
707 762.4455

Nicholson, Rick
2310 Denison, Cleveland, OH 44109
216 398.1494

Nickel, David
700 1/2 Cedar St, Santa Monica, CA 90405
310 399.5549

Nickle, John
298 Seventh Ave, Brooklyn, NY 11215
718 788.7310

Nicolini Associates
4046 Maybelle Ave, Oakland, CA 94619
510 531.5569

Nielsen, Terese
9044 E Ardendale Ave, San Gabriel, CA 91775
818 285.9966

Nielson, Judy
200 Culver Blvd, Playa Del Rey, CA 90293
310 823.5153

Nigida, Karen
812 W Van Buren, Chicago, IL 60607
312 421.5137

Niklewicz, Adam
26 Great Quater Road, Sandy Hook, CT 06482
203 270.8424

Niles-Lusk, Nancy
7700 W 83rd St, Overland Park, KS 66204
913 648.2616

Nimoy, Nancy
10534 Clarkson Rd, L.A., CA 90064
310 202.0773

Ning, Amy
19608 Mildred Ave, Torrance, CA 90503
310 433.6645

Nipp, Bob
8960 Central Pike, Mt Juliet, TN 37122
615 754.4992

Nishibeppu, Mariko
4325 Franklin Ave, L.A., CA 90027
213 665.8747

Nishinaka, Jeff
654 Pier Ave, Santa Monica, CA 90405
310 392.4877

Nitta, Kazushige
41 Union Sq W, NYC, NY 10003
212 807.6627

Nitto, Tomio
51 Camden St, Toronto, ON,
Canada M5V 1V2
416 362.1913
fax 416 362.6356
page 227

Nitzberg, Andrew
1333 Broadway, NYC, NY 10018
212 736.6398

Nixon, Tony
7210 Robinson, Overland Park, KS 66204
913 384.5444

No Steroids Studios
1409 N Alta Vista Blvd, L.A., CA 90046
213 850.8209

Noah, Merikay
12953 Moorpark, Studio City, CA 90039
818 981.7567

Nobens, C A Illustration
3616 Rhode Island Ave S,
St Louis Park, MN 54426
612 935.9130

Noche, Mario
6529 College Ave, Indpls, IN 46220
317 475.0277

Noiset, Michele
900 W Jackson Blvd, Chicago, IL 60607
312 944.5680

Noll, Cheryl Kirk
19 Hooker St, Providence, RI 02908
401 861.5869

Nolte, Larry
2901 Mermec, St Louis, MO 63118
314 481.6983

Noonan, Julia
19 Stuyvesant Oval, NYC, NY 10009
212 505.9342

Norcia, Ernest
3451 Houston Rd, Waynesville, OH 45068
513 862.5761

Nordell, Dale
8615 26th Ave NE, Seattle, WA 98115
206 527.8223
fax 206 527.8223
page 136

Nordenhok, Nancy
315 Calle Familia, San Clemente, CA 92672
714 361.2210

Nordling, Todd
315 First Ave S, Seattle, WA 98104
206 624.4996
page 139

Nordmann, Suzanne
3201 Crossbend, Plano, TX 75203
214 596.7565

Noreika, Robert
201 E 28th St, NYC, NY 10016
212 532.0928

Norlien, Kim
11808 Van Buren St, Blaine, MN 55434
612 767.9276

Norman, Barbara
43 W 24th St, NYC, NY 10010
212 229.9447

Norman, Gary
7517 Manchester Ave, L.A., CA 90045
310 578.2191

Norman, Marty
Five Radcliff Blvd, Glen Head, NY 11545
516 671.4482

Norris, Andrew
1312 Grandview Dr, Nashville, TN 37215
615 298.3681

Norris, Bruce
1725 17th St, Wash, DC 20009
202 387.5771

North, Jan
25 W 45th St, NYC, NY 10036
212 398.9540

Northerner, Will
520 N Michigan Ave, Chicago, IL 60611
312 787.4459

Norton, Larry
1918 N Craig Ave, Altadena, CA 91001
818 797.9837

Norvell, Jill Calligraphy
2123 Cabots Point Ln, Reston, VA 22091
703 264.0600

Norwell, Jeff Illustration
2451 Eglinton Ave E, Toronto, ON,
Canada M4P 3C2
416 483.6225ext651
fax 416 489.8782
page 70

Notarile, Chris
11 Hamilton Ave, NYC, NY 10017
212 986.5680

Novak, Bob
6878 Fry Rd,
Middleburg Hts, OH 44130
216 234.1808
page 430

Novak, Justin
156 Fifth Ave, NYC, NY 10010
212 243.1333

Novak, Tony Illustration
5010 Idaho Ave, Nashville, TN 37209
615 385.4368

Noyes, David
353 W 53rd St, NYC, NY 10019
212 682.2462

Nunley, Vivian
3952 N Sheridan, Chicago, IL 60613
312 929.2115

Nuttle, Jim
14904 Wellwood Rd, Silver Spring, MD 20905
301 989.0942

O'Brien, Kathy
1205 W California Ave, Mill Valley, CA 94941
415 383.9026

O'Brien, Tim
60 E 42nd St, NYC, NY 10165
212 953.7088

O'Connell, Frank
10219 Brecksville Rd, Brecksville, OH 44141
216 526.1870

O'Connell, Jennifer Barrett
5510 Glenwood Rd, Bethesda, MD 20817
301 654.4603

O'Connell, Kathy
1494 Cold Springs Rd,
Pottstown, PA 19464
610 326.8038
fax 610 326.6173
page 438

O'Connell, Mitch
6425 N Newgard, Chicago, IL 60626
312 743.3848
page 424

O'Connor, Cathy Christy
420 Lexington Ave, NYC, NY 10170
212 986.5680
fax 212 818.1246
page 91

O'Connor, Jeff
331 S Taylor, Oak Park, IL 60302
708 383.6698

O'Connor, John
2010 Scott Dr, Blacksburg, VA 24060
703 953.2744

O'Donnell, William
3159 Byrnes Mill Rd, Eureka, MO 63025
314 677.5592

O'Malia, Carol
770 E 73rd St, Indpls, IN 46240
317 255.1197

O'Malley, Kevin
Nine Babbling Brook Ln, Suffern, NY 10901
914 368.8606

O'Neil, Sharron
409 Alberto Way, Los Gatos, CA 95032
408 354.3816

O'Neill, Fran
539 Shawmut Ave, Boston, MA 02118
617 267.9215
page 99

O'Regan, Bernice
134 Smith St, Brooklyn, NY 11201
718 243.2824

O'Reilly, Michael
156 Fifth Ave, NYC, NY 10010
212 243.1333

O'Shaughnessy Studio
2519 Columbia Dr, Costa Mesa, CA 92626
714 545.1663

O'Shea, Kevin
828 S Lawson Rd,
Camano Island, WA 98292
206 387.7669
fax 206 387.7366
page 129

O'Sullivan, John
20 Neck Hill Rd, Mendon, MA 01756
508 473.2310

O'Sullivan, Tom
156 Fifth Ave, NYC, NY 10010
212 243.1333

O'Toole, Tim
3443 Wade St, L.A., CA 90066
310 390.9595

Oakes, Jim
6638 N 13th St, Phoenix, AZ 85014
602 263.8990
fax 602 277.0680
page 156

Oakes, Terry
11 Kings Ridge Rd, Long Valley, NJ 07853
908 813.8718

Oasis Art Studio
972 Medina Rd, Wayzata, MN 55391
612 860.1701

Oasis Studio
118 E 26th St, Mpls, MN 55404
612 871.4539

Oberheide, Heide
295 Washington Ave, Brooklyn, NY 11205
718 622.7056

Ochagavia, Carlos
211 New Canaan Rd, Wilton, CT 06897
212 355.0910

Ochsner, Dennis
311 First Ave S, Seattle, WA 98104
206 464.4033

Oden, Dick
PO Box 867, Silverado, CA 92676
714 649.2690

Oden, Ron
1612 View Way, El Cajon, CA 92020
619 447.0389

Odom, Mel
252 W 76th St, NYC, NY 10023
212 724.9320

Ogai, Masaaki
PO Box 1160, L.A., CA 96708
310 826.1332

Ogburn, Greg
1826 Asheville Pl, Charlotte, NC 28203
704 372.6007

Ogden, Robin Artist Rep
3722 W 50th St, Mpls, MN 55410
612 925.4174
fax 612 925.4174
page 224

Ogle, Shawn
6001 219th SW,
Mountlake Ter, WA 98043
206 775.9198
page 141

Oglesby, Gavin
60 Lakefront St, Irvine, CA 92714
714 733.1743

Oh, Jeffrey
Six Challenger Ct,
Baltimore, MD 21234
410 661.6064
page 114

Oh, Steve
2525 Franklin Ave, Mpls, MN 55406
612 338.8642

Ohlsson, Eskil Associates Inc
450 Lexington Ave, NYC, NY 10017
212 907.4303

Okamoto, Alan H Illustration
152 Central Ave, San Francisco, CA 94117
415 626.2501

Oko & Mano Inc
Ten E Second St, NYC, NY 10003
212 387.9209

Olbinski, Rafal
425 W 23rd St, NYC, NY 10011
212 242.6367

Olbinski, Tomek
211 E 89th St, NYC, NY 10128
212 289.5514

Old Mill Graphics
1942 Huntington Dr,
South Pasadena, CA 91030
818 799.1360

Oldroyd, Mark
11 Kings Ridge Rd, Long Valley, NJ 07853
908 813.8718

Olds, Scott
2100 W Big Beaver Rd, Troy, MI 48084
810 643.6000

Olimb Grafix
11454 Elbert Way, San Diego, CA 92126
619 566.6247

Oliver, Mindy
1001 S Alfred St, L.A., CA 90035
310 556.1439
fax 213 653.5696
page 386

Olivere, Ray
65 W 55th St, NYC, NY 10019
212 767.0260

Oliveros & Friends
2112 Bishopsgate Dr, Toledo, OH 43614
419 385.8100

Olivia
3723 Birch,
Newport Beach, CA 92660
714 252.1147
page 354

Olivieri, Teofilo
1001 Willow Ave, Hoboken, NJ 07030
201 216.1284

Olmstead, David
1300 Nicollet Mall, Mpls, MN 55403
612 339.2112
fax 612 339.2233
page 52

Olsen Graphics
PO Box 1103, Sun Valley, CA 91353
818 767.1210

Olson, Ed
4521 N Vistapark Dr, Moorpark, CA 93021
805 529.3101

Olson, Erik
221 W Maple St, Monrovia, CA 91016
818 303.2455

Olson, Rik
749 Circle Ct S, San Francisco, CA 94080
415 589.4392

Olson, Robert
118 E 26th St, Mpls, MN 55404
612 871.4539

Olson, Stan
817 Westwood Dr S, Mpls, MN 55416
612 374.3169

Olson, Terri
520 N Michigan Ave, Chicago, IL 60611
312 527.0351

Olson, Victor
19 Old Stagecoach Rd,
West Redding, CT 06896
203 938.2863

Onasch, Carole Retouching
350 Townsend, San Francisco, CA 94107
415 896.5595

One of One/Patricia Shrimpton
860 Second St, San Francisco, CA 94107
415 388.1018

Ong, Diana
Deerwood Park, Jacksonville, FL 32256
800 828.4545

Opal Arts
107 W Van Buren St, Chicago, IL 60605
312 922.3027

Opasinski, Gary
1409 W Gregory St, Chicago, IL 60640
312 275.8729

Oppenheimer, Jennie
PO Box 292, Lagunitas, CA 94938
415 331.0834

Orlowski, Neil
1605 Regency Dr, Kearney, MO 64060
816 635.4391

Ormai, Stella
26 E Manning St, Providence, RI 02906
401 272.0407

Orr, Tom
3931 N Paulina, Chicago, IL 60613
312 583.8146

Ortega, Jose
524 E 82nd St, NYC, NY 10028
212 772.3329
page 257

Ortiz, Jose Luis
66 W 77th St, NYC, NY 10024
212 877.3081

Orvidas, Ken
16724 NE 138th Ct, Woodinville, WA 98072
206 885.7437

Osaka, Richard
14-22 30th Dr, L.I.C., NY 11102
718 956.0015

Oshidari, Houmann
Hand Carved Lettering in Stone,
Lexington, MA 02173
617 862.1583

Osiecki, Lori
123 W Second St, Mesa, AZ 85201
602 962.5233
fax 602 962.5233
page 178

Osmundsen, Mary
4790 N Diversey Blvd,
Whitefish Bay, WI 53211
414 961.1416

Osser, Stephanie
150 Winding River Rd,
Needham, MA 02192
617 237.1116
page 413

Ostroushko, George
14039 Dunbar Ct, Apple Valley, MN 55124
612 423.2026

Ostrow, Carol
2933 N Sheridan Rd, Chicago, IL 60657
312 348.6965

Othrow, Marge
417 Washington Ave, Brooklyn, NY 11238
718 789.1619

Otnes, Fred
211 E 51st St, NYC, NY 10022
212 755.1365

Otnes, Mark
Four Illini Cir, Urbana, IL 61801
217 337.1717

Otsuka, Ken
22 E 36th St, NYC, NY 10016
212 685.4580

Otteson, Gary
200 51st Ter, Kansas City, MO 64112
816 561.0590

Oudekerk, Doug
2003 Goodrich Ave, St Paul, MN 55105
612 884.8083

Oughton, Taylor
Box 355, Jamison, PA 18929
215 598.3246

Out Of My Mind Illustration
1221 W Ben White Blvd, Austin, TX 78704
512 326.8383

Out of the Blue Inc
1906 Welbourne Dr NE, Atlanta, GA 30324
404 875.1363

Ovies, Joseph M
Four E Ohio, Chicago, IL 60611
312 944.1330

Owens, James
3000 Chestnut Ln, Baltimore, MD 21211
410 243.0324

Pace, Annie
Box 257, Pleasantville, NY 10570
914 747.2220

Pace, Julie
PO Box 491, Sky Forest, CA 92385
909 337.0731
fax 909 337.5703
page 453

Paciulli, Bruno
125 W 77th St, NYC, NY 10024
212 799.6532

Padfield, Jane
6239 Elizabeth Ave, St Louis, MO 63139
314 781.8851

Pagaza, Joy
306 Comstock Ave, San Marcos, CA 92069
619 471.8835

Page, Frank
5315 Oakdale Ave, Woodland Hills, CA 91364
818 346.0816

Pagowski, Filip
113 W 106th St, NYC, NY 10025
212 662.3601

Pahl, Peter
580 Washington, San Francisco, CA 94111
415 362.8280

Paillot, Jim
4907 Holly, Kansas City, MO 64112
816 561.8045
fax 816 561.6201
page 58

Pakula, Joani
918 NE 109th Ter,
Kansas City, MO 64155
816 734.4344
page 407

Palazzo Productions
5215 Agnes Ave, North Hollywood, CA 91607
818 840.5162

Palencar, John Jude
249 Elm St, Oberlin, OH 44074
216 774.7312

Palmatier, Gary
5256 Aero Dr, Santa Rosa, CA 95403
707 542.4301

Palmer, Gary
1826 Asheville Pl, Charlotte, NC 28203
704 372.6007

Palmer, Tom
40 Chicasaw Dr, Oakland, NJ 07436
201 337.8638

Palombo, Lisa A
226 Willow Ave, Hoboken, NJ 07030
201 653.1501

Palulian, Dick
18 McKinley St, Rowayton, CT 06853
203 866.3734
fax 203 857.0842
page 28

Palulian, Dick
NYC, NY
212 581.8338
page 28

Palulian, Joanne
18 McKinley St, Rowayton, CT 06853
203 866.3734
fax 203 857.0842
pages 17-29

Palulian, Joanne
NYC, NY
212 581.8338
pages 17-29

Paluso, Christopher
3217 Sweetwater Springs Blvd,
Spring Valley, CA 91978
619 670.4907

Pantuso, Mike
240 Union St, Doylestown, PA 18901
215 340.0158

Paperny, Vladimir
10625 Magnolia Blvd, N Hollywood, CA 91601
818 506.4596

Papi, Liza
231 W 25th St, NYC, NY 10001
212 627.7438

Papitto, Aurelia
300 Commercial St, Boston, MA 02109
617 742.3108

Parallel Inc
1181 Centerfield Ave, Niles, MI 49120
616 683.2800

Pardo, Jackie
116 E 27th St, NYC, NY 10016
212 725.3806

Paredes, Victor
4504 Kingswell Ave, L.A., CA 90027
213 660.2369

Parios Studio
65 W 55th St, NYC, NY 10019
212 767.0260

Parisi, Richard
194 Third Ave, NYC, NY 10003
212 475.0440

Park, Chang
52-05 39th Rd, Woodside, NY 11377
718 651.3764

Park, Darcie
2461 Roswell Ave, Long Beach, CA 90815
310 985.0506

Park, Elliott
PO Box 2193, Grapevine, TX 76099
817 481.2212
fax 817 481.2908
page 359

Park, WB
110 Park Ave S, Winter Park, FL 32789
407 644.1553

Parker, Curtis
1946 E Palomino Dr, Tempe, AZ 85284
602 831.8322

Parker, Diana
2904 University Blvd, Houston, TX 77005
713 661.5844

Parker, Earl
PO Box 155, Passaic, NJ 07055
201 472.1225

Parker, Edward
58 W 15th St, NYC, NY 10011
212 741.2539

Parker, Hank
PO Box 2811, Dillon, CO 80435
303 468.2632

Parker, Robert Andrew
155 W 15th St, NYC, NY 10011
212 989.8770

Parks, Melanie Marder
Five Broadview Ln, Red Hook, NY 12571
914 758.0656

Parks, Phil
806 Woodcrest, Royal Oak, MI 48067
313 545.6477

Parnell, Miles
597 Riverside Ave,
Westport, CT 06880
203 226.4724
fax 203 454.9904
page 69

Parrish, George I Jr
330 W Fourth St, NYC, NY 10014
212 688.1080

Parson, Leon
217 E 86th St, NYC, NY 10022
212 355.0910

Parsons, Glenn
8522 National Blvd, Culver City, CA 90232
310 559.6571

Parsons, Jennifer
251 Steilen Ave, Ridgewood, NJ 07450
201 652.7122

Parsons, John
420 Lexington Ave, NYC, NY 10170
212 697.8525

Parton, Steve
400 W 43rd St, NYC, NY 10036
212 868.0539

Paschkis, Julie
309 NE 94th St, Seattle, WA 98115
206 525.5205
fax 206 525.0831
page 125

Paslavsky, Ivan
510-7 Main St N, Roosevelt Island, NY 10044
212 759.3985

Passantino, Robert
566 Seventh Ave, NYC, NY 10018
212 221.8090

Passarelli, Charles
353 W 53rd St, NYC, NY 10019
212 582.0023
fax 212 582.0090
page 147

Passey, Kim
115 Hurlbut, Pasadena, CA 91105
818 441.4384

Pasternak, Robert
114 W 27th St, NYC, NY 10001
212 675.0002

Pastrana, Robert
473-A Riverdale Dr, Glendale, CA 91204
818 548.6083

Pastucha, Ron
121 1/2 N Glassell St, Orange, CA 92666
714 744.1505

Pate, Judith Arlene
699 County Home Rd, Reidsville, NC 27320
910 342.3729

Pate, Martin
32 Wesley St, Newman, GA 30263
404 251.5286

Pate, Randy
15296 Bitner Pl, Moorpark, CA 93021
805 529.8111

Paterson, James
4312 Mt Olney Ln, Mt Olney, MD 20832
301 774.8329

Patnode, Lou Illustration
1408 Post Alley, Seattle, WA 98101
206 622.2950

Patrick, Cyndy
71 Swan St, Everett, MA 02149
617 387.4296

Patrick, John
68 E Franklin, Dayton, OH 45459
513 433.8383

Patti, Joyce
194 Third Ave, NYC, NY 10003
212 475.0440

Patton Brothers
3768 Miles Ct, Spring Valley, CA 91977
619 463.4562

Patton, Edd
905 W 29th, Austin, TX 78705
512 478.3338

Paul, Jon
15 W 72nd St, NYC, NY 10023
212 799.2231

Paul, Virginia
1823 Santa Clara, Alameda, CA 94501
510 769.0296

Pavlovits, Ivan
5183 Overland Ave, Culver City, CA 90230
310 558.3325

Pavy, F Xavier
210 Gordon St, La Fayette, LA 70501
318 232.6682

Payne, Adair
5921 E Inca, Mesa, AZ 85205
602 641.7345
fax 602 641.7345
page 206

Payne, CF
121 Madison Ave, NYC, NY 10016
212 683.1362

Payne, Liane
11 Kings Ridge Rd, Long Valley, NJ 07853
908 813.8718

Payne, Tom
19 Stuyvesant Oval, NYC, NY 10009
212 505.9342

Peacock Productions
PO Box 5083, Dockton, WA 98070
206 463.9462

Peake, Kevin
8930 SW 95th Ave, Miami Beach, FL 33176
305 576.0142

Pearl Design
1616 Butler Ave, L.A., CA 90025
310 473.4935

Pearson, Patricia
3916 Sacramento St, San Francisco, CA 94118
415 751.3028

Pearson, Rick
5611 Joe Sayers Ave, Austin, TX 78756
512 454.9853

Pechanec, Vladimir M
34-43 Crescent St, L.I.C., NY 11106
718 729.3973

Pechenik, Mark
408 Columbus Ave, s.F., CA 94133
415 982.9181

Peck, Marshall
3443 Wade St, L.A., CA 90066
310 390.9595

Peck, Scott
2701 Thorndale, Plano, TX 75074
214 422.7438
page 377

Peck, Suzanne
420 Lexington Ave, NYC, NY 10017
212 986.5680

Peck, Virginia
73 Winthrop Rd, Brookline, MA 02146
617 232.1653

Pederson, Judy
280 Madison Ave, NYC, NY 10016
212 545.9155

Peirson to Peirson Studio
23409 Gilmore St, West Hills, CA 91307
818 888.5709

Pelavin, Daniel
80 Varick St, NYC, NY 10013
212 941.7418

Pels, Winslow Pinney
RR One Box 504, Port Royal, PA 17082
717 527.2689

Pembroke, Richard
353 W 53rd St, NYC, NY 10019
212 682.2462

Pen Station
11661 W Bluemound Rd, Milwaukee, WI 53226
414 771.3181

Penca, Gary
8335 NW 20th St, Coral Springs, FL 33071
305 752.4699

Pendleton, Roy
28 Pimlico Dr, Commack, NY 11725
516 543.0003

Pendragon Ink
27 Prospect St, Whitinsville, MA 01588
508 234.6843

Peng, Leif
731 N 24th St, Phila, PA 19130
215 232.6666
fax 215 232.6585
pages 328-329

Pennington, Jack
8882 Woodsman, Washington, MI 48094
203 226.4724

Penny & Stermer Group
19 Stuyvesant Oval, NYC, NY 10009
212 505.9342

Penpoint & Design Studio
PO Box 15828, Chevy Chase, MD 20825
202 466.1694

Pepper, Bob
157 Clinton St, Brooklyn, NY 11201
718 875.3236

Pepper, Brenda
157 Clinton St, Brooklyn, NY 11201
718 875.3236

Pepper, Missy Representative
35 Stillman, San Francisco, CA 94107
415 543.6881
fax 415 882.0848
page 245

Peralta, Bella
PO Box 1093, Weaverville, CA 96093
916 623.4872

Percivalle, Rosanne
132 W 21st St, NYC, NY 10011
212 727.9158

Perera, Edmund
1763 Keyes Rd, Memphis, TN 38116
901 346.1739

Perez, Alex
11331 E Elliot Ave, El Monte, CA 91732
310 553.0971

Perez, Luis F
72 Park Ter W, NYC, NY 10034
212 567.4883

Perez, Vincent Studio
1279 Weber St, Alameda, CA 94501
510 521.2262

Peringer, Stephen
17808 184th Ave NE, Woodinville, WA 98072
206 788.5767

Perini, Ben
PO Box 421443,
San Francisco, CA 94142
415 647.5660
fax 415 285.1102
page 378

Perkins, Donna
3443 Wade St, L.A., CA 90066
310 390.9595

Perkins, Ken
5938 W 41st Ave, Denver, CO 80212
303 422.2557

Perkins, Robert
11 Cupania Cir, Monterey Park, CA 91755
213 887.2663

Perry, Alfred
82 Pokorny Rd, Higganum, CT 06441
203 345.2910

Perry, Joe
3561 Ebenezer Rd, Marietta, GA 30066
404 973.0010

Perry, Marcia
160 via Paraiso, Monterey, CA 93940
408 373.7443

Perry, Rex
407 E 25th St, Chicago, IL 60616
312 808.0033

Pesek, Marjorie E
603 Orchid Ave,
Corona Del Mar, CA 92625
714 721.9805
page 267

Pesek, Marjorie E
1888 Century Park E, L.A., CA 90067
310 826.1332
fax 310 284.3290
page 267

Petan, Greg
One Irving Pl, NYC, NY 10003
312 787.9490

Peteet, Rex
965 Slocum St, Dallas, TX 75207
214 761.9400

Peter X (+C) Ltd
200 Varick St, NYC, NY 10014
212 366.6600

Peters, Bob
108 E 35th St, NYC, NY 10016
212 889.3337

Peters, David
12812 Wood Valley Ct, St Louis, MO 63131
314 821.8701

Peters, David Design
2141 Walnut Ave, Venice, CA 90291
310 390.3528

Petersen, Chris
1635 E 22nd St, Oakland, CA 94606
510 535.0495

Petersen, Don
3451 Guido St, Oakland, CA 94602
510 482.3808

Peterson, Bryan/Square Dogs II
405 N Wabash Ave, Chicago, IL 60611
312 321.1336

Peterson, Chris
1630 N Main St, Walnut Creek, CA 94596
510 942.0257

Peterson, Eric
270 Termino Ave, Long Beach, CA 90803
310 438.2785

Peterson, Keith
2509 Park St, Rolling Meadows, IL 60008
708 577.2279

Peterson, Ron
44255-F Fremont Blvd, Fremont, CA 94538
510 623.7043

Peterson, Zig
28 Shelton St, London,
England WC2H 9JN
011 44.71 240 2077
fax 011 44.71 836 0199
page 121

Petrauskas, Kathy
1660 N LaSalle, Chicago, IL 60614
312 642.4950
fax 312 642.6391
page 259

Petrucci, Sam
275 Newbury St, Boston, MA 02116
617 267.0618

Petter, Noel
1716 Hillside Dr, Glendale, CA 91208
213 245.5455

Pettit, David
1400 N Hayworth Ave,
West Hollywood, CA 90046
213 851.7737

PG Representatives
E Main St, Ware, MA 01082
413 967.9855

Phalen, Jim
36 N Pleasant, Oberlin, OH 44074
216 774.1728

Phalen, Mary Jo
405 N Wabash Ave, Chicago, IL 60611
312 321.1336

Phoenix, Harold
10807 McClearen Dr, Houston, TX 77096
713 723.1474

Philbrook & Associates
20927 Wolfe Way, Woodland Hills, CA 91364
818 348.4255

Philbrook, Diana
20927 Wolfe Way, Woodland Hills, CA 91364
818 348.4255

Phillippidis, Evangelia
57 S Monroe Ave, Columbus, OH 43205
614 469.0847

Phillips, Chet
6527 Del Norte, Dallas, TX 75225
214 987.4344

Phillips, Gary
50 Fuller Brook Rd, Wellesley, MA 02181
617 235.8658

Phillips, Jared
21 Woodmont Dr, Woodcliff Lake, NJ 07675
201 573.1053

Phillips, Laura
164 Spencer Ave, Sausalito, CA 94965
415 331.1660

Phillips, Mike
2325 Old Northpark Ln, Alpharetta, GA 30201
404 751.0731

Phoenix Studio
1456 N Dayton, Chicago, IL 60622
312 649.9144

Photocom
3005 Maple Ave, Dallas, TX 75201
214 720.2272

Photonics Graphics
700 W Pete Rose Way, Cincinnati, OH 45203
513 723.4440

Piampiano, John
380 S Euclid, Pasadena, CA 91101
818 584.1589

Piazza, Gail
866 UN Plz, NYC, NY 10017
212 644.2020

Pica, Steve
4215 E Bay Dr, Clearwater, FL 34624
813 532.0912

Picasso, Dan
2211 Emerson Ave N, Mpls, MN 55411
612 588.0567

Piejko, Alex
5796 Morris Rd, Marcy, NY 13403
315 732.4852

Pierazzi, Gary
13997 Emerald Ct, Grass Valley, CA 95945
916 477.1950

Pierre, Keith
5200 SW Tenth Ct, Margate, FL 33068
305 726.0401

Pietrobono, Janet
Five Spring St, Mt Kisco, NY 10549
914 666.4730

Pietzsch, Steve
9802 B Hundred Oaks Cir, Austin, TX 78750
512 331.8755

Pifko, Sigmund
108 E 35th St, NYC, NY 10016
212 889.3337

Pig Pen Studios
235 Carmelita Dr, Mountain View, CA 94040
415 961.5674

Pijet, Andre
4760 Cote des Neiges, Montreal, QU,
Canada H3V 1G3
514 341.1560

Piland Goodell Inc
24 Greenway Plz, Houston, TX 77046
713 965.0453

Piloco, Richard
Seven East End Ave, NYC, NY 10028
212 988.2072

Pilon, Alain
Six St Viateur W, Montreal, QU,
Canada H2T 2K6
514 274.1540

Pina, C David
409 S Beachwood Dr, Burbank, CA 91506
818 972.9239

Pinaha, Bob
24 Patton Dr, Sayreville, NJ 08872
908 257.3228

Pincus, Harry
160 Ave of the Americas, NYC, NY 10013
212 925.8071

Pinkney, Brian
41 Furnace Dock Rd, Croton, NY 10520
914 271.5238

Pinkney, Jerry
41 Furnace Dock Rd, Croton, NY 10520
914 271.5238

Pinkney, Myles
1355 N Union, Colorado Springs, CO 80909
719 635.8848

Pippo, Louis
56 Westminster Rd,
Yorktown Heights, NY 10598
914 245.8267

Pirman, John
330 W 76th St, NYC, NY 10023
212 721.9787

Pisano, Al
6061 N Bay Rd, Miami Beach, FL 33040
305 693.0611

Pittard Sullivan Fitzgerald
6430 Sunset Blvd, Hollywood, CA 90028
213 462.1190

Pittman, Jackie
1728 N Rock Spgs Rd, Atlanta, GA 30324
404 874.2014

Pitts, Ted
68 E Franklin St, Dayton, OH 45459
513 433.8383

Pizzo, Robert
288 E Devonia Ave, Mount Vernon, NY 10552
914 664.4423

Planet X Productions
3536 Moore St, L.A., CA 90066
310 390.5266

Plank, Michael
5833 Monrovia, Shawnee Mission, KS 66216
913 631.7021

Platz III, H Rusty
15922 118th Pl NE, Bothell, WA 98011
206 488.9171

Plotkin, Barnett
126 Wooleys Ln, Great Neck, NY 11023
516 487.7457

Plumley Design
3817 W 226th St, Torrance, CA 90505
310 373.7722

Plummer, Anita Ellescas
1872 Holly Tree Ln, Santa Ana, CA 92705
714 838.0227

Podevin, Jean-François
5812 Newlin Ave, Whittier, CA 90601
310 945.9613

Pohl, David
1629 Rhine St, Pittsburgh, PA 15212
412 231.0838

Poje, Elizabeth
1001 S Alfred St, L.A., CA 90035
310 556.1439
fax 213 653.5696
pages 385-387

Polenghi, Evan
159-25th St, Brooklyn, NY 11232
718 499.3214

Polentz, Chris
420 E Ninth Ave, Escondido, CA 92025
619 489.8419

Polfus, Roberta
226 N Lombard, Oak Park, IL 60302
708 383.3651

Polk, Katherine
5214 E 19th St, Tucson, AZ 85711
602 790.1439

Polkinghorne, Sharron
856 Fifth St, Manhattan Beach, CA 90266
310 379.7323

Pollack, Lou M
3319 SW First Ave,
Portland, OR 97201
503 228.1658
fax 503 228.1658
page 233

Pollack, Scott
78 Hidden Ridge Dr,
Syosset, NY 11791
516 921.1908
fax 516 921.2383
page 343

Pollock, Marty
306 Pleasant St, Pasadena, CA 91101
818 796.1417

Pollock, Matthew
695 Atlantic Ave, Boston, MA 02111
617 342.3832

Polonsky, Gabriel
274 LaGrange St, Chestnut Hill, MA 02167
617 965.3035

Polson, Steven
225 E 79th St, NYC, NY 10021
212 734.3917

Pomerantz, Lisa
731 N 24th St, Phila, PA
215 232.6666
fax 215 232.6585
page 325

Pomilla, Joseph
58 Forest Ave, Ronkonkoma, NY 11779
516 471.2728

Pompelli, Lisa
2550 Amherst Ave, L.A., CA 90064
310 473.9694

Poole, David L
4039 Prescott Ave, Dallas, TX 75219
214 559.4003

Popadics, Joel
109 Alta Vista Dr, Ringwood, NJ 07456
201 831.7381

Pope, Kevin
3286 Ivanhoe, St Louis, MO 63139
314 781.7377

Popeo, Joanie
1001 S Alfred St, L.A., CA 90035
310 556.1439
fax 213 653.5696
page 386

Popp, Wendy
19 Hall Ave, Larchmont, NY 10538
212 833.3520

Porfirio, Guy
4101 E Holmes, Tucson, AZ 85711
602 881.7708

Porras & Lawlor Associates
15 Lucille Ave, Salem, NH 03079
603 893.3626

Porter, John
PO Box 1323, Washington Grove, MD 20880
301 921.0545

Porter, Pat
28 W 69th St, NYC, NY 10023
212 799.8493

Porter, Walter
4010 W El Camino del Cerro,
Tucson, AZ 85745
602 743.9821
fax 602 743.9821
page 205

Portraits & Caricatures
2613 NE Garfield St, Mpls, MN 55418
612 789.5650

Portwood, Andrew
5049 Rollingway Rd, Chesterfield, VA 22832
804 744.2901

Porzio, Ed
59 Channing Rd, Belmont, MA 02178
617 489.6572

Posey, Pam
2763 College Blvd, Oceanside, CA 92056
619 724.3566

Post, Jim Graphics
1411 W Olympic Blvd, L.A., CA 90015
213 387.4572

Potts, Carolyn & Associates Inc
Four E Ohio, Chicago, IL 60611
312 944.1130

Powell, Andrew
212 Third Ave N, Mpls, MN 54401
612 349.6611

Powell, Charles
3028 College Ave, Berkeley, CA 94705
510 652.5811

Powell, Tana
531 Hugo St, San Francisco, CA 94122
415 759.6453

Power, Mary
23-30 24th St, L.I.C., NY 11105
718 932.5817

Pozzatti, Illica
1901 E Tenth St, Bloomington, IN 47408
812 855.0476

Prapas, Christine
8402 SW Woods Creek Ct,
Portland, OR 97219
503 246.9511
fax 503 246.6016
pages 346-356

Pratt, Pierre
Two Silver Ave, Toronto, ON,
Canada M6R 3A2
416 530.1500

Pratt, Russell E
171 Ogden Ave, Jersey City, NJ 07307
201 222.2887

Prendergast, Michael
12 Merrill St, Newburyport, MA 01950
508 465.8598

Prentice, Vicki Associates Inc
1888 Century Park E, L.A., CA 90067
310 826.1332
fax 310 284.3290
pages 260-267

Presslor, Joan
770 E 73rd St, Indpls, IN 46240
317 255.1197

Preston, Heather
20 Savannah Ave, San Anselmo, CA 94960
415 454.4099

Preuitt, Clayton
420 South Detroit St, Los Angeles, CA 90036
213 965.8285

Previn, Stacy
Four E Ohio, Chicago, IL 60611
312 944.1130

Pribble, Holly
7428 W 57th St, Summit, IL 60501
708 458.0387

Pribble, Laurie
653 Pomfret Rd, Hampton, CT 06247
203 455.0811
fax 203 455.1933
pages 107, 355

Pribble, Laurie
Arcadia, CA
818 574.0288
fax 818 574.3940
pages 107, 355

Price, Jim
20 W Hubbard, Chicago, IL 60610
312 222.1361

Primeau, Chuck
116 Dowd Ave, Canton, CT 06019
203 693.0535

Prince, Kevin
24436 Ward St, Torrance, CA 90505
310 375.9232

Prince, Vanna
Eight Jordan, San Francisco, CA 94118
415 668.0622

Pro Art
2008 Polaris, N St Paul, MN 55109
612 770.7011

Probert, Jean
3286 Ivanhoe, St Louis, MO 63138
314 241.4014

Proctor, Jack
12185 N Robin Rd, Maple Grove, MN 55369
612 424.4511

Product Illustration
233 E Ontario, Chicago, IL 60611
312 943.7311

Prud'Homme, Jon
1119 Colorado Ave, Santa Monica, CA 90401
310 394.5031

Pryor, Robert
2153 Charlemagne Ave, Long Beach, CA 90815
310 597.6161

Przewodek, Camille
522 E D St, Petaluma, CA 94952
707 762.4125

PT Pie Illustrations
33 Stonegate Dr, Southbury, CT 06488
203 264.0908

Ptasynski, Fritz
2619 Gates Ave, Redondo Beach, CA 90278
310 214.9035

Puckett, David
16 Prairie Falcon, Aliso Viejo, CA 92656
714 837.4417

Pulver, Harry Jr
105 Meadow Lane N, Mpls, MN 55422
612 377.1797
fax 612 377.1797
page 384

Punchatz, Don Ivan
2605 Westgate Dr, Arlington, TX 76015
817 469.8151

Punin, Nikolai
161 W 16th St, NYC, NY 10011
212 727.7237

Purcell, R Scott
543 W Rolling Rd, Springfield, MA 19064
610 544.0874

Purdom, Bill
2805 Oleander Dr, Wilmington, NC 28403
910 763.1208

Purple Rhino Design
328 Rowan Dr, Berea, OH 44017
216 234.3137

Pushpin Group
215 Park Ave S, NYC, NY 10003
212 674.8080

Putnam, Denise
716 Sanchez St, San Francisco, CA 94114
415 285.8267

Pyk, Jan
340 E 93rd St, NYC, NY 10128
212 876.9749

Pyle, Charles
946 B St, Petaluma, CA 94952
707 765.6734

Pyle, Chris
770 E 73rd St, Indpls, IN 46240
317 255.1197
fax 317 254.9693
page 222

Pyle, Liz
155 W 15th St, NYC, NY 10011
212 989.8770

Quackenbush, Robert
460 E 79th St, NYC, NY 10021
212 744.3822

Quanrud Illustration & Design
6441 NE Tara Ln, Bainbridge Isl, WA 98110
206 842.6063

Queen of Arts
12325 S 90th Ave, Palos Park, IL 60464
708 361.0679

Quinlan, Stephen Ills Ltd
1957 Creston Pl, Burlington, ON,
Canada L7P 2Y5
416 485.8277
fax 416 485.8277
page 399

Quon Design Office
568 Broadway, NYC, NY 10012
212 226.6024

R/Greenberg Associates
350 W 39th St, NYC, NY 10018
212 239.6767

Rabin, Bill & Associates
680 N Lake Shore Dr, Chicago, IL 60611
312 944.6655

Rabi, Lorraine
629 Glenwood Ave,
Teaneck, NJ 07666
201 836.4283
page 445

Rachko, Barbara
1311 W Braddock Rd, Alexandria, VA 22302
703 998.7496

Radigan, Robert
742 Pyrula, Sanibel Island, FL 33957
813 472.0910

Rae, Ron
2100 W Big Beaver Rd, Troy, MI 48084
313 643.6000

Rafei, Bob
21 Overlook Ave, Emerson, NJ 07630
210 261.4564

Raff, Lyne
9501 Rolling Oak Trl, Austin, TX 78750
512 219.1208

Ragland, Greg
2500 Lucky John Dr, Park City, UT 84060
801 645.9232

Ramage, Alfred
Winthrop, MA
617 846.5955

Ramba Design
1776 Columbus Rd, Cleveland, OH 44113
216 621.1776

Ramirez, Roberto
1410 W First St, Winston-Salem, NC 27101
910 722.5113

Ramon, John
Box 257, Pleasantville, NY 10570
914 747.2220

Ramsay-In The Black Inc
1128 Smith St, Honolulu, HI 96813
808 537.2787

Ramune
210 Hillside Ave, Needham, MA 02194
617 444.1185
page 363

Rancorn, Chuck
750 94th Ave N, St Petersburg, FL 33702
813 579.4499

Randazzo, Anthony
353 W 53rd St, NYC, NY 10019
212 582.0023
fax 212 582.0090
page 147

Random Arts
2617 E Hedrick Dr, Tucson, AZ 85716
602 881.8882

Rangel, Fernando
45-38 47th St, Sunnyside, NY 11104
718 729.6065

Rangne, Monica
210 First Ave, NYC, NY 10009
212 260.5121

Rapp, Gerald & Cullen
108 E 35th St, NYC, NY 10016
212 889.3337
fax 212 889.3341
page 170

Rappy & Co
150 W 22nd St, NYC, NY 10011
212 989.0603

Ratz de Tagyos, Paul
30 Eastchester Rd, New Rochelle, NY 10801
914 636.2313

Ravanelli, Terry
1400 S Highway Dr, Fenton, MO 63094
314 827.2840

Ravenwolf, Patricia Randall
One Gilmore Rd, Trenton, NJ 08628
609 882.3066

Rawson, Jon M
1225 S Hamilton St, Lockport, IL 60441
312 266.4884

Ray, Dennis Paul
2199 Wildflower Ct, Corona, CA 91719
909 371.4655

Ray, Les
3443 Wade St, L.A., CA 90066
310 390.9595

Rayevsky, Robert
403 Garwood Dr,
Cherry Hill, NJ 08003
609 427.6970
fax 609 427.6970
page 468

Raymer, Louis
529 S Seventh St, Mpls, MN 55415
612 338.2022

Raymond, Victoria
234 W 21st St, NYC, NY 10011
212 741.0005

Rea, Tracy
3301A S Jefferson Ave, St Louis, MO 63118
314 773.2600

Reactor
51 Camden St, Toronto, ON,
Canada M5V 1V2
416 362.1913 800 730.8945
fax 416 362.6356
pages 226-229

Reactor Worldwide
156 Fifth Ave, NYC, NY 10010
800 730.8945
pages 226-229

Read, Steve
28 Shelton St, London,
England WC2H 9JN
011 44.71 240 2077
fax 011 44.71 836 0199
page 123

Reagan, Mike
200 Aquetong Rd,
New Hope, PA 18938
215 862.2091
fax 215 862.2641
page 281

Reay, Richard
6010 Liebig Ave, Riverdale, NY 10471
718 884.2317

Reben, Ken
305 E 46th St, NYC, NY 10017
212 421.8190

Rector, Melinda
9271 Velardo Dr, Huntington Beach, CA 92646
714 964.7486

Red Owl, Richard
Box 257, Pleasantville, NY 10570
914 747.2220

Redgrafix
19750 W Observatory, New Berlin, WI 53146
414 542.5547

Redman, Dina
45 Brosnan St, San Francisco, CA 94103
415 863.1074

Redner, Ann
2100 W Big Beaver Rd, Troy, MI 48084
313 643.6000

Redowl, Richard
Box 257, Pleasantville, NY 10570
914 747.2220

Redwood, Jo-Anne
5371 Wilshire Blvd, L.A., CA 90036
213 936.1156

Reed, Chris
17 Edgewood Rd, Edison, NJ 08820
908 548.3927
fax 908 603.0842
page 76

Reed, Dan
65 Keene St, Providence, RI 02906
401 521.1395

Reed, Judy
1808 Manning Ave, L.A., CA 90025
310 641.8556

Reed, Lynn Rowe
420 Lexington Ave, NYC, NY 10170
212 986.5680
fax 212 818.1246
page 83

Reed, Mike
1314 Summit Ave, Mpls, MN 55403
612 374.3164

Reed, Susie
2175 Francisco Blvd, San Rafael, CA 94901
415 456.8267

Reeser, Renee
4639 Franklin Ave, L.A., CA 90027
213 664.8046

Rehbein, Richard
643 Newark Ave, Kenilworth, NJ 07033
908 241.0743

Reich, Allen J
64 S Parker Dr, Wesley Hills, NY 10952
914 354.3202

Reid, Andrew
924 Lincoln Rd, Miami Beach, FL 33139
305 531.7338

Reid, Glenn
430 Ventura Pl, Vero Beach, FL 32963
617 236.1920

Reilly, Donald
211 Newtown Tpk, Wilton, CT 06897
203 834.0067

Reilly, Kerry Reps
1826 Asheville Pl, Charlotte, NC 28203
704 372.6007

Reiner, Annie
10532 Blythe, L.A., CA 90064
310 559.0831

Reiner, John
27 Watch Way, Lloyd Neck, NY 11743
516 385.4261

Reinert, Kirk
251 Longview Rd, Clinton Corners, NY 12514
914 266.3227

Reingold, Alan
155 E 38th St, NYC, NY 10016
212 697.6170

Reingold, Michael
310 Warwick Rd, Haddonfield, NJ 08033
609 354.1787

Reinhardt, Dorothy
466 Melrose Ave,
San Francisco, CA 94127
415 584.9369
fax 415 584.9369
page 364

Reinman, Mick
5183 Overland Ave, Culver City, CA 90230
310 558.3325

Reisch, Jesse
135 Elinor Ave, Mill Valley, CA 94041
415 388.8704

Rekosh, Jana
145 N 84th St, Seattle, WA 98104
206 282.8558

Renard Represents
501 Fifth Ave, NYC, NY 10017
212 490.2450
fax 212 697.6828
pages 40, 286-308

Rendeiro, Charlene
643 Santa Clara Ave, Venice, CA 90291
310 396.8308

Rendon, Maria
1001 E First St, L.A., CA 90012
212 687.3664

Renfro, Ed
250 E 83rd St, NYC, NY 10028
212 879.3823

Renlie, Frank
500 Aurora Ave N, Seattle, WA 98109
206 284.4701

Reott, P
731 N 24th St, Phila, PA 19130
215 232.6666

Repertoire
5521 Greenville, Dallas, TX 75206
214 369.6990
fax 214 369.6938
pages 362, 457

Reppel, Aletha
905 W 29th St, Austin, TX 78705
512 478.0853

Reyes, Eduardo
454 W 36th St, NYC, NY 10018
212 967.6756

Reynaldo Associates
26211 Vera Way, Calabasas, CA 91302
818 880.6269

Reynolds, Keith L
RR 2 Box 387, Sanbornville, NH 03872
603 522.8765

Reynolds, Mark Andrew
396 Pine Hill Rd, Stinson Beach, CA 94941
415 383.3348

Rez, Jenny
4128 Manila Ave, Oakland, CA 94609
510 655.5032

Ricceri, David
505 Court St, Brooklyn, NY 11231
718 852.8987

Riccio, Frank
420 Lexington Ave, NYC, NY 10170
212 986.5680

Rice, Cecil
5784 Salem Terr, Acworth, GA 30102
404 974.0684

Rich Art Graphics
1309 Vine St, Phila, PA 19107
215 922.1539

Richards, Dan
2811 McKinney Ave, Dallas, TX 75204
214 922.9080

Richards, Kenn
Three Elwin Pl, East Northport, NY 11731
516 499.7575

Richards, Linda
27 Bleeker St, NYC, NY 10012
212 673.1600

Richardson, Jeff
2416 1/2 McKinney, Dallas, TX 75201
214 747.3122

Richart Studio
4160-12B Hutchinson RPE, Bronx, NY 10475
718 320.2779

Richer, Paul
2109 45th Ave, L.I.C., NY 11101
718 472.0859

Richter, Andrea
Seven Trout Way, Salisbury, MA 01952
508 462.0527

Rickel, Irwin F
2878 Dunleer Pl, L.A., CA 90064
310 839.1517

Rickert, David Studio
4608 Upton Ave S, Mpls, MN 55410
612 922.4587

Rickwood, Jake
28 Shelton St, London,
England WC2H 9JN
011 44.71 240 2077
fax 011 44.71 836 0199
page 120

Riding, Linda
280 Madison Ave, NYC, NY 10016
212 545.9155

Ridley, Dave
Seven Flintlock Rd, Norwalk, CT 06850
203 866.5865

Rie, Carolyn
22-03 Astoria Blvd, L.I.C., NY 11102
718 721.4360

Riedy, Mark
68 E Franklin St, Dayton, OH 45459
513 433.8383

Rieser, Bonnie
934 NE 33rd St, Portland, OR 97232
503 452.2210
page 101

Rieser, William
361 Magee Ave, Mill Valley, CA 94941
415 389.0332

Rigie, Mitchell
41 Union Sq W, NYC, NY 10003
212 807.6627

Riley Illustration
155 W 15th St, NYC, NY 10011
212 989.8770

Riley, Frank
108 Bamford Ave, Hawthorne, NJ 07506
201 423.2659

Riley, Kelly
213 Village St, Millis, MA 02054
508 376.5477

Riley, Susan
1347 N Dearborn, Chicago, IL 60610
312 751.1313

Riskin, Martin
12 Tidewinds Ter, Marblehead, MA 01945
617 631.2073

Risko, Robert
155 W 15th St, NYC, NY 10011
212 255.2865

Risser Digital Studio
5330 Electric Ave, Milwaukee, WI 53234
414 545.1270

Ristau, Paul
307 N Michigan Ave, Chicago, IL 60601
312 855.9336

Ritchey Associates
900 N Franklin, Chicago, IL 60610
312 642.5763

Riveros, Victoria
2820 E Sixth St, L.A., CA 90023
213 264.3123

Riverworks
2521 Palisade Ave, Riverdale, NY 10463
718 884.5315

Rivoche, Paul
Two Silver Ave, Toronto, ON,
Canada M6R 3A2
416 530.1500
fax 416 530.1401
page 463

Rixford, Ellen
308 W 97th St, NYC, NY 10025
212 865.5686

RKB Studios Inc
420 N Fifth St, Mpls, MN 55401
612 339.7055
fax 612 339.8689
page 57

Robb, Corey
1121 S Glenstone, Springfield, MO 65804
417 864.5866

Roberts, Brad
7006 Lanewood Ave, Hollywood, CA 90028
213 856.9951

Roberts, Eva
540 Erbes Rd, Thousand Oaks, CA 91362
805 495.2266

Roberts, Ken
12121 Wilshire Blvd, L.A., CA 90025
310 826.9378

Roberts, Peggi
13075 N 75th Pl, Scottsdale, AZ 85260
602 991.8568

Roberts, Scott
Six N Main St, Bel Air, MD 21014
410 879.3362
fax 410 879.3362
page 98

Roberts, Stephanie
909 11th St, Santa Monica, CA 90403
310 395.4688

Roberts, Tom
15 W 72nd St, NYC, NY 10023
212 799.2231

Robertson, Chris
3708 Watseka, L.A., CA 90034
310 836.8968

Robinette, Ilene Illustration
120 W Illinois, Chicago, IL 60610
312 527.1805

Robins, Lili Petrov
3014 Cruiser Dr, Stafford, VA 22554
703 720.6592

Robins, Mike
726 1/2 E 12 1/2 St, Houston, TX 77008
713 868.9871

Robinson, Gwen
14133 Paddock St, Sylmar, CA 91342
818 367.6430

Robinson, Kristin
112 Nakota Dr, Spicer, MN 56228
612 796.5670

Robinson, Lynn
791 Sunbury Rd, Columbus, OH 43147
614 252.4771

Robinson, Mark V
9050 Loreleigh Way, Fairfax, VA 22031
703 280.4123

Rocha, Peter
2417 Bryant St, San Francisco, CA 94110
415 648.9007

Roche, Barbara
4350 Browndale Ave, St Louis Park, MN 55424
612 925.7829

Roche, Diann Represents
200 W 51st Ter,
Kansas City, MO 64112
816 561.0590
fax 816 531.5103
pages 319, 374-375

Rockwell, Barry
344 Beaver Dam Rd, Brookhaven, NY 11719
516 286.5808

Rockwell, Richard
Box 257, Pleasantville, NY 10570
914 747.2220

Roda, Bot
78 Victoria Ln, Lancaster, PA 17603
717 393.1406

Rodan, Don
Box 58, Oak Island, NC 28465
910 278.1888

Rodela, Rene
7819 Broadway, El Paso, TX 79915
915 778.4838

Roden, Susan
1501 Tramway Blvd NE,
Albuquerque, NM 87112
505 293.1873

Rodorigo, Sandro
23-17 33rd St, Astoria, NY 11105
718 274.2764

Rodriguez, Claudio
304 Mulberry St, NYC, NY 10012
212 941.0573

Rodriguez, Jose
14521 Cullen St, Whittier, CA 90603
310 693.1031

Rodriguez, Robert
501 Fifth Ave, NYC, NY 10017
212 490.2450
fax 212 697.6828
page 307

Roehr, KE
230 Babcock St, Brookline, MA 02146
617 566.1137

Rogan, Michael
733 Bounty Dr, Foster City, CA 94404
415 378.6715

Rogers, Adam
414 W Pender St, Vancouver, BC,
Canada V6B 1T5
604 684.6826

Rogers, Bryant K
1853 Renada Cir, N Las Vegas, NV 89030
702 649.7279

Rogers, Buc
1025 W Madison, Chicago, IL 60607
312 421.4132
page 318

Rogers, Glenda
4049 Marlton Cir, Liverpool, NY 13090
315 451.3220

Rogers, Joe
Two N 112 Virginia, Glen Ellyn, IL 60137
708 682.0515

Rogers, Kathy
19220 Hackamore Rd, Corcoran, MN 55340
612 478.9897

Rogers, Lilla
Six Parker Rd, Arlington, MA 02174
617 641.2787

Rogers, Mike
17711 Margate St, Encino, CA 91316
818 344.8609

Rogers, Nip
212 S Front St, Phillipsburg, PA 16866
814 342.6572
page 165

Rogers, Nip
848 Greenwood Ave,
Atlanta, GA 30306
404 875.1363 800 347.0734
fax 404 875.9733
page 165

Rogers, Paul
12 S Fair Oaks, L.A., CA 91105
818 564.8728

Rogers, Randy
1212 N Post Oak, Houston, TX 77055
713 688.0637
fax 713 688.9988
page 162

Rogerson, Zebulon
1312 18th St NW, Wash, DC 20036
202 293.1687

Rogondino & Associates
779 Holly Oak Dr, Palo Alto, CA 94303
415 852.9493

Rohrbacher, Patricia
1374 Midland Ave, Bronxville, NY 10708
914 776.1185

Rohrer, Neal
725 17th St, Kenosha, WI 53140
414 551.7233

Rolin Graphics
5620 W Broadway, Crystal, MN 55428
612 533.2494

Roman, Barbara J
345 W 88th St, NYC, NY 10024
212 362.1374

Roman, Helen Associates
177 Newtowne Tpke, Weston, CT 10023
203 222.1608

Roman, Irena & John
369 Thomas Clapp Rd, Scituate, MA 02066
617 545.6514

Roman, John
PO Box 571, Scituate, MA 02066
617 545.6514

Rombola, John
3804 Farragut Rd, Brooklyn, NY 11210
212 645.8000

Romeo Empire Design
154 Spring St, NYC, NY 10012
212 274.0214

The Romeo Studio
1066 NW 96th St, Ft Lauderdale, FL 33322
305 472.0072

Romer, Dan V
176 Fifth Ave, Brooklyn, NY 11217
718 789.8442

Romero, Javier Design Group
24 E 23rd St, NYC, NY 10010
212 420.0656
fax 212 420.1168
page 419

Roper, Marty
6115 Brookside Blvd,
Kansas City, MO 64113
816 361.8589
page 375

Rosandich, Dan
PO Box 410, Chassell, MI 49916
906 482.6234

Rosch, Brucie
64 Hollywood Ave, Albany, NY 12208
518 459.3261

Rosco, Delro
91-822B Pohakupuna Rd, Ewa Beach, HI 96706
808 689.4635

Rose, David
1623 N Curson Ave, L.A., CA 90046
213 876.0038

Rose, Drew
1728 N Rock Spgs Rd, Atlanta, GA 30324
404 874.2014

Rose, Lee
4250 TC Jester Blvd, Houston, TX 77018
713 686.4799

Rose, Peggy J
53 Sonora Way, Corte Madera, CA 94925
415 924.6485

Rosebush Co
154 W 57th St, NYC, NY 10019
212 581.3000

Rosefsky, Flora
PO Box 177, Binghamton, NY 13903
607 771.3442

Rosen, Jake
34 Bal Harbour, St Louis, MO 63146
314 432.0941

Rosen, Jonathon
408 Second St, Brooklyn, NY 11215
718 499.3911

Rosenbaum, Jon & Georgina
Four Carroll St, Stamford, CT 06907
203 324.4558

Rosenberg, Beb Kilen
2405 NW Thurman St, Portland, OR 97210
503 225.9687

Rosenberry, Vera
144 Munsell Rd, East Patchogue, NY 11772
516 286.3903

Rosenblum, Richard
Two Grace Ct, Brooklyn, NY 11201
718 237.1318

Rosenfeld, Julie
15 N Meramec, St Louis, MO 63105
314 725.3434

Rosenheim, Cindy Salans
15 Westgate Dr, San Francisco, CA 94127
415 334.2723

Rosenhouse, Irwin
256 Mott St, NYC, NY 10012
212 226.2848

Rosenthal Represents
3443 Wade St, L.A., CA 90066
310 390.9595

Rosenthal, Marc
Eight Rte 66, Malden Bridge, NY 12115
518 766.4191

Rosenthal, Marshal M
231 W 18th St, NYC, NY 10011
212 807.1247

Rosenwald, Laurie
54 W 21st St, NYC, NY 10010
212 675.6707

The Rosner Studio
PO Box 980175, Houston, TX 77098
713 528.5446

Rosner, Meryl
21 Gramercy Park S, NYC, NY 10003
212 254.7668

Ross Associates
42 Partridge Rd, Methuen, MA 01844
508 682.5794

Ross, Dave
531 41st St, Brooklyn, NY 11232
718 854.1006

Ross, Ian
203 W 84th St, NYC, NY 10024
212 721.5268

Ross, Larry
53 Fairview Ave, Madison, NJ 07940
201 377.6859

Ross, Marc
20 W Hubbard, Chicago, IL 60610
312 222.1361
fax 312 222.0753
pages 422-423

Ross, Mary
San Francisco, CA
415 776.3833
page 276

Ross, Richard
545 Eighth Ave, NYC, NY 10018
212 330.0411

Ross, Scott
731 N 24th St, Phila, PA 19130
215 232.6666

Rossiter, Nan
597 Riverside Ave,
Westport, CT 06880
203 226.4724
fax 203 454.9904
page 68

Roth, Arnold
157 W 57th St, NYC, NY 10019
212 333.7606

Roth, Larry I
1544 W Grace, Chicago, IL 60613
312 880.0182

Roth, Marc
323 W Kennedy Dr, Streamwood, IL 60107
312 837.8899

Roth, Robert
2022 Jones St, San Francisco, CA 94133
415 928.0457

**Roth, Roger
7227 Brent Rd,
Upper Darby, PA 19082
610 352.3235
fax 610 352.3235
page 411**

Rother, Sue
19 Brookmont Cir, San Anselmo, CA 94960
415 454.3593

Rotunno, Betsy
3443 Wade St, L.A., CA 90066
310 390.9595

Roundy, Laine
42 Buttonball Dr, Sandy Hook, CT 06482
203 426.9531

Rouner, Elizabeth
339 Chestnut St, St Paul, MN 55102
612 298.0059

Rowe, Charles
133 Aronimink Dr, Newark, DE 19711
302 738.0641

Rowe, Greg Alan
900 E First St, L.A., CA 90012
213 626.6563

Rowe, John
316 Mellow Ln, La Can Flintrdge, CA 91011
818 790.2645

Roy, Joanna
549 W 123rd St, NYC, NY 10027
212 663.7876

Royo, Luis
11 Kings Ridge Rd, Long Valley, NJ 07853
908 813.8718

Rubess, Balvis
260 Brunswick Ave, Toronto, ON,
Canada M5S 2M7
416 927.7071

Rubin Photo Illustration
4140 Arch Dr, Studio City, CA 91604
818 508.9028

Rubin, Al
250 Mercer St, NYC, NY 10012
212 674.4535

Ruchlewicz, Mark
17 Castor Cres, Scarborough, ON,
Canada M1G 3R1
416 439.2082

Rudd, Greg
Pine Rd HCR, Neversink, NY 12765
914 985.2936

**Rudnak, Theo
501 Fifth Ave, NYC, NY 10017
212 490.2450
fax 212 697.6828
page 297**

Ruegger, Rebecca
333 E 49th St, NYC, NY 10017
212 982.6533

Ruemmele Design
1825 N Pennsylvania St, Indpls, IN 46202
317 924.0606

**Ruff, Donna
18 Crockett St, Rowayton, CT 06853
203 866.8626
fax 203 866.8005
pages 118-119**

Ruhman, Rick
1150 W Winton Ave, Hayward, CA 94545
510 783.4482

Ruiz, Art
43 E 19th St, NYC, NY 10003
212 254.4996

Rummel, Moira B
4105 Linden Hills Blvd, Mpls, MN 55410
612 920.5502

Ruscha, Paul
940 N Highland Ave, L.A., CA 90038
213 856.0008

Rush, John
123 Kedzie St, Evanston, IL 60202
708 869.2078

**Russell, Bill
949 Filbert St, San Francisco, CA 94133
415 474.4159
fax 415 474.5464
page 228**

Russell, David M
823 Seamaster, Houston, TX 77062
713 488.2302

Russell, Mike
427 First St, Brooklyn, NY 11215
718 499.3436

Russo, Anthony
51 Fogland Rd, Tiverton, RI 02878
401 351.1770

Russo, Camille
1521 Continental Sq Dr, Lexington, KY 40505
606 293.6150

Russo, David Anson
41 Union Sq W, NYC, NY 10003
212 807.6627

Russo, Jeffrey
3421 Gray St, Tampa, FL 33609
813 877.3639

Ruszkowski, Joe
8800 N I H35, Austin, TX 78753
512 339.6133

Rutherford, John
563 Ocean, Ferndale, CA 95536
707 786.4055

Ryan, Cheri
PO Box 19412, Seattle, WA 98109
206 634.1880

Ryan, David
1408 Pacific Ave, Alameda, CA 94501
415 752.8277

Ryan, Donna
2405 NW Thurman St, Portland, OR 97210
503 225.9687

Ryan, Terry
8020 Grenfell St, Kew Gardens, NY 11415
212 688.1080

Rybka, Stephen
3119 W 83rd St, Chicago, IL 60202
312 737.1981

Rydberg, Steven
14 W 103rd St, NYC, NY 10025
212 663.0332

Ryden, Mark
541 Ramona Ave, Sierra Madre, CA 91024
818 303.3133

S.F. Society of Illustrators
690 Market St, San Francisco, CA 94104
415 399.1681

Sabanosh, Michael
433 W 34th St, NYC, NY 10001
212 947.8161

Sabella, Jill
2607 Ninth Ave W, Seattle, WA 98104
206 285.4794

Sabin, Tracy
13476 Ridley Rd, San Diego, CA 92129
619 484.8712

Sable, Paul
3314 Washburn Ave N, Mpls, MN 55412
612 529.2644

Sachs, Jenny
157 E 32nd St, NYC, NY 10016
212 684.0565
page 313

Sacks, Cal
721-B Heritage Vlg, Southbury, CT 06488
203 262.1427

Sadowski, Victor
211 E 89th St, NYC, NY 10128
212 289.5514
fax 212 987.2855
page 202

Saffioti, Lino
69 E Rouges Path, Huntington Sta, NY 11746
516 673.3760

Saffold, Joe
501 Fifth Ave, NYC, NY 10017
212 490.2450
fax 212 697.6828
page 288

Saiki, Lorel Keiko
1842 Glendon Ave, L.A., CA 90025
310 470.2898

Saint-Jivago Desanges
PO Box 24 AA2, L.A., CA 90024
213 931.1984

Sakahara, Dick
28826 Cedar Bluff Dr, Rancho Palos, CA 90274
310 541.8187

Saksa Art & Design
10 Hidden Hollow Dr,
Hamilton Township, NJ 08620
609 259.7792

Sala, John
PO Box 155, Passaic, NJ 07055
201 472.1225

Salazar, Miro
PO Box 421443,
San Francisco, CA 94142
415 647.5660
fax 415 285.1102
pages 379, 381

Salcido, Henry R
36 Viewpoint Cir, Philips Ranch, CA 91766
909 865.0268

Salentine, Katherine
Ten Summerhill Ct, San Rafael, CA 94903
415 499.9329

Salerno, Steven
41 Union Sq W, NYC, NY 10003
212 929.5590
page 243

Sales, David Art
108 E 35th St, NYC, NY 10016
212 889.3337

Salinas, Kim
7014 Captain Dr, Houston, TX 77036
713 955.0353

Salinas, Ruben
716 E Eight 1/2 St, Houston, TX 77000
713 880.4985

Salk, Lawrence
19029 Sprague St, Tarzana, CA 91356
818 776.1992

Salmela, Don
24262 E Typo Drive NE, Stacy, MN 55079
612 884.4045

Salmon, Chris
866 W Aldine St, Chicago, IL 60657
312 871.8570

Salmon, Paul
5826 Jackson's Oak Ct, Burke, VA 22015
703 250.4943

Salvati, Jim
6600 Royer Ave, West Hills, CA 91307
818 348.9012

Salzman, Richard W
Chicago, IL
312 252.2244
pages 186.187

Salzman, Richard W
NYC, NY
212 997.0115
pages 186-187

Salzman, Richard W
London, England
011 44.71.636.7141
pages 186-187

Salzman, Richard W
L.A., CA
310 276.4298
pages 186-187

Salzman, Richard W
716 Sanchez St,
San Francisco, CA 94114
415 285.8267
fax 415 285.8268
pages 186-187

Samanich, Barbara
PO Box 712, Taos, NM 87571
505 758.4859

Sammel, Chelsea
25 Esquiline Rd, Carmel Valley, CA 93924
408 659.1813

Sams, BB
PO Box A, Social Circle, GA 30279
404 464.2956

Samul, Cynthia
15 Pacific St, New London, CT 06320
203 442.5695

Sanchez, Carlos
3301 A S Jefferson Ave, St Louis, MO 63118
314 773.2600

Sandbox Digital Playground
203 N Wabash, Chicago, IL 60601
312 372.1170

Sanders, Bruce
Four Prospect St, Beverly, MA 01915
508 921.0887

Sanders, James
2066 Lyric Ave, L.A., CA 90039
213 669.1879

Sanders, Liz Agency
30166 Chapala Ct, Laguna Niguel, CA 92677
714 495.3664

Sandford, John
Pine Rd HCR, Neversink, NY 12765
914 985.2936

Sandro, Cindy
834 Briarcliff Rd, Atlanta, GA 30306
404 872.7193

Sands, Trudy Artist Rep
1350 Chemical St, Dallas, TX 75207
214 748.8663

Sanfilippo, Margaret
530 Ramona, Palo Alto, CA 94301
415 322.2057

Sanford, Sandy
1103 Glengarry Dr, Walnut Creek, CA 94596
510 933.3884

Sanford, Steve
41 Union Sq W, NYC, NY 10003
212 243.6119

Sano, Kazuhiko
501 Fifth Ave, NYC, NY 10017
212 490.2450
fax 212 697.6828
page 306

Sano, Kazuhiko
105 Stadium Ave,
Mill Valley, CA 94941
415 381.6377
page 306

Sanson, Jeff
1212 N Post Oak, Houston, TX 77055
713 688.0637
page 161

Santa-Donato Studios
25 W 39th St, NYC, NY 10018
212 921.1550

Santalucia, Francesco
420 Lexington Ave, NYC, NY 10017
212 986.5680

Santelli, Helen
410 N Michigan Ave, Chicago, IL 60611
312 689.3442

Santiago, Rafael
72-10 37th Ave, Jackson Hts, NY 11372
718 565.6772

Santillan, Steve A
1700 W Cerritos St, Anaheim, CA 92804
714 635.7630

Santoliquido, Dolores R
60 W Broad St, Mt Vernon, NY 10552
914 667.3199

Santore, Charles
138 S 20th St, Phila, PA 19103
215 563.0430

Saputo, Joe
737 Milwood Ave, Venice, CA 90291
310 301.8059

Sardella, Ferruccio
211 E 89th St, NYC, NY 10128
212 289.5514
fax 212 987.2855
page 199

Sarecky, Melody
3601 Connecticut Ave NW, Wash, DC 20008
202 347.5276

Sargent, Claudia Karabaic
15-38 126th St, College Point, NY 11356
718 461.8280

Sarley, Michael
1400 N Hayworth Ave,
West Hollywood, CA 90046
213 851.7737

Sattler, Peter
824 N 26th St, Phila, PA 19127
215 765.9197

Sauber, Robert
10 Plz St, Brooklyn, NY 11238
718 636.9050

Sauer, Jennifer
5183 Overland Ave, Culver City, CA 90230
310 558.3325

Saunders, Fred
4829 18th Ave SW, Seattle, WA 98106
206 762.6737
page 134

Saunders, Rob
34 Station St, Brookline, MA 02146
617 566.4464
fax 617 739.0040
page 372

Savage, Mike
2817 W 49th St, Westwood, KS 66025
913 677.5979

Sawecki, Michael
410 N Michigan Ave, Chicago, IL 60611
312 689.3442

Sayess, Shirley Kathan
205 Indian Meadow Dr, Northboro, MA 01532
508 393.7435

Sayles Graphic Design
308 Eighth St, Des Moines, IA 50309
515 243.2922

Scanlan, David
1600 18th St,
Manhattan Beach, CA 90266
310 545.0773
fax 310 545.7364
page 447

Scanlan, Mike
27 Brookwood Dr, Normal, IL 61761
309 452.6408

Scanlan, Peter
713 Willow Ave, Hoboken, NJ 07030
201 792.1575

Scanlon, Susan
417 E 87th St, NYC, NY 10128
212 996.0591

Scardova, Jaclyne
17 Redwood Rd, Fairfax, CA 94930
415 721.0707

Scarola, Vito-Leonardo
24872 Via Sonoma, Laguna Niguel, CA 92656
714 831.1270

Scarpulla, Caren
2832 Waverly Dr, L.A., CA 90039
213 913.2458

Schaefer, Alex
380 S Euclid, Pasadena, CA 91101
818 584.1589

Schaffer, Amanda
445 Hanson Ln, Ramona, CA 92065
619 788.0388

Scheffler, Harlan C
520 N Michigan Ave, Chicago, IL 60611
312 527.0351

Schein, Barry
NYC, NY 11415
212 432.6844

Schell, Paul
1608 E 51st St, Brooklyn, NY 11234
718 951.8976

Scherman, John
310 E 12th St, NYC, NY 10003
212 473.7237

Scheuer, Lauren
77 Pierce Rd, Watertown, MA 02172
617 924.6799
page 74

Scheuer, Phil
126 Fifth Ave, NYC, NY 10011
212 620.0728

Schilling, John
8507 137th NE, Redmond, WA 98052
206 867.1074

Schilling, Stephanie
111 Atlantic Ave, Boston, MA 02110
617 723.2333

Schiwall-Gallo, Linda
PO Box 258, Ashfield, MA 01330
413 628.4735

Schlecht, Richard
2724 S June St, Arlington, VA 22202
703 684.8035

Schleinkofer, David
420 Lexington Ave, NYC, NY 10017
212 986.5680

Schlowsky, Lois
73 Old Rd, Weston, MA 02193
617 899.5110

Schmelzer, JP
1002 S Wesley, Oak Park, IL 60304
708 386.4005

Schmid, Paul
1911 NE 80th St, Seattle, WA 98115
206 522.1839

Schmidt Associates
20296 Harper Ave, Harper Woods, MI 48225
313 881.8075

Schmidt, Brad
60 E 42nd St, NYC, NY 10017
212 867.8092

Schmidt, Chuck
1715 Ramona Ave, South Pasadena, CA 91030
213 256.0815

Schmidt, George
183 Steuben St, Brooklyn, NY 11205
718 857.1837

Schmidt, John
7308 Leesville Blvd, Springfield, VA 22151
703 750.0927

Schneider, Douglas
9016 Danube Ln, San Diego, CA 92103
619 695.6796

Schneider, RM
597 Riverside Ave,
Westport, CT 06880
203 226.4724
fax 203.454.9904
page 62

Schofield, Den
7013 Hegerman, Phila, PA 19135
215 624.8143

Schofield, Glen
Four Hillside Ave, Roseland, NJ 07068
201 226.5597

Schofield, Mark
1201 First Ave S, Seattle, WA 98134
206 623.9539

Scholl, Heather
223 Prospect, Seattle, WA 98109
206 282.8558
fax 206 285.4304
page 135

Scholl, Oliver
1400 N Hayworth Ave,
West Hollywood, CA 90046
213 851.7737

Scholle, Kim
495 Carolina St, San Francisco, CA 94107
415 863.4969

Schongut, Emanuel
247 Main St, Mountain Dale, NY 12763
914 434.8964

Schott, Cathleen
3443 Wade St, L.A., CA 90066
310 390.9595

Schreck, John
101 Springhill Rd, Fairfield, CT 06430
203 259.6824

Schreiber, Dana
36 Center St, Collinsville, CT 06022
203 693.6688

Schreier, Joshua
466 Washington St, NYC, NY 10013
212 925.0472

Schreiner, John
206 N First St, Mpls, MN 55401
612 332.2361

Schrier, Fred
770 E 73rd St, Indpls, IN 46240
317 255.1197

Schroeder, Mark
414 Jackson St, San Francisco, CA 94111
415 421.3691

Schroeder, Michael
5801 La Vista Ct, Dallas, TX 75206
214 821.9834
page 357

Schuchman, Bob
5347 Linda Dr, Torrance, CA 90505
310 376.1448

Schuett, Stacey
PO Box 15, Duncans Mill, CA 95430
707 632.5123

Schulenberg, Paul
24 Captain Connolly Road,
Brewster, MA 02631
508 385.8845

Schuler, Mark
5410 W 68th St, Prairie Village, KS 66208
913 384.0646

Schulte, Lynn
121 S Eighth St, Mpls, MN 55402
612 334.3440

Schulte, Tom
13 Carson, Irvine, CA 92720
714 551.5631

Schumacher, Michael
101 Yesler Way, Seattle, WA 98104
206 447.1600

Schumaker, Ward
466 Green St, San Francisco, CA 94133
415 398.1060

Schumann & Co
2472 Bolsover, Houston, TX 77005
713 523.8444
fax 713 523.8485
page 443

Schumock, Cindy
2405 NW Thurman St,
Portland, OR 97210
503 225.9687
fax 503 228.6030
pages 233-235

Schuna Group, The
30 N First St, Mpls, MN 55401
612 343.0432
fax 612 375.1952
page 47

Schurig, Ingrid
2244 Holly Dr, L.A., CA 90068
213 463.4981

Schuster, Rob
2233 Kemper Ln, Cincinnati, OH 45206
513 861.1400

Schwab, Michael
501 Fifth Ave, NYC, NY 10017
212 490.2450
fax 212 697.6828
page 287

Schwartz, Carol
8311 Frontwell Cir, Gaithersburg, MD 20879
301 926.4776

Schwartz, Daniel
48 E 13th St, NYC, NY 10016
212 683.1362

Schwartz, Judith
231 E Fifth St, NYC, NY 10003
212 777.7533

Schwartz, Sara
130 W 67th St, NYC, NY 10023
212 877.4162

Schwarz, Joanie
194 Third Ave, NYC, NY 10003
212 475.0440

Schwarze, Evan
20 W Hubbard, Chicago, IL 60610
312 222.1361

Schweigert, Carol
Nine Lawnwood Pl, Boston, MA 02129
617 242.3901
fax 617 242.3901
page 412

Schwerin, Ron
889 Broadway, NYC, NY 10003
212 228.0340

Schwering, Jim
PO Box 665, Stinson Beach, CA 94970
415 868.1062

Sciacca, Tom
77-39 66th Dr, Middle Village, NY 11379
718 326.9124

Scible, Betsy
3115 Gosheff Ln, Gambrills, MD 21054
410 721.2137

Scientific Illustration West
PO Box 1025, Camarillo, CA 93011
805 484.7533

Scott, Bill
925 Elm Grove Rd,
Elm Grove, WI 53122
414 785.1940
fax 414 785.1611
page 215

Scott, Bob
4108 Forest Hill Ave, Richmond, VA 23225
312 944.5680

Scott, Elizabeth
4236 25th St, San Francisco, CA 94114
415 647.6304

Scott, Freda
244 Ninth St, San Francisco, CA 94103
415 621.2992
fax 415 621.5202
pages 95, 319, 322-323

Scott, Jack
899 S Plymouth Ct, Chicago, IL 60605
312 922.1467

Scott, Karen
1643 N Alvernon, Tuscon, AZ 85712
602 795.3027

Scott, Maren
Pine Rd HCR, Neversink, NY 12765
914 985.2936

Scott, Steven
PO Box 470818, San Francisco, CA 94147
415 383.9026

Scratchy Studio
539 Shawmut Ave, Boston, MA 02118
617 267.9215
page 99

Scribner, Joanne
N 3314 Lee St, Spokane, WA 99207
509 484.3208

Scrofani, Joseph
353 W 53rd St, NYC, NY 10019
212 582.0023
fax 212 582.0090
page 146

Scroggy, Hal
171 Court Dr, Fairlawn, OH 44333
216 666.4757

Scullin, Dick
6603 Blue Spruce Ct,
West Bloomfield, MI 48324
810 360.1603

Scullin, Maureen
109 W Hanover Ave, Randolph, NJ 07869
201 895.8858

Sczepanski, Stan
3634 W 105th St, Chicago, IL 60655
312 779.8448

Sea Dog Studios
2560 Bancroft Way, Berkeley, CA 94704
510 540.8658

Seabaugh, Max
246 First St, San Francisco, CA 94105
415 543.7775

Seaholm, Eric
1311 Harold, Houston, TX 77006
713 526.4250

Searle, Ronald
15 E 76th St, NYC, NY 10021
212 288.8010

Sears, Richard
1835 S Alta Vista Ave, Monrovia, CA 91016
818 359.3410

Sears, Stan
1125 S Kenlston Ave, L.A., CA 90019
213 930.0224

Seaver, Jeff
130 W 24th St, NYC, NY 10011
212 741.2279

Secker, Peter T
614 Grant St, Winfield, IL 60190
708 690.7632

Seibert, David
488 Curtis Corner Rd, S Kingston, RI 02879
401 782.2103

Seibold, J Otto
41 E 22nd St, NYC, NY 10010
212 366.4949

Seiffer, Alison
305 Canal St, NYC, NY 10013
212 941.7076

Seiffert, Claire
25 W 45th St, NYC, NY 10036
212 398.9540

Sekine, Hisashi
Three Crested Butte Cir,
Laguna Niguel, CA 92677
714 363.0705

Selby, Andrea
280 Madison, NYC, NY 10016
212 545.9155

Sell Inc
333 N Michigan Ave,
Chicago, IL 60601
312 578.8844
fax 312 578.8847
pages 42, 44, 389

Selwyn, Paul
229 Berkely St, Boston, MA 02116
617 266.3858

Sempe, JJ
155 W 15th St, NYC, NY 10011
212 989.8770

Senn, Oscar
1001 S Alfred St, L.A., CA 90035
310 556.1439
fax 213 653.5696
page 387

Setterlund, Theresa
7019 Waldheim Ct, San Jose, CA 95120
408 997.9662

Sevalrud, Thom
26 Gifford St, Toronto, ON, Canada M5A 321
416 922.9303

Seventeenth St Studios
455 17th St, Oakland, CA 94612
510 835.1717

Severn, Jeff
Six Monterey Terr, Orinda, CA 94563
510 253.9451

Shaffer, Shelly
HC 30 Box 1025, Sedona, AZ 86336
602 282.6303
page 356

Shaller, Bernice
10101 Grosvner Pl, Rockville, MD 20852
301 897.9495

Shanahan, Danny
155 W 15th St, NYC, NY 10011
212 989.8770

Shannon, David
333 N Screenland Dr, Burbank, CA 91505
818 563.6763

Shap, Sandra
853 Broadway, NYC, NY 10003
212 677.9100
fax 212 353.0954
page 382

Shareff Creative Concepts
81 Irving Pl, NYC, NY 10003
212 475.3963

Sharp, Bruce
2125 Western Ave, Seattle, WA 98121
206 443.0326

Sharpe & Associates
7536 Ogelsby Ave, L.A., CA 90045
310 641.8556

Shaw, Ned
2770 N Smith Pike, Bloomington, IN 47401
812 333.2181

Shaw, Paul
785 West End Ave, NYC, NY 10025
212 666.3738

Shay, RJ/Studio X
3301 S Jefferson Ave,
St Louis, MO 63118
314 773.9989
fax 314 773.6406
page 148

Sheban, Chris
1807 W Sunnyside Ave, Chicago, IL 60640
312 525.4955

SHEd
924 Lincoln Rd, Miami Beach, FL 33139
305 531.7338

Shed, Greg
716 Sanchez St,
San Francisco, CA 94114
415 285.8267
fax 415 285.8268
page 186

Shed, Greg
5707 Baltimore Dr,
San Diego, CA 91942
619 299.5576
page 186

Sheehan, Elizabeth
19 Ruxview Ct, Baltimore, MD 21204
410 828.4020

Shega, Marla
4401 Edinburg Ln,
Hanover Park, IL 60103
708 830.4745
fax 708 830.4745
page 409

Shelly, Jeff
55 Mercer St, NYC, NY 10013
212 663.4403

Shelly, Roger
716 Montgomery St, San Francisco, CA 94111
415 433.1222

Shema, Bob
600 N Bishop Ave, Dallas, TX 75208
214 946.6569

Shemeta, Karen
416 W Franklin St, Richmond, VA 23220
804 788.0400

Shen, Lin H
10162 St Bernard St, Cypress, CA 90630
714 828.1535

Sherbak, Yvonne
33459 Mulholland Hwy, Malibu, CA 90265
818 889.6593

Sherbo, Dan
4208 38th St, Wash, DC 20016
202 244.0474

Sheridan, Brian
481 Main St, New Rochelle, NY 10801
914 636.0075

Sherman, Oren
30 Ipswich St, Boston, MA 02215
617 437.7368

Sherman, Scott
4137 Alla Rd, L.A., CA 90066
310 398.5083

Sherman-Eckert
853 Ridge Rd, Webster, NY 14580
716 288.8000

Sherwin, Cynthia
2515 NE Expressway, Atlanta, GA 30345
404 248.1453

Sherwood, Alyssa
107 S Arden Blvd, L.A., CA 90004
213 934.6852

Shields, Bill
14 Wilmot St, San Francisco, CA 94115
415 346.0376

Shields, Gretchen
10834 Blix St, Toluca Lake, CA 91602
818 760.0746

Shiff, Andrew
153 Clinton St, Hopkinton, MA 01748
508 435.3607

Shigley Illustration
17696 Montero Rd, San Diego, CA 92128
619 451.1101

Shigley, Neil
853 Broadway, NYC, NY 10003
212 677.9100

Shihada, Hani
45 Tudor City Plz, NYC, NY 10017
212 972.8981

Shilstone, Arthur
42 Picketts Ridge Rd, W Redding, CT 06896
203 438.2727

Shock, Steve
405 N Wabash Ave, Chicago, IL 60611
312 321.1336

Shoemaker, Doug
5009 Excelsior Blvd, Mpls, MN 55416
612 925.1745

Shoemaker, Russ
2801 Ocean Dr, Vero Beach, FL 32963
407 234.8001

Shohet, Marti
41 Union Sq W, NYC, NY 10003
212.206.0066

Shoopack, Joseph
4340 Cannington Dr, San Diego, CA 92117
619 560.5824

Shooting Star
1441 N McCadden Pl, Hollywood, CA 90028
213 469.2020

Shoreline Graphics
27205 Harper, St Clair Shores, MI 48081
313 773.4000

Short, Kevin A
34562B Via Catalina,
Capistrano Beach, CA 92624
714 240.6979

Showalter, Paul Design
9173 Camino Real, San Gabriel, CA 91775
818 285.4731

Shultz, David
1863 S Pearl St, Denver, CO 80210
303 733.0128

Shure, Mick
410 N Michigan Ave, Chicago, IL 60611
312 689.3442

Shutz, David
410 N Michigan Ave, Chicago, IL 60611
312 689.3442

SI Int'l
43 E 19th St, NYC, NY 10003
212 254.4996

Sibley, Don
965 Slocum, Dallas, TX 75207
214 761.0103

Siciliano, Gerald
Nine Garfield Pl, Brooklyn, NY 11215
718 636.4561

Sicoransa, John Storyboards
280 First Ave, NYC, NY 10009
212 674.0541

Siddal-Germack, Stephanie
70 St Mary's Pky, Buffalo Grove, IL 60089
708 808.1863

Side Effects
117 Denmark Rd, London, England SE5 9LB
011 44.71.738.6324

Siegel, Estelle
74 Laurel Hollow Ct, Edison, NJ 08820
908 753.9722

Siegel, Kimberley
105 Calle Sol, San Clemente, CA 92672
714 498.5604

Siegel, Sharon
47 Peyster St, Albany, NY 12208
518 482.2336

Sienkowski, Laurie
199 Deer Run, Ada, MI 49301
616 676.3040

Sierra, Dorothea
One Fitchburg St, Somerville, MA 02143
617 625.8070

Sigal, Anya
27951 Chiclana, Mission Viejo, CA 92692
714 458.9597

Sigala, Anthony
657 Main St, Brawley, CA 92227
619 351.1880

Sign Smith/Art of Lettering
537 W Arrow Hwy, Upland, CA 91786
909 981.6369

Signorino, Slug
PO Box 387, Michigan City, IN 46360
219 879.5221

Sigwart Design
1033 S Orlando Ave, L.A., CA 90035
213 655.7734

Sikorski, Tony
237 Fourth Ave, Pittsburgh, PA 15222
412 391.8366

Silcox, Juana
770 E 73rd St, Indpls, IN 46240
317 255.1197

Silent Sounds Studio
Five Irwin St, Winthrop, MA 02152
617 846.5955

Sillen, Florence
55 W 11th St, NYC, NY 10011
212 243.9490

Silva, Elaine
104 Adams St, Fairhaven, MA 02719
508 997.7111

Silverman, Burton
324 W 71st St, NYC, NY 10023
212 799.3399

Silvers, Bill
420 Lexington Ave, NYC, NY 10170
212 986.5680
fax 212 818.1246
page 89

Silvers, William
2020 Euclid Ave, Cleveland, OH 44115
216 694.2020

Silverstraw Productions
10635 Riverside Dr, Toluca Lake, CA 91620
818 752-9040

Silvestri, Lorraine
122 Plimpton St, Walpole, MA 02081
508 668.0111
fax 508 668.0111
page 270

Simard, Remy
5051 Marquette, Montreal, QU,
Canada H2J 3Z1
514 526.9065

Simison, DJ
720 Third Ave, San Francisco, CA 94118
415 221.1917

Simon & Oberman
119 Morris St, Yonkers, NY 10705
914 963.6906

Simon, Dennis Illustration
16312 Yeoho Rd, Sparks, MD 21152
410 329.3983

Simon, William
9431 Bonhomme Woods, St Louis, MO 63132
314 993.3522

Simons, Art
12300 Marion Ln W, Minnetonka, MN 55305
612 333.6681

Simons, Kim
3443 Wade St, L.A., CA 90066
310 390.9595

Simpson, Bob
6202 Pacific Coast Hwy,
Redondo Beach, CA 90277
310 375.5406

Simpson, Gretchen Dow
117 Everett Ave, Providence, RI 02906
401 331.4514

Simpson, Jet
500 N Michigan, Chicago, IL 60611
312 661.1717

Simson, David
95 Horatio St, NYC, NY 10014
212 807.0840

Sinclair, Brian
S 2203 Grand Blvd, Spokane, WA 99203
509 747.8041

Sinclair, Valerie
501 Fifth Ave, NYC, NY 10017
212 490.2450
fax 212 697.6828
page 296

Singer, Alan D
206 Edgewood Ave, Rochester, NY 14618
716 473.4115

Sinovcic, Miro
60 E 42nd, NYC, NY 10017
212 867.8092

Sipp, Geo
380 Garden Ln NW, Atlanta, GA 30309
404 876.0312

Siracusa, Catherine
112 W 74th St, NYC, NY 10023
212 580.8084

Siren
#403-1040 Hamilton St, Vancouver, BC,
Canada V6B 2R9
604 662.8630

Sirrell, T
768 Red Oak Dr, Bartlett, IL 60103
708 213.9003
fax 708 213.9003
page 450

Sis, Peter
252 Lafayette St, NYC, NY 10012
212 226.2203

Siu, Peter
11936 W Jefferson Blvd,
Culver City, CA 90230
310 390.8663

Sizemore, Ted
60 E 42nd St, NYC, NY 10017
212 867.8092

Sizer, Dale
1400 N Hayworth Ave, L.A., CA 90046
213 874.0155

Skarda, John
1420 Godwin St, Houston, TX 77023
713 944.0768

Skelton, Steve
3205 Fifth St, Boulder, CO 80304
303 546.0117

Sketch Pad Studio
2605 Westgate Dr, Arlington, TX 76015
817 469.8151

Skidmore Inc
2100 W Big Beaver Rd, Troy, MI 48084
313 643.6000

Skinner, Cortney
32 Churchill Ave, Arlington, MA 02174
617 648.2875

Sklut-Lettire, Meryl
721 Pleasant Valley Way,
West Orange, NJ 07052
201 669.8078

SKM Designs
351 Spruce St, Paynesville, MN 56362
612 243.3964

Skopp, Jennifer
165 Emmons Ave, Brooklyn, NY 11235
718 646.2344

Skorodumov, Alexander
385 Ft Washington Ave, NYC, NY 10033
212 923.7787

Skrzelowski, David
2233 Kemper Ln, Cincinnati, OH 45206
513 861.1400

Slabbers, Ronald
32 W 31 St, NYC, NY 10001
212 239.4283

Slack, Chuck
Nine Cambridge Ln, Lincolnshire, IL 60069
708 948.9226

Slaske, Steve
PO Box 92314, Milwaukke, WI 53202
414 272.1193

Slater, Jim
17832 Dunblaine, Birmingham, MI 48025
313 258.5930

Slater, Joann Dufau
1608 Via Machado, Palos Verdes, CA 90274
310 373.9090

Slatky, Tom
1119 Colorado Ste 23,
Santa Monica, CA 90401
310 394.5031

Slightly Touched
PO Box 1175, Fairfax, CA 94978
415 607.1162

Sloan, Michael
458 Eighth Ave, Brooklyn, NY 11215
718 788.5437
fax 718 499.8958
page 188

Sloan, Rick Design
9432 Appalachian Dr, Sacramento, CA 95827
916 364.5844

Sloan, William A
236 W 26th St, NYC, NY 10001
212 463.7025

Slobodian, Barbara
6519 Fountain Ave, L.A., CA 90028
213 464.2341

Small, David
25626 Simpson Rd, Mendon, MI 49072
616 496.8193

Smallbone, Norma C
2905 Piedmont Ave, La Crescenta, CA 91214
818 249.1823

Smalley, Guy
5340 Date Palm St, Cocoa, FL 32927
407 639.0936

Smallwood, Steve
4702 Summer Creek Ln SE,
Grand Rapids, MI 49508
616 249.2845

Smeck Graphicsn
676 N St Clair, Chicago, IL 60611
312 280.9444

Smith, Christopher
7954 Queens Rd, Glen Burnie, MD 21061
301 277.6371

Smith, Doug
121 Madison Ave, NYC, NY 10016
212 683.1362

Smith, E Silas
14303 Sandown Ct, Poway, CA 92064
619 748.7142

Smith, Eileen
Rte Five Box 62, Walterboro, SC 29488
803 893.3252

Smith, Elwood H
Two Locust Grove Rd, Rhinebeck, NY 12572
914 876.2358

Smith, Gary
PO Box 155, Passaic, NJ 07055
201 472.1225

Smith, J
1141 Brunswick Ln, Aurora, IL 60504
708 820.7188

Smith, J Peter
PO Box 69559, L.A., CA 90069
213 464.1163

Smith, J Randall
927 Lincoln Way, Auburn, CA 95603
916 888.0484

Smith, JA
5430 Lisette Ave, St Louis, MO 63109
314 353.8580

Smith, Jeffrey
639 Geary St, San Francisco, CA 94102
415 274.2221

Smith, Jere
2814 NW 72nd St, Seattle, WA 98117
206 784.1136

Smith, Jonathan
1829 W 25th St, L.A., CA 90018
213 734.4470

Smith, Jos A
159 John St, NYC, NY 10038
212 825.1475

Smith, Kirk Richard
492 Armstrong St,
Columbus, OH 43215
614 464.0928
page 277

Smith, Lane
43 W 16th St, NYC, NY 10011
212 627.8364

Smith, Laura
6545 Cahuenga Ter, Hollywood, CA 90068
213 467.1700

Smith, Marcia
112 Linden St, Rochester, NY 14620
716 461.9348

Smith, Mark T
15 E 21st St, NYC, NY 10010
212 673.8446

Smith, Marty
30166 Chipala Ct, Laguna Niguel, CA 92677
714 495.3664

Smith, Michael T
9833 Tolworth Cir, Randallstown, MD 21133
410 655.2486

Smith, Monica
111 Fourth Ave, NYC, NY 10003
212 529.5195

Smith, Owen
1020 Westchester Pl, L.A., CA 90019
213 731.4168

Smith, Pete
265 Westminster Rd, Rochester, NY 14607
716 244.6956

Smith, Raymond E
602 Willow Ave, Hoboken, NJ 07030
201 653.6638

Smith, Rick
1236 Tranquilla, Dallas, TX 75218
214 321.6264

Smith, Roy
3720 Hartford St, St Louis, MO 63116
314 776.5542

Smith, Samantha Carol
3818 Greenmount Ave, Baltimore, MD 21218
410 243.6184

Smith, Susan
537 Chestnut St, Needham, MA 02192
617 449.7761
fax 617 449.9092
page 158

Smith, Terry E
1713 Dryden Way, Crofton, MD 21114
301 858.0734

Smith, Theresa
666 Greenwich St, NYC, NY 10014
212 675.5719

Smith, Vicki
430 Ventura Pl, Vero Beach, FL 32963
617 236.1920

Smola, Jim
94 Maple Hill Ave, Newington, CT 06111
203 665.0305

Smollin, Mark
2112 Queensbury Rd, Pasadena, CA 91104
818 798.5999

Smythe, Danny
6103 Knight Arnold St, Memphis, TN 38115
901 794.5883

Snapp, Dann
4203 Montrose Blvd, Houston, TX 77006
713 522.1555

Snider, Jackie & Steve
RR Seven Hwy 30, Brighton, ON, Canada
K0K 1H0
613 475.4551
pages 394-395

Snow, Scott
1537 S Main St, Salt Lake City, UT 84115
801 484.0419

Snyder, David
4812 Burris Dr, Louisville, KY 40291
502 239.2075

Snyder, Teresa
25727 Mountain Dr, Arlington, WA 98223
206 435.8998

Sobel, June
2131 Lindengrove St,
Westlake Village, CA 91361
805 495.0626

Sobey, Mike
520 N Michigan Ave, Chicago, IL 60611
312 527.0351

Society of Illustrators
128 E 63rd St, NYC, NY 10021
212 838.2560

Soderlind, Kirsten
194 Third Ave, NYC, NY 10003
212 475.0440

Sofo, Frank
16 Branch Ln, Levittown, NY 11756
516 681.8745

Soileau, Hodges
350 Flax Hill Rd, Norwalk, CT 06854
203 852.0751

Sokolowski, Ted
RD Two Box 208, Lake Ariel, PA 18436
717 937.4527

Solarz Illustration
7610 N Eastlake Ter, Chicago, IL 60626
312 761.5218

Soldat & Associates
307 N Michigan Ave, Chicago, IL 60601
312 201.9662

Solie, John
PO Box 249, Seal Rock, OR 97376
503 563.5225

Sollenberger, Terry Lee
3820 CR 603B, Burleson, TX 76028
817 561.9191

Solomon, Debra
143 Greene St, NYC, NY 10012
212 473.0060
fax 212 473.7163
page 269

Solomon, Gary
6236 Teesdale Ave, N Hollywood, CA 91606
818 508.9381

Solomon, Richard
121 Madison Ave, NYC, NY 10016
212 683.1362

Soltis, Linda DeVito
PO Box 462, Woodbury, CT 69798
203 263.4019

Soman, Liana
1940 Elizabeth Ave, Rahway, NJ 07065
908 382.3230

Sommel, Chelsea
30166 Chapala Ct, Laguna Niguel, CA 92677
714 495.3664

Sonneville, Dane & Associates Inc
PO Box 155, Passaic, NJ 07055
201 472.1225

Soos, Erne
2469 Pine Ave, Long Beach, CA 90806
310 424.5765

Soper, Pat
50 Fuller Brook Rd, Wellesley, MA 02181
617 235.8658

Sopin, Nan Grover
Nine Bradley Dr, Freehold, NJ 07728
908 462.7154

Sorel, Edward
156 Franklin St, NYC, NY 10013
212 966.3949

Sorensen, Marcos
3740 25th St, San Francisco, CA 94110
415 282.5796

Sorensen, Robert
22 Strathmore Ave, Milford, CT 06460
203 874.6381

Sornat Studio
4521 Sidereal Dr, Austin, TX 78727
512 836.9528

Sorren, Joe
2149 Lyon, San Francisco, CA 94115
415 921.7140

Soulé, Robert
15229 Baughman Dr,
Silver Spring, MD 20906
301 598.8883 800 364.5589
page 230

Soules, Dick
897 University St, Grosse Point, MI 48230
313 881.0094

Sours, Michael
1350 Chemical St, Dallas, TX 75207
214 748.8663

South, Randy
2000 Clybourn Ave, Burbank, CA 91505
818 985.9306

Southern Draw
5025 Arapaho Rd, Addison, TX 75248
214 387.5667

Soyka, Ed
231 Lafayette Ave, Peekskill, NY 10566
914 737.2230

Spacek, Peter
43 Murray St, NYC, NY 10007
212 962.7383
fax 212 571.4705
page 285

Spain, Valerie
83 Franklin St, Watertown, MA 02172
617 923.1989
fax 617 923.1989
page 272

Spalenka, Greg
21303 San Miguel St, Woodland Hls, CA 91364
818 992.5828

Spanfeller, Jim
Mustato Rd, Katonah, NY 10536
914 232.3546

Spangler, Noel
2844 N Hackett Ave, Milwaukee, WI 53211
414 964.4005

Sparacin, Ernest
3111 Cole Ave, Dallas, TX 75204
214 855.5405

Spark Studios
1245 Pearl St, Boulder, CO 80302
303 440.9019

Sparks, Richard
597 Riverside Ave, Westport, CT 06851
203 226.4724

Spear, Charles
456 Ninth St, Hoboken, NJ 07030
201 798.6466

Specht, Richard Studios
305 Apache Trl, Woodland Park, CO 80863
719 687.3947

Spector, Dori
821 Hunt Rd, Newtown Sq, PA 19073
610 353.8670

Spector, Joel
Three Maplewood Dr, New Milford, CT 06776
203 355.5942

Spectrum Studio
206 N First St, Mpls, MN 55401
612 332.2361

Spellman, Susan
50 Fuller Brook Rd, Wellesley Hills, MA 02181
617 235.8658

Spencer, Joe
11201 Valley Spring Ln, Studio City, CA 91602
818 760.0216

Spencer, Mary
1888 Century Park E, L.A., CA 90067
310 826.1332
fax 310 284.3290
page 261

Spencer, Mary
7816 Connie Dr,
Huntington Beach, CA 92648
714 848.4954
page 261

Spencer, Torrey
11201 Valley Spring Ln, Studio City, CA 91602
818 505.1124

Spengler, Ken
2668 17th St, NYC, NY 95818
916 441.1932

Spiak, Sharon
146 Reade St, NYC, NY 10013
212 941.4680

Spiece Graphics
1811 Woodhaven, Ft Wayne, IN 46819
219 747.3916

Spiegelman, Art
27 Greene St, NYC, NY 10013
212 226.0146

Spiers, Herbert
43 E 19th St, NYC, NY 10003
212 254.4996

Spinney Associates
23 Gordon Ave, Pelham, NH 03076
603 635.9014

Spirin, Gennady
45 Nursery Rd, Titusville, NJ 08560
609 882.9186

Splash Page
4300 N Narragansett, Chicago, IL 60634
708 670.0912

Spokesfolks
333 N Michigan Ave, Chicago, IL 60601
312 332.3984

Spollen, Chris
362 Cromwell Ave, Ocean Breeze, NY 10305
718 979.9695

Spoon, Wilfred
PO Box 421443,
San Francisco, CA 94142
415 647.5660
fax 415 285.1102
page 378

Sposato, John
43 E 22nd St, NYC, NY 10010
212 477.3909

Spridel, Sandra
5015 Clinton St, L.A., CA 90004
213 957.2327

Sprouls, Kevin
One Schooner Ln, Sweetwater, NJ 08037
609 965.4795

Spurll, Barbara
366 Adelaide St E, Toronto, ON, Canada
M5A 3X9
416 594.6594
fax 416 601.1010
page 402

Spurlock, J David
3000 Carlisle, Dallas, TX 75204
214 871.1180

St Clair, Linda
7028 Wabash Cir, Dallas, TX 75214
214 328.6662

St James, Synthia
PO Box 27683, L.A., CA 90027
213 464.8381

Staake, Bob
726 S Ballas Rd, St Louis, MO 63122
314 961.2303

Stabin, Victor
100 W 15th St, NYC, NY 10011
212 243.7688

Stabler, Barton
831 Willow Grove Rd, Westfield, NJ 07090
908 789.7415

Stadler, Greg
2706 Tenth Ave, Seattle, WA 98119
206 284.2231

Stafford, KW
PO Box 11920, Costa Mesa, CA 92627
714 261.7553

Stagg, James
272 Bay Vista Cir, Sausalito, CA 94965
415 332.7856

Stahl, Ben
15 W 72nd St, NYC, NY 10028
212 799.2231

Stahl, Nancy
470 W End Ave, NYC, NY 10024
212 362.8779

Stallard, Peter
199 Wild Turkey Pl, Drake, CO 80515
303 663.5460

Stamm, Jan
4908 Hawley Blvd, San Diego, CA 92116
619 534.4037

Stanfill, Mike
2330 Jonesboro, Dallas, TX 75228
214 320.2293

Stanford, Ginny Gouch
PO Box 15152, Santa Rosa, CA 95402
707 579.1535

Stanford, Walter
1826 Asheville Pl, Charlotte, NC 28203
704 372.6007

Stanger, Susan E
1311B Dominus St, Honolulu, HI 96822
808 521.1885

Stankiewicz, Steven
317 E 18th St, NYC, NY 10003
212 477.4229

Stanley, Rob Design
1528 NE 86th Ave, Portland, OR 97220
503 255.1234

Stanton, Frank L
12540 Pepperwood Dr, St Louis, MO 63146
314 576.6216

Stark, Emma
1209 Reynolds, Bryan, TX 77803
409 779.0722
page 448

Starks, Gloria
961 S Plymouth Blvd, L.A., CA 90019
213 935.5328

Starr, Jim
138 W 25th St, Baltimore, MD 21218
410 889.0703
fax 410 889.5498
pages 142-143

Starrett, Terri
19 Stuyvesant Oval, NYC, NY 10009
212 505.9342

Stasolla, Mario
37 Cedar Hill Ave, South Nyack, NY 10960
914 353.3086

Staunton, James
4813 Oregon St, San Diego, CA 92103
619 283.5975

Steadman, Broeck
12056 Summit Cir, Beverly Hills, CA 90210
310 276.5282

Steadman, Ralph
146 E 19th St, NYC, NY 10003
212 420.8585

Steam Inc
1335 Union St, San Francisco, CA 94109
415 776.4247

Stearney, Mark
621 S Plymouth Ct, Chicago, IL 60605
312 360.9033

Steele, Mark
539 Tremont St, Boston, MA 02116
617 424.0604

Steele, Robert Gantt
41 Union Sq W, NYC, NY 10003
212 929.5590
page 253

Steen, Karen
909 Lyndon St, S Pasadena, CA 91030
213 259.8722

Steever, Rebecca
1305 Williams St NE, Pullman, WA 99163
509 335.1817

Stefanko, Kenneth
7837 Whitsett Ave, N Hollywood, CA 91605
818 765.8250

Stefanski, Janice
2022 Jones St, San Francisco, CA 94133
415 928.0457

Steffenhagen, C Bruce
8520 De Soto Ave, Canoga Park, CA 91304
818 341.9440

Stefl, Jim
17830 Winterberry St,
Fountain Valley, CA 92708
714 964.8771

Steiger, Cheryl
1790 Spruce Ave, Highland Park, IL 60035
708 831.2294

Stein, August
3030 Homer, San Diego, CA 92106
619 223.3042
page 193

Steinberg, James
41 Fruit St, Worcester, MA 01609
508 792.0372

Steiner, Frank
507 Cool Dell Ct, Manchester, MO 63021
314 827.2182

Steiner, Peter
1948 Rockingham St, McLean, VA 22101
703 237.9576

Steirnagle, Michael
353 W 53rd St, NYC, NY 10019
212 582.0023
fax 212 582.0090
page 146

Stentz, Nancy
PO Box 19412, Seattle, WA 98109
206 634.1880

Stepanek, Michael
1014 S Scoville, Chicago, IL 60304
312 222.1361

Stergulz, Richard
452 W Aldine, Chicago, IL 60657
312 528.4475

Sterk, Bo
Ten Milton St, St Augustine, FL 32085
904 824.1441

Stermer, Dugald
600 The Embarcadero,
San Francisco, CA 94107
415 441.4384

Stern, Kalika
308 E 79th St, NYC, NY 10021
212 734.4503

Sterrett, Jane
160 Fifth Ave, NYC, NY 10010
212 929.2566

Stevens, Georgian
4727 E Warner Rd, Phoenix, AZ 85044
602 496.9658

Stevens, Heidi
22 Tenth St, Petaluma, CA 94952
707.769.1252
fax 707.769.1252
page 61

Stevens, James
5750 Fontenelle St, Houston, TX 77035
713 723.1373

Stevens, Mick
PO Box 344, W Tisbury, MA 02575
508 693.2981

Stevens, Robin
410 N Michigan Ave,
Chicago, IL 60611
312 689.3442
page 447

Stevenson, Dave
522 Colonial Cir, Vacaville, CA 95687
707 447.5720

Stewart, April Blair
177 Newtowne Tpke, Weston, CT 06883
203 222.1608

Stewart, Don
117 W Green Ct, Greensboro, NC 27407
910 854.2769

Stewart, John
11323 Blythe St, Sun Valley, CA 91352
213 875.2012

Stewart, JW
41 Union Sq W, NYC, NY 10003
212 929.5590
pages 238-239

Stewart, Steven
420 W Sixth St, Claremont, CA 91711
909 625.3789

Stewart, Walt
PO Box 621, Stinson Beach, CA 94970
415 868.0481

Stieferman, Guy
5744 Magnolia Woods Dr, Bartlett, TN 38134
901 372.2902

Stieger, Marcia
136 Scenic Rd, Fairfax, CA 94930
415 459.7560

Stiglich, Joyce
727 Forest Glen Ct, Maitland, FL 32751
407 644.5294

Stiles, Jeff
1339 Charlestown Dr, Edgewood, MD 21040
410 679.3517

Stiles, Pat
117 Brooks Ave, Venice, CA 90291
310 396.2186

Still, Wayne Anthony
1801 Butler Pike, Conshohocken, PA 19428
215 940.1551

Stillman, Susan
25 Alexander Ave, White Plains, NY 10606
914 682.3771

Stimson, David
60 Haven Ave, NYC, NY 10032
212 927.6594

Stine, Christopher
731 SE 41st St, Portland, OR 97214
503 238.1820

Stine, Debra
716 Sanchez St, San Francisco, CA 94114
415 285.8267

Stirnweis, Shannon
31 Fawn Pl, Wilton, CT 06897
203 762.7058

Stock, Jeffrey
30 Doaks Ln, Marblehead, MA 01945
617 639.8384

Stone, David K
106 Stonybrook Rd, Chapel Hill, NC 27516
919 929.0853

Stone, Marly
2405 NW Thurman St, Portland, OR 97210
503 225.9687

Stone, Sylvia
24 Prudence Dr, Stamford, CT 06907
203 322.2634

Storey, Barron
852 Union St, San Francisco, CA 94133
415 986.4086

Storey, Lee
6565 Green Valley Cir, Culver City, CA 90230
310 670.3477

Stork, Bill
PO Box 19906, Greensboro, NC 27419
910 292.2224

Storm, Mark
2322 University Blvd, Houston, TX 77005
713 523.1529

Storozuk, Walter
25 W 45th St, NYC, NY 10036
212 398.9540

Storyboard/Animatic Art Studio
65 E Wacker, Chicago, IL 60601
312 266.1417

Stott, Dorothy
666 Greewich St, NYC, NY 10014
212 675.5719

Stottlemyer, John
445 Suzanne Ave, Shoreview, MN 55126
612 241.3256

Stout, Tim
405 N Wabash, Chicago, IL 60611
312 329.1370

Stout, William
1468 Loma Vista St, Pasadena, CA 91104
818 798.6490

Stovall, Lorna Design
1088 Queen Anne Pl, L.A., CA 90019
213 931.5984

Strandoo, Paul
1318 Tenth Ave, San Francisco, CA 94122
415 661.1650

Strang, Helen
14618 Tyler Foote Blvd,
Nevada City, CA 95959
916 292.3433

Stratton, Michael
3500 Tangle Brush, The Woodlands, TX 77381
713 292.7581

Straub, Matt Illustration
128 E Fourth St, NYC, NY 10003
212 995.9359

Streamline Graphics Inc
210 Eleventh Ave, NYC, NY 10001
212 633.0021

Strebel, Carol
2930 Hackberry St, Cincinnati, OH 45206
513 281.6837

Street, Suzanne
3106 Robinhood St, Houston, TX 77005
713 666.3409

Streetworks Studio
13908 Marblestone Dr, Clifton, VA 22024
703 631.1650

Streff, Michael
2766 Wasson Rd, Cincinnati, OH 45209
513 731.0360

Strelecki, Karen
4019 Rockmill Dr, Atlanta, GA 30062
404 875.1363 800 347.0734
fax 404 875.9733
page 169

Strokes
1423-A Sanchez St, San Francisco, CA 94131
415 282.2141

Stromoski, Rick
569 N Main St, Suffield, CT 06078
203 668.8738

Stroster, Maria
2057 N Sheffield Ave,
Chicago, IL 60614
312 525.2081
fax 312 525.3114
page 258

Stroud, Steven
1031 Howe Ave, Shelton, CT 06484
203 924.2460

Structo
537 Duncan St, San Francisco, CA 94131
415 647.5190

Struthers, Doug
501 Fifth Ave, NYC, NY 10017
212 490.2450

Struzan, Drew
624 Eaton Dr, Pasadena, CA 91107
818 578.7291

Stuart, Walter
716 Sanchez St, San Francisco, CA 94114
415 285.8267

Stubbs, Diane N
3355 Spring Mountain Rd, Las Vegas, NV 89102
702 871.2711

Stubbs, Elizabeth
27 Wyman St, Arlington, MA 02174
617 646.0785

Studio 2034
2034 Oak Glen Pl, L.A., CA 90039
213 661.2241

Studio 70 Architectural Illust
PO Drawer E, Algonquin, IL 60102
708 658.6519

Studio Artworks
502 W Cypress, Phoenix, AZ 60225
602 258.6318

Studio Associates Inc
5850 Chase Rd, Dearborn, MI 48126
313 581.1030

Studio Bustamante
2400 Kettner Blvd, San Diego, CA 92101
619 234.8803

Studio D Inc
7026 SW 106th Pl, Miami, FL 33173
305 598.7431

Studio DNA
One S Fair Oaks Ave, Pasadena, CA 91105
818 683.3078

Studio Edidt
14733 Janet Ln, Guerneville, CA 95446
707 869.3155

Studio G
M645 Birch St, Marshfield, WI 54449
715 384.0092

Studio G Inc
755 Marine Ave, Manhattan Beach, CA 90266
310 545.7709

Studio Liddell
217 E 86th St, NYC, NY 10028
212 355.0910

Studio MD
1512 Alaskan Way, Seattle, WA 98101
206 682.6221

Studio One
7300 Metro Blvd, Edina, MN 55439
612 831.6313

Studio Solo
650 Bamboo Ter, San Rafael, CA 94903
415 472.7656

Studio West Inc
1005 W Franklin Ave, Mpls, MN 55405
612 871.2900

The Studio
216 E 45th St, NYC, NY 10017
212 661.1363

Stuhmer, Robert
50 W 72nd St, NYC, NY 10023
212 877.2390

Sturman, Sally Mara
195 Prospect Pl, Brooklyn, NY 11238
718 857.6743

Sturrock, William
2075 E Third St, Long Beach, CA 90814
310 438.4921

Sturtz, Donald Prescott
758 Hacienda Ave, Campbell, CA 95008
408 370.7106

Stutzman, Laura
100 G St, Mt Lake Park, MD 21550
301 334.4086
fax 301.334.4186
pages 112-113

Stutzman, Mark
100 G St, Mt Lake Park, MD 21550
301 334.4086
fax 301 334.4186
pages 112-113

Succinct Ink
5442 E Flower St, Phoenix, AZ 85018
602 840.5635

Suchit, Stewart G
284 Fourth St, Jersey City, NJ 07302
201 963.3011

Sudavicius, Dalia
5619 Burdette St, Omaha, NE 68104
402 556.5842

Suggs, Margaret Anne
4083 Gladney Dr NE, Atlanta, GA 30340
404 493.8136

Suhre-Garza, Christine
5816 W Ave M-6, Quartz Hill, CA 93536
805 943.2540

Sullivan & Associates
3805 Maple Ct, Marietta, GA 30066
404 971.6782

Sullivan, Dave
101 Monmouth St, Brookline, MA 02146
617 277.0921

Sullivan, Don
912 S Telluride St, Aurora, CO 80017
303 671.9257
fax 303 752.3037
page 92

Sullivan, James
26 Pulaski Ave, Carteret, NJ 07008
908 541.2926

Sullivan, Melinda May
834 Moultrie St, San Francisco, CA 94110
415 648.2376

Sullivan, Michael
1949 Stemmons Fwy, Dallas, TX 75207
214 698.1777

Sullivan, Steve
25 W 45th St, NYC, NY 10036
212 398.9540

Sulski, Victoria
PO Box 7709, Santa Cruz, CA 95060
408 426.4247

Suma, Doug
654 Pier Ave, Santa Monica, CA 90405
310 392.4877

Sumichrast, Jozef
501 Fifth Ave, NYC, NY 10017
212 490.2450

Summers, Ethan
353 W 53rd St, NYC, NY 10019
212 682.2462

Summers, Mark
12 Milverton Close, Watertown, ON,
Canada LOR 2HD
416 632.2646

Sumpter, Will & Associates
1728 N Rock Springs Rd,
Atlanta, GA 30324
404 874.2014
fax 404 874.8173
page 432

Surles, Michael
300 Stony Point Rd, Santa Rosa, CA 95401
707 575.7367

Sutton, Jim Illustration
822 W Altgeld, Chicago, IL 60614
312 525.8812

Sutton, Judith
239 Dean St, Brooklyn, NY 11217
718 834.8851

Suvityasiri, Sarn
2419 Bonar St, Berkeley, CA 94702
510 548.8218

Suzan, Gerardo
50 Fuller Brook Rd,
Wellesley, MA 02181
617 235.8658
pages 110-111

Swaine, Michael
6735 N Tenth Pl, Phoenix, AZ 85014
602 264.5400

Swales, Scott
1019 Main St, Phoenix, NY 13135
315 695.4519

Swan, Susan Illustration
83 Saugatuck Ave, Westport, CT 06880
203 226.9104

Swanson, James
15 Richmond Ave,
La Grange Park, IL 60525
708 352.3081
fax 708 352.3082
page 373

Swanson, Ted
7517 Manchester Ave, L.A., CA 90045
310 578.2191

Swarts, Jeff
PO Box 289, Danville, OH 43014
614 599.6516

Sweat, Lynn
Cornwall Br, CT 06754
203 672.0059

Sweeney, Jerry
1644 Beryl Dr, Pittsburgh, PA 15227
412 884.5704

Sweeny, Glynis
346 W Webster St, Ferndale, MI 48220
716 633.4679

Sweeny, Steve
25 W 45th St, NYC, NY 10036
212 398.9540

Sweet, Brian
11 Kings Ridge Rd, Long Valley, NJ 07853
908 813.8718

Sweet, Ron Represents
716 Montgomery St, San Francisco, CA 94111
415 433.1222

Sweny, Stephen
3121 Hollywood Dr, Decatur, GA 30033
404 299.7535

Swerdlow, Trina
PO Box 23987, Pleasant Hill, CA 94523
510 687.6499

Swift, Michael
5183 Overland Ave, Culver City, CA 90230
310 558.3325

Swift, Steve
600 N Bishop Ave, Dallas, TX 75208
214 946.6569

Switlik, Mark
502 W Jackson St, Phoenix, AZ 85003
602 254.7840

Sylvain
1400 N Hayworth Ave,
West Hollywood, CA 90046
213 851.7737

Sylvestre, Daniel
3643 St Laurent, Montreal, QU, Canada
514 587.7668

Syntax International
1790 Fifth St, Berkeley, CA 94710
510 849.4313

Syska, Richard
1905 W Foster, Chicago, IL 60640
312 728.2738

Syzygy Design Group Inc
7037 Matilija Ave, Van Nuys, CA 91405
818 785.4989

Szabo, Leslie
44 S Main St, South Norwalk, CT 06854
203 838.2155

Szpura, Beata
48-02 69th St, Woodside, NY 11377
718 424.8440

T-26
852 W Roscoe, Chicago, IL 60657
312 281.4663

Tachiera, Andrea
7416 Fairmount Ave, El Cerrito, CA 94530
510 525.3484

Tagel, Peggy
666 Greenwich St, NYC, NY 10014
212 675.5719

Taggart, Tom
31 Huff Rd, Wayne, NJ 07470
201 633.0323

Tainer, Dario
445 W Erie, Chicago, IL 60610
312 951.1656

Takahashi, Takeshi
1228 Spruce St, Phila, PA 19107
215 735.4846

Takakjian, Asdur
PO Box 696, Truro, MA 02666
508 349.3021

Takei, Koji
4136 McLaughlin Ave, L.A., CA 90066
310 391.1214

Talanay, Keith
6701 De Soto St, Canoga, CA 91303
818 715.9095

Talaro, Lionel
25 W 45th St, NYC, NY 10036
212 398.9540

Talbot, Jim
E Main St, Ware, MA 01082
413 967.9855

Talbott, Eugenia
PO Box 39, Mayhew, MS 39753
601 328.5534

Talcott, Julia Illustration
38 Linden St, Brookline, MA 02146
617 232.7306

Taleporos, Plato
333 E 23rd St, NYC, NY 10010
212 689.3138

Tamara
3490 Piedmont Rd, Atlanta, GA 30305
404 262.1209

Tamura, David
412 N Midland, Upper Nyack, NY 10960
212 686.4559

Tanaka, Lynn
4018 W 44th St, Edina, MN 55424
612 926.8923
fax 612 926.8933
page 273

Tanenbaum, Robert
5505 Corbin Ave, Tarzana, CA 91356
818 345.6741

Tanhauser, Gary
716 Sanchez St,
San Francisco, CA 94114
415 285.8267
fax 415 285.8268
page 186

Tank, Darrel
716 Montgomery St, San Francisco, CA 94111
415 433.1222

Tarabay, Sharif
597 Riverside Ave,
Westport, CT 06880
203 226.4724
fax 203 454.9904
page 65

Targete, Jean Pierre
Ten N Ridgewood Rd, S Orange, NJ 07079
201 763.7330

Tarlow, Phyllis
42 Stratford Rd, New Rochelle, NY 10804
914 235.9473

Tarnowski, Glen P
4217 Dixie Canyon Ave,
Sherman Oaks, CA 91423
818 783.3710

Tarrish, Laura
123 Townsend St, San Francisco, CA 94107
415 442.1866

Tate, Clarke
301 Woodford St, Gridley, IL 61744
309 747.3388 800 828.3008
fax 309 747.3008
page 432

Tate, Don
112 W Fourth St, Gridley, IL 61744
309 747.2929

Tatopoulos, Patrick
1400 N Hayworth Ave,
West Hollywood, CA 90046
213 851.7737

Taubleb, Naomi
PO Box 447, NYC, NY 10009
212 505.6539

Taulman, Derek
4331 Dickason, Dallas, TX 75219
214 880.0888

Tauss, Herbert
South Mountain Pass, Garrison, NY 10524
914 424.3765

Taxali, Gary
1589 Lovelady Crescent,
Mississauga, ON, Canada L4W 2Y9
905 625.1079

Taylor, BK
24940 S Cromwell, Franklin, MI 48025
810 626.8698

Taylor, C Winston
17008 Lisette St, Granada Hills, CA 91344
818 363.5761

Taylor, Dahl
194 Third Ave, NYC, NY 10003
212 475.0440

Taylor, David
1449 N Pennsylvania St, Indpls, IN 46202
317 634.2728

Taylor, Jay
21-16 28th St, L.I.C., NY 11105
718 204.6184

Taylor, Jimmie
5901 JFK Blvd, N Little Rock, AR 72116
501 771.4251

Taylor, Joseph
2117 Ewing Ave, Evanston, IL 60201
708 328.2454
page 56

Taylor, Scott
Five Mandeville Ct, Monterey, CA 93940
408 649.1332

Taylor, Tim
PO Box 591, Roseland, NJ 07068
201 267.7081

Taylor-Palmer, Dorothea
490 Stone Mtn Lithonia Rd,
Stone Mountain, GA 30088
404 413.8276

Teach, Buz Walker
3006 Fourth Ave, Sacramento, CA 95817
916 454.3556

Teare, Brad
270 Pk Ave S, NYC, NY 10017
212 260.5680

Teemlet, Trudy
3671 Bear St, Santa Ana, CA 92704
714 850.1964

Templeton, Sandra
495 Carolina St, San Francisco, CA 94107
415 863.4969

Ten, Arnie
37 Forbus St, Poughkeepsie, NY 12601
914 485.8419

Tennison, James
5500 Bradley Ct, Arlington, TX 76017
817 483.6280

Tenret, Carla Calli & Design
623 Cornell Ave, Albany, CA 94706
510 526.7545

Tenud, Tish
3427 Folsom Blvd,
Sacramento, CA 95816
916 455.0569
fax 916 451.6037
page 271

Terrence & Associates
1809-B Mar W, Tiburon, CA 94920
415 435.8562

Terres, Gene Art Studio
4051 Blaisdell Ave S, Mpls, MN 55409
612 825.4512

Terreson, Jeffrey
420 Lexington Ave, NYC, NY 10017
212 986.5680

Terrones, Craig
140 Lakeside Ave, Seattle, WA 98122
206 325.9504

Terry, Emerson
511 Wyoming St, Pasadena, CA 91103
213 681.4115

Terry, Will
11505 Montgomery Rd, Beltsville, MD 20705
301 937.9038

Tessler, Benny
5183 Overland Ave, Culver City, CA 90230
310 558.3325

Tessler, John
1409 R St, Sacramento, CA 95821
916 443.9080

The Studio by Lynne Tucker
2001 S Barrington, L.A., CA 90025
310 996.6767

Theakston, Greg
88 Lexington Ave, NYC, NY 10016
212 686.0652

Theodore, Jim
1270 W Peachtree St, Atlanta, GA 30309
404 873.2287

Thewlis, Diana
5755 San Juan Way, Pleasanton, CA 94566
415 484.9777

Thomas & Hagen
105 S Main, Seattle, WA 98104
206 682.6799

Thomas, Pat Medical Ills
711 Carpenter Ave, Oak Park, IL 60304
708 383.8505

Thomas, Rod
16 Grasmere Rd, Needham, MA 02194
617 449.0480
page 429

Thomas, Troy
1247 Portage Ln, Woodstock, IL 60098
815 338.9455

Thomas-Bradley Illust & Design
411 Center St, Gidley, IL 61744
309 747.3266

Thomas. Charles
4617 Lost Horizon Dr, Tucson, AZ 85745
602 743.3613

Thomassie, Juan
319 Prospect Ave, Long Beach, CA 90814
310 439.7246

Thompson, Art
39 Prospect Ave, Pompton Plains, NJ 07444
201 835.3534

Thompson, Darren
404 E 38th St, Anderson, IN 46013
317 641.7046

Thompson, Doug
3301A S Jefferson Ave, St Louis, MO 63118
314 773.2600

Thompson, Ellen
67 De Leon Cir, Franklin Park, NJ 08826
908 422.0233

Thompson, Emily
34-50 28th St, Astoria, NY 11106
718 937.2388

Thompson, George
34-50 28th St, Astoria, NY 11106
718 937.2388

Thompson, John M
118 Parkview Ave, Weehawken, NJ 07087
201 865.7853

Thompson, John P
5454 Newcastle, Houston, TX 77081
713 660.7039

Thompson, M Kathryn
190 Forrest Ave, Fairfax, CA 94930
415 459.8835

Thompson, Nick
3443 Wade St, L.A., CA 90066
310 390.9595

Thompson, Thierry
212 Dorchester Ln, Alamo, CA 94507
510 210.0155

Thomssen, Kate
1336 Scheffer Ave, St Paul, MN 55116
612 698.9129

Thoner, Dan
3485 Copley Ave, San Diego, CA 92116
619 282.0031

Thonnessen, Sabina
141 Wooster St, NYC, NY 10012
212 254.7436

Thordarson, Tom
320 W Wilson Ave, Glendale, CA 91203
818 547.1900

Thorn, Dick
353 W 53rd St, NYC, NY 10019
212 582.0023
fax 212 582.0090
page 145

Thornburgh, Bethann
1673 Columbia Rd NW, Wash, DC 20009
202 667.0147

Thornley, Blair
1251 University Ave, San Diego, CA 92103
619 299.3874

Thornton, Jeremy
302 N La Brea Ave, L.A., CA 90036
213 655.0998

Thornton, Michael
7844 Starward Dr, Dublin, CA 94568
510 828.5032

Thorpe, Peter
254 Park Ave S, NYC, NY 10010
212 477.0131

Thorspecken, Thomas
615 E 14th St, NYC, NY 10009
212 995.5647

Those 3 Reps
2909 Cole Ave, Dallas, TX 75204
214 871.1316
fax 214 880.0337
pages 414-415

Thrash & Cortez Design
16812 Red Hill Ave, Irvine, CA 92714
714 955.1045

Thrun, Rick
207 E Buffalo St, Milwaukee, WI 53202
414 277.7743

Thrun, Thomas
36 Cory Rd, Flanders, NJ 07836
201 927.7316

Thurston, Russell Studio
2315 W Huron, Chicago, IL 60612
312 235.6257

Tiani, Alex
PO Box 4530, Greenwich, CT 06830
203 661.3891

Tiberi Graphics
3725 W Morse Ave, Lincolnwood, IL 60645
708 933.9424

Tierney, John
659 Churchill St, Pittsfield, MA 01201
413 442.8428

Tiessen, Ken
900 W Jackson Blvd, Chicago, IL 60607
312 994.5680

Tilley, Debbie
2051 Shadetree Ln, Escondido, CA 92029
619 432.6282

Tillinghast, David
221 W Maple Ave, Monrovia, CA 91016
818 359.4083

Timmons, Bonnie
446 Springdell RD Five,
Coatesville, PA 19320
610 380.0292
fax 610 380.0479
pages 20-21

Timmons, Bonnie
18 McKinley St, Rowayton, CT 06853
203 866.3734
fax 203 857.0842
pages 20-21

Timmons, Bonnie
NYC, NY
212 581.8338
pages 20-21

Tinkelman, Murray
75 Lakeview Ave W, Peekskill, NY 10566
914 737.5960

Tinney, Robert
410 E Carriere St, Washington, LA 70589
318 826.3003

Tipich, Sharon
1417 W 13th St, San Pedro, CA 90732
404 872.8811

Tirado, Alicia
168 H St, Chula Vista, CA 91910
619 422.2645

Titcombe, Harry
Nine Deveron Way, Essex, England RM1 4UL
011 44.708.743.777

Tkaczuk, Stanley
E Main St, Ware, MA 01082
413 967.9855

Tocchet, Mark J
225 Weldy Ave, Oreland, PA 19075
215 885.1292

Toelke, Cathleen
PO Box 487, Rhinebeck, NY 12572
914 876.8776

Tofanelli, Mike
1100 Howe Ave,
Sacramento, CA 95825
916 927.4809
fax 916 927.4809
page 446

Tokmakoff, Karen
2366 Jane Ln, Mountain View, CA 94043
415 969.7829

Tom, Jack
135 Lazy Brook Rd, Monroe, CT 06468
203 452.0889

Tomaka, Jeffrey
228 E 25th St, NYC, NY 10010
212 684.2636

Tomarchio, Linda
5050 Klump, N Hollywood, CA 91601
818 508.9055

Tomas, Mary
3514 Oak Grove, Dallas, TX 75204
214 296.4124

Tomasello, Sam
36-01 31st Ave, Astoria, NY 11106
718 728.4914

Tomasulo, Patrick
76 Howard St, Dumont, NJ 07628
201 385.4350

Tomei, Lorna & Gordon
3443 Wade St, L.A., CA 90066
310 390.9595

Tomlinson, Richard
319 E 24th St, NYC, NY 10010
212 685.0552

Tompkins, Tish
1660 Redcliff St, L.A., CA 90026
213 662.1660

Toomer, George Sr
3923 Cole Ave, Dallas, TX 75204
214 522.1171
fax 214 528.3588
pages 414-415

Toos, Andrew
50 Bullymuck Rd, New Milford, CT 06776
203 350.3718

Tople, Larry
Fisher Bldg, Detroit, MI 48202
313 871.2188

Torline, Kevin
2233 Kemper Ln, Cincinnati, OH 45206
513 861.1400

Torres, April
8402 SW Woods Creek Ct,
Portland, OR 97219
503 246.9511

Torres, Carlos
192 17th St, Brooklyn, NY 11215
718 768.3296

Torres, Cecilia
1156 Western Ave, Glendale, CA 91201
818 243.0501

Torres, Daniel
11 Kings Ridge Rd, Long Valley, NJ 07853
908 813.8718

Torres, Leyla
14 N Henry St, Brooklyn, NY 11222
718 389.6101

Torrisi, Gary
50 Fuller Brook Rd, Wellesley, MA 02181
617 235.8658

Torstenson-Vertlieb, Shirley
801 S Weymouth Ave, San Pedro, CA 90732
310 548.7181

Torzecka, Marlena
211 E 89th St, NYC, NY 10128
212 289.5514
fax 212 987.2855
pages 195-203

Tosch, Jamie
8732 Fair Oaks Blvd, Carmichael, CA 95608
916 944.2097

Toyama, Ken
870 Market St, San Francisco, CA 94102
415 989.2023

Tracy, Susan
2031 State St, Santa Barbara, CA 93105
805 687.8014

Tragerman, Jay
6651 Capistrano Ave, West Hills, CA 91307
818 340.6974

Trang, Winson
2233 W Main St, Alhambra, CA 91801
818 570.8718

Travis, Janet
2531 B McKinney Ave, Dallas, TX 75201
214 871.6064

Traxion Studios
1029 W Lee St, Greensboro, NC 27403
910 275.6773

Traynor, Elizabeth
848 Greenwood Ave NE,
Atlanta, GA 30306
404 875.1363   800 347.0734
fax 404 875.9733
page 166

Treadway, Todd
778 S Swadley St,
Lakewood, CO 80228
303 763-9288
page 437

Treatner, Meryl
Two Daisy Ln, Maple Glen, PA 19002
215 540.9993

Tregeagle, Steve
2994 S Richards St, Salt Lake City, UT 84115
801 484.1673

Triad Productions
9400 Mission Rd, Praire Village, KS 66206
913 341.8988

Trimmer, Ralph
13100 Pandora, Dallas, TX 75238
214 553.8005

Trimpe Studios
Rte Four Box 221 F, Charlottesville, VA 22901
804 973.1317

Trimpe, Susan & Co
2717 Western Ave, Seattle, WA 98121
206 728.1300

Trina Represents
San Francisco, CA
415 325.9677
fax 415 325.9781
page 162

Troncalli Illustration
PO Box 863, Brandon, FL 33509
813.681.2331

Trought Associates Inc
270 Washington Ave, Belleville, NJ 07109
201 751.0330

Trout & Trout
739 Bryant St, San Francisco, CA 94107
415 896.5275

Trout, Cary Michael
739 Bryant St, San Francisco, CA 94107
415 896.5275

Truxaw, Richard
6404 W 125th St, Overland Park, KS 66209
913 338.4224

Truzzi, Pat Illus & Design
5010 Willis Rd, Grass Lake, MI 49240
517 522.3552

Tucker, Greg
1915 Lakeview SW,
Albuquerque, NM 87105
505 873.3727
page 50

Tucker, Joseph
1743 W 35th St, L.A., CA 90018
213 732.0360

Tughan, James
50 Queen St, Georgetown, ON,
Canada L7G 2E7
905 877.2683

Tuke, Joni
325 W Huron, Chicago, IL 60610
312 787.6826

Tull, Bobbi
6103 Beachway Dr, Falls Church, VA 22041
703 998.9292

Tull, Jeff
622 E Main St, Louisville, KY 40202
502 584.1333

Turaski, David
4541 Cambury Dr, La Palma, CA 90623
310 860.6132

Turgeon, Jim
405 N Wabash Ave, Chicago, IL 60611
312 644.1444

Turgeon, Pol
41 Union Sq W, NYC, NY 10003
212 929.5590
page 240

Turk, Melissa/Artist Network
Nine Babbling Brook Ln, Suffern, NY 10901
914 368.8606

Turk, Natasha
PO Box 17193, Phoenix, AZ 85011
602 954.8116

Turk, Stephen
927 Westbourne Dr, L.A., CA 90069
310 788.0682

Turnbaugh & Associates
89 W Main St, West Dundee, IL 60118
708 426.6081

Turner, David
1001 S Alfred St, L.A., CA 90035
310 556.1439
fax 213 653.5696
page 387

Turner, Jeanne
6900 Chestnut Ave, Falls Church, VA 22042
703 237.1108

Turner, Ray
Pier 33 N, San Francisco, CA 94111
415 956.4750

Tuschman, Richard
221 Rockland Rd, Pearl River, NY 10965
914 735.9259

Tuttle, Jean
145 Palisade St,
Dobbs Ferry, NY 10522
914 693.7681
fax 914 693.8123
page 229

Tuveson, Christine
1119 Hi-Point St, L.A., CA 90035
213 936.5851

Twelvetrees Studio
23336 Williams Ave, Euclid, OH 44123
216 261.2505

Ty Reps
920 1/4 N Formosa Ave, L.A., CA 90046
213 850.7957

Tylden-Wright, Jenny
11 Kings Ridge Rd,
Long Valley, NJ 07853
908 813.8718
fax 908 813.0076
page 35

Tysko, Lisa
308 Crescent Ave, Mercerville, NJ 08619
609 890.6645

Uhl, David Illustration
1501 Boulder St, Denver, CO 80211
303 455.3535
fax 303 455.1603
pages 14-15

Uhlir, April
504 W Wisconsin St, Chicago, IL 60614
312 944.4969

Ulan, Helen Cerra
4227 San Juan Dr, Fairfax, VA 22030
703 691.0474

Ulatowski, Joseph P
130 Juniper Dr, Norwood, MA 02062
617 762.2239

Ulay, Ayse
146 S Michigan Ave, Pasadena, CA 91106
818 796.4615

Ulriksen, Mark
841 Shrader St,
San Francisco, CA 94117
415 387.0170
fax 415 387.1913
page 231

Ulve, Kristen
1549 N Wells St, Chicago, IL 60610
312 951.0009

Undercuffler, Gary
1214 Locust St, Phila, PA 19107
215 545.3973

Unger, Elaine
23650 Via Beguine, Valencia, CA 91355
805 259.2174

Unger, Judy J
16014 Lahey St, Granada Hills, CA 91344
818 368.2111

Unruh, Jack
2706 Fairmount, Dallas, TX 75201
214 871.0187

Upston, Jack
1895 W 262nd St, Lomita, CA 90717
310 325.6094

Uram, Lauren
838 Carroll St, Brooklyn, NY 11215
718 789.7717

Urban Arts
3411 Belle Isle Dr, San Diego, CA 92105
619 280.5144

Urbanovic, Jackie/Cartoonist
420 N Fifth St, Mpls, MN 55401
612 673.9323
fax 612 333.4823
page 452

Uyehara, Elizabeth
1020 Westchester Pl, L.A., CA 90019
213 731.4168

Vaccarello, Paul
320 Bee Brook Rd, Washington, CT 06777
203 868.1011

Vaccaro, Victor
Six Sunny Dr, Bellport, NY 11713
516 286.6266

Vadun, Chuck
14814 Priscilla St, San Diego, CA 92129
619 672.0212

Vaes, Alain
29 Wareham St, Boston, MA 02118
617 542.5285

Vahaid
PO Box 470818, San Francisco, CA 94147
415 552.4252

Vainisi, Jennine
58 Middagh St, Brooklyn, NY 11201
718 858.4914

Valderrama, Rosario
50 Fuller Brook Rd,
Wellesley, MA 02181
617 235.8658
pages 110-111

Valk, Tinam
2111 Henderson Ave, Silver Spring, MD 20902
301 946.6583

Valko, Diane
235 S Beach Blvd, Anaheim, CA 92804
714 826.3440

Valla, Victor R
19 Prospect St, Falls Village, CT 06031
203 824.5014

Vallejo, Dorian
1940 Elizabeth Ave, Rahway, NJ 07065
908 382.3230

Valley, Gregg
128 Thomas Rd, McMurray, PA 15317
412 941.4662
fax 412 941.3490
page 449

Van Amerongen, Jerry
2533 Washburn Ave S, Mpls, MN 55416
612 374.9574

Van Genderen, Rick
PO Box 193523, San Francisco, CA 94119
510 534.2218

The Van Noy Group
19750 S Vermont Ave, Torrance, CA 90502
310 329.0800

Van Nutt, Robert
194 W Tenth St, NYC, NY 10014
212 255.7815

Van Riper, Janet
7072 Raleigh Tavern Dr, Manassas, VA 22111
703 791.3073

Van Seters, Kim
1202 Lessie Ct, Marietta, GA 30066
404 425.5707

Van Severen Studio
826 S Quincy St, Green Bay, WI 54301
414 435.6313

Van Zanten, Hugh
116 W Illinois, Chicago, IL 60610
312 644.2890

Vance, Jay
310 Avenida Granada,
San Clemente, CA 92672
714 498.8468

Vance, Steve
11936 W Jefferson Blvd,
Culver City, CA 90230
310 390.8663

Vanden Broeck, Fabricio
50 Fuller Brook Rd,
Wellesley, MA 02181
617 235.8658
pages 110-111

Vander Jagt Creative
1216 E McLellan Blvd, Phoenix, AZ 85014
602 265.0675

Vandervoort, Gene
3201 S Ramona Dr, Santa Ana, CA 92707
714 549.3194

Vandruff, Marshall
2627 W Broadway, Anaheim, CA 92804
714 952.9040

Vangsgard, Amy
517 N Beachwood Dr, L.A., CA 90004
213 461.3094

Vann, Bill Studio
420 Lexington Ave, NYC, NY 10170
212 986.5680
fax 212 818.1246
page 85

Varga, Peter
73-23 194th St, Fresh Meadows, NY 11366
718 468.7052

Varner, Charles
702 E College, Grandview, TX 76050
817 866.2415

Vasconcellos, Daniel
225 Old Washington St, Pembroke, MA 02359
617 829.8815

Vasquez, Madeline
3627 Niblick Dr, La Mesa, CA 91941
619 465.8683
fax 619 267.6649
page 355

Vass, Rod
353 W 53rd St, NYC, NY 10019
212 582.0023

Vaughan, Jack
1826 Asheville Pl, Charlotte, NC 28203
704 372.6007

Vaughn, Susan Stewart
1026 St Georges Ln, Landenberg, PA 19350
610 274.0702

Vaux, Jacquie
165 E 32nd St, NYC, NY 10016
212 686.3514

Vella, Ray
20 N Broadway Bldg 1-240,
White Plains, NY 10601
914 997.1424

Veno, Joe
50 Fuller Brook Rd, Wellesley, MA 02181
617 235.8658

Venola, Trici
5183 Overland Ave, Culver City, CA 90230
310 558.3325

Venti, Anthony
25 Claredon Rd, Rockland, ME 04841
207 596.7660

Ventura, Andrea
152 Madison Ave, NYC, NY 10016
212 689.4330

Verougstraete, Randy
10537 Pine Grove St, Spring Valley, CA 91978
619 670.5152

Verzaal, Dale
2445 East Pebble Beach Dr, Tempe, AZ 85282
602.813.2528

Vetromile, Alfred
18 Clapboard Hill Rd,
Old Say Brook, CT 06475
203.388.1843

Vibbert, Carolyn
244 Ninth St, San Francisco, CA 94103
415 621.2992

Vidinghoff, Carol M
11 Lloyd Rd, Watertown, MA 02172
617 924.4846

Villa, Roxana
16771 Addison St,
Encino, CA 91436
818 906.3355
fax 818 906.3377
page 236

Vincent, Wayne
957 N Livingston St, Arlington, VA 22205
703 532.8551

Vingelli, Michael
4360 N Camino Real, Tucson, AZ 85718
602 577.0902

Vinson, WT
4118 Vernon, Glen Avon, CA 92509
909 685.7697

Virnig, Janet
2532 Kipling Ave S, Mpls, MN 55416
612 926.5585
fax 612 926.3347
page 315

Visionary Art Resources
3972 Barranca Pky, Irvine, CA 92714
714 241.0604

Vismara, Paul
3521 N Wilton, Chicago, IL 60657
312 248.7084
fax 312 248.7084
page 314

Viss, Troy
4914 35th St, San Diego, CA 92116
619 233.9633

Visser, Karen
1979 Yonge St, Toronto, ON, Canada M4S 1Z6
416 484.3779

Visual Images Inc
1626 Franklin St, Denver, CO 80218
303 388.5366

Visual Logic
724 Yorklyn Rd, Hockessin, DE 19707
302 234.5707

Visual Science Studio
932 S Water Reed Dr, Arlington, VA 22204
703 979.3931

Vitale, Stefano
41 Union Sq W, NYC, NY 10003
212 929.5590
page 252

Viviano, Sam
25 W 13th St, NYC, NY 10011
212 242.1471

Vizbar, Milda
55 Bethune St, NYC, NY 10014
212 675.6293

Vogelsang, Johanna
4583 Via San Marco, Las Vegas, NV 89103
702 362.9785

Voigt, David
1011 Wellman Ave, Montgomery, IL 60538
708 892.3186

Volp, Kathleen
91 Bristers Hill Rd, Concord, MA 01742
508 371.1384

Volz, Laura L
1638 Ano Nuevo Dr, Diamond Bar, CA 91765
909 861.3868

von Arx, Diane M
3340 Bryant Ave S, Mpls, MN 55408
612 825.6520

von Buhler, Cynthia
16 Ashford St, Boston, MA 02134
617 783.2421
page 466

Von Eiff, Damon
Two W Argyle St, Rockville, MD 20850
301 251.0381

Von Haeger, Arden
416 Ramble Wood Cir, Nashville, TN 37221
615 646.7022

von Ulrich, Mark
One Union Square W, NYC, NY 10003
212 989.9325
page 256

Von Wolffersdorff, Joy
1115 Hope St, S Pasadena, CA 91030
818 441.0795

Voo, Rhonda
8800 Venice Blvd, L.A., CA 90034
310 839.1532

Voss, Tom Illustration
1888 Century Park E, L.A., CA 90067
310 826.1332
fax 310 284.3290
page 262

Voss, Tom Illustration
632 McDonald Ln,
Escondido, CA 92025
619 747.3946
page 262

Voth, Greg
67 Eighth Ave, NYC, NY 10014
212 807.9766

Voth, Pam
PO Box 155, Passaic, NJ 07055
201 472.1225

Voyles, Dick
2822 Breckenridge Ind Ct, St Louis, MO 63144
314 968.3851

Vye, Mike
3112 Bryant Ave S, Mpls, MN 55408
612 827.7302

W W Two Design
250 Post Rd E, Westport, CT 06880
203 454.2550

W.E.T. Studios
750 Second St, San Francisco, CA 94107
415 764.1992

Wack, Jeff
3614 Berry Dr, Studio City, CA 91604
818 508.0348

Waggaman, GF
1112 Waters Ave, Aspen, CO 81611
303 925.2126

Waggaman, Jim
PO Box 141, Cardiff, CA 92007
619 931.5931

Waggoner, Dug
740 Gilman St, Berkeley, CA 94710
510 524.6288

Waggoner, Richard W
202 Drexel Ave, Decatur, GA 30030
404 378.6403

Wagner, Kathleen
8450 Cambridge, Houston, TX 77054
713 795.0760

Wagner, Marijke Paquay
1085 Hickory View Cir, Camarillo, CA 93012
805 987.1123

Wagner, Patricia Ann
604 Matchwood Pl, Azusa, CA 91702
818 334.3923

Wagner, Stephen
Rte One Box 978, Washington, VA 22747
703 675.3046

Wagoner, Jae
654 Pier Ave, Santa Monica, CA 90405
310 392.4877

Wahle, Elizabeth
57 Packard Ave, Somerville, MA 02144
617 628.2803

Waitzman, William
805 Union St, Brooklyn, NY 11215
718 638.3120

Wald, Carol
5280 Lakeshore Rd, Burlington, ON,
Canada L7L 5R1
416 681.3280

Waldman, Bruce
19 Westbrook Rd, Westfield, NJ 07090
908 232.2840

Waldman, Neil & Bryna
63 Livingston Ave, Dobbs Ferry, NY 10522
914 693.2782

Waldrep, Richard L
15804 Ensor Mill Rd,
Sparks, MD 21152
410 472.2328
fax 410 472.1288
page 44

Waldron, Sarah Illustration
24 Western Ave, Petaluma, CA 94952
707 778.0848

Walker, Brad
90 Rowley Rd, Woodbury, CT 06798
203 263.0530

Walker, John
4423 Wilson Ave, Downers Grove, IL 60515
708 963.8359

Watts, Stan
7517 Manchester Ave, L.A., CA 90045
310 578.2191

Watts-Clark, Cynthia
36 Haggerty Hill Rd, Rhinebeck, NY 12572
914 876.2615

Wawiorka, Matt
770 E 73rd St, Indpls, IN 46240
317.255.1197
fax 317 254.9693
page 223

Wax, Wendy
322 E 55th St, NYC, NY 10022
212 371.6156

Wayman, Dena
11693 San Vicente Blvd, L.A., CA 90049
310 820.1824

Weakley, Mark
105 N Alamo Rd, San Antonio, TX 78205
210 222.9543

Weast & Weast
1215 18th St, Sacramento, CA 95814
916 441.4231

Webb, Darren
72 Orchard St, Hamburg, NJ 07419
201 827.9608

Webb, Jim
2036 Pacifics St, Brooklyn, NY 11233
718 345.7610

Weber, John
3637 Ridgewood Dr, Hilliard, OH 43026
614 777.0631

Weber, Richard
229 W Illinois, Chicago, IL 60610
312 802.5343

Weber, Tricia/The Weber Group
125 W 77th St, NYC, NY 10024
212 799.6532

Wedmore, Keith
PO Box 275, Mill Valley, CA 94942
415 381.4456

Wehrman, Richard
247 N Goodman St, Rochester, NY 14607
716 271.2280

Wehrman, Vicki
265 Westminster Rd, Rochester, NY 14607
716 657.7910

Weil, Martha
295 Park Ave So, NYC, NY 10010
212 260.8743

Weiland, Garison
19 Barry Pl, Falmouth, MA 02540
508 540.2551

Weimann, Roy
68 E Franklin St, Dayton, OH 45459
513 433.8383

Weinberg & Clark
160 E Dana St, Mountain View, CA 94041
415 962.1752

Weinman, Brad
310 E Santa Anita, Burbank, CA 91502
818 843.2249
fax 818 843.3008
page 346

Weinstein, Ellen
84 Forsyth St, NYC, NY 10002
212 274.9055

Weinstein, Morey
807 Larkwood Dr, Greensboro, NC 27410
910 854.5161

Weinstock, Bruce
25-98 36th St, Astoria, NY 11103
718 956.1670

Weir-Quiton, Gregory
1800 Benedict Canyon, Beverly Hills, CA 90210
310 278.2852

Weisbach, Jonathan
E Main St, Ware, MA 01082
413 967.9855

Weisbecker, Philippe
155 W 15th St, NYC, NY 10011
212 989.8770

Weisberg, Pam
PO Box 1795, Pacific Palisade, CA 90272
310 459.4878

Weiss, Conrad
40 Mohawk Trl, W Milford, NJ 07480
201 697.7226

Weiss, Gary
525 Sweet Creek Dr, Lawrenceville, GA 30244
404 339.9266

Weisser, Carl Silhouette
38 Livingston St, Brooklyn, NY 11201
718 834.0952

Weistling, Morgan
3443 Wade St, L.A., CA 90066
310 390.9595

Welch, Michael
925 Eighth Ave, Sacramento, CA 95818
916 446.5691

Welkis, Allen
53 Heights Rd, Fort Salonga, NY 11768
516 261.4160

Weller, Don
PO Box 726, Park City, UT 84060
801 649.9859

Weller, Linda
PO Box 959, Ridgefield, CT 06887
203 438.8386

Wells, Karen Represents
14027 Memorial Dr,
Houston, TX 77079
713 293.9375
fax 713 688.9988
pages 161-163

Wells, Peter/Square Dogs Illus
405 N Wabash Ave, Chicago, IL 60611
312 321.1336

Wells, Stephen
1212 N Post Oak, Houston, TX 77055
713 688.0637
fax 713 688.9988
page 163

Wells, Susan & Associates
5134 Timber Trl NE, Atlanta, GA 30342
404 255.1430

Wend, Daniel
3220 15th Ave, Seattle, WA 98119
206 286.8091

Wende, Philip
1728 N Rock Spgs Rd, Atlanta, GA 30324
404 874.2014

Wenngren, Anders
450 Sixth Ave, NYC, NY 10011
212 353.1248

Wepplo, Mike
Ten Ranch Creek Ct,
Pomona, CA 91766
909 865.5056
fax 909 865.5056
page 355

Werner, Jerry
PO Box 133, Sisters, OR 97759
503 549.9130

Wesen, Michele
75 Leonard St, NYC, NY 10013
212 226.6710

West End Studios
12121 Wilshire Blvd, L.A., CA 90025
310 826.9378

West, Jeffery Design
736 N 17th, San Jose, CA 95112
408 971.0504

Westerfield, David
3525 W Peterson Ave, Chicago, IL 60659
312 588.4995

Westermeyer, Todd
2233 Kemper Ln, Cincinnati, OH 45206
513 861.1400

Westin, Janey
4600 Oak Dr, Edina, MN 55424
612 925.9411

Westman, Barbara
420 Riverside Dr, NYC, NY 10025
212 666.3588

Westmoreland, Scott
16005 La Meseta Way, Whittier, CA 90603
310 943.8626

Weston, Will
7517 Manchester Ave, L.A., CA 90045
310 578.2191

Westphal, Ken
325 W Huron St, Chicago, IL 60610
312 787.6826

Westwater, James
3443 Wade St, L.A., CA 90066
310 390.9595

Westwood, William
327 State St, Albany, NY 12210
518 432.5237

Wet Paint
1684 Grand Ave, St Paul, MN 55105
612 698.6431

Wetterhahn, Kristin
1314 Kearny St, San Francisco, CA 94133
415 398.1953

Wetzel, Marcia
758 Brookridge Dr, Atlanta, GA 30306
404 872.7980

Wexler, Ed
4701 Don Pio Dr, Woodland Hills, CA 91364
818 888.3858

Wharton, Jennifer Heyd
128 Beechtree Dr, Broomall, PA 19008
215 356.0362

Wheatley, Mark
7844 St Thomas Dr, Baltimore, MD 21236
410 661.6897

Wheatley, Misty
2233 Kemper Ln, Cincinnati, OH 45206
513 861.1400

Wheaton, Liz
16780 Dry Creek Ct,
Morgan Hill, CA 95037
408 776.1325
fax 408 779.1285
page 105

Wheaton-O'Leary Associates
2500 39th Ave NE, Mpls, MN 55421
612 788.4201

Whelan, Michael
23 Old Hayrake, Danbury, CT 06811
203 792.8089

Whelan, Patrick James
490 S Coast Hwy, Laguna Beach, CA 92651
714 494.8175

Whipple, Rick
PO Box 2193, Grapevine, TX 76099
817 481.2212
fax 817 481.2908
page 359

Whistl'n Dixie
6111 Peachtree Dunwoody Rd,
Atlanta, GA 30328
404 391.9929

White Picket Studio
95 North Main, Petersham, MA 01366
508 724.8810

White, B Perry
6918 Whitaker Ave, Van Nuys, CA 91604
818 785.0929

White, Bill
7707 18th Ave, Seattle, WA 98115
206 526.1175

White, Caroline
126 Ashfield Mountain Rd, Ashfield, MA 01330
413 628.4042

White, Jeff
3820 SW 96th Ave, Portland, OR 97225
503 297.9490

White, Jim
6231 Forest Ave, Hammond, IN 46324
219 932.6394

White, Meg
2110 Shumate Rd, Ekron, KY 40117
502 828.8400

White, Roger
160 West End Ave, NYC, NY 10023
212 362.1848

Whitehead, Danny
1909 W 48th Ter, Westwood Hills, KS 66205
913 362.4544

Whitehead, Samuel B
200 E 27th St, NYC, NY 10016
212 686.5250

Whitehouse, Debora
8650 Gulana Ave, Playa del Rey, CA 90293
310 827.7545

Whiting, Jim
773 S Nardo, Solana Beach, CA 92075
619 755.7449

Whitlatch, Terryl
804 Arlington Way,
Martinez, CA 94553
510 228.7675
fax 510 372.7613
page 371

Whitt, Gregory
1008 Pine Shadow Dr, Apopka, FL 32712
407 889.8184

Whitver, Harry
208 Reidhurst Ave, Nashville, TN 37203
615 320.1795

Whytock, John
PO Box 964, Sugarloaf, CA 92386
909 585.9355

Wickart, Mark
731 N 24th St, Phila, PA 19130
215 232.6666
fax 215 232.6585
page 331

Wicks, Ren
5455 Wilshire Blvd, L.A., CA 90036
213 937.4472

Wickstrom, Richard Inc
209 Marion Ave, Mill Valley, CA 94941
415 383.5498

Widener, Terry
2215 Old Megarrah Rd, McKinney, TX 75070
214 540.2360

Wieland, Don
420 Lexington Ave, NYC, NY 10170
212 986.5680
fax 212 818.1246
page 87

Wiemer, Dan
3825 E 26th St, Mpls, MN 55406
612 729.1774

Wiener, Mark
164 E 37th St, NYC, NY 10016
212 696.1792

Wiese, Loretta
306 Raymond, Ojai, CA 93023
805 646.2316

Wiggins, Bryan
229 Berkely St, Boston, MA 02116
617 266.3858

Wiggins, Mick
1103 Amador Ave, Berkeley, CA 94707
212 741.2539

Wightman, Ron
558 S Venice Blvd, Venice, CA 90291
310 827.7736

Wilcox, David
5955 Sawmill Rd, Doylestown, PA 18901
215 297.0849

Wild Onion Studio
431 S Dearborn, Chicago, IL 60605
312 663.5595

Wiley, David Artist Representative
870 Market St, San Francisco, CA 94102
415 989.2023

Wiley, Paul
410 W 24th St, NYC, NY 10011
212 627.8071

Wilgus, Robin
1826 Asheville Pl, Charlotte, NC 28203
704 372.6007

Wilkie, Rich
315 E Commonwealth Ave,
Fullerton, CA 92632
714 449.9582

Wilkinson, Joel
39 Blair St, Greenville, SC 29607
803 235.4483

Wilkinson, Peter
2756 Autumnwood Ln, Minnetonka, MN 55305
612 542.2256

Willard, Chuck
2321 Barberry Dr, Dallas, TX 75211
214 946.9141

Willard, Mike
2450 Mesquite Ter, Olathe, KS 66061
913 782.5512

Willard, Paul Associates
10415 N 38th St, Phoenix, AZ 85028
602 257.0097

Willardson & Associates
194 Third Ave, NYC, NY 10003
212 475.0440

The Williams Group
1270 W Peachtree St, Atlanta, GA 30309
404 873.2287

Williams, Arlene
7401 Oakcrest Ln, Clarksville, MD 21029
301 498.6479

Williams, Carolyn
680 S Federal, Chicago, IL 60605
312 427.2189

Williams, Dean
1817 E Ocean Blvd, Long Beach, CA 90802
310 436.5352

Williams, Donna
440 Brightmore Downs, Alpharetta, GA 30202
310 436.5352

Williams, Garry
7045 California Ave, Hammond, IN 46323
219 844.8002

Williams, Jack
PO Box 34464, Richmond, VA 23234
804 796.4797

Williams, Jim
2233 Kemper Ln, Cincinnati, OH 45206
513 861.1400

Williams, Karin
3443 Wade St, L.A., CA 90066
310 390.9595

Williams, Kent
102 Sidney Green St, Chapel Hill, NC 27516
919 968.1496

Williams, Kurt Alan
680 S Federal, Chicago, IL 60605
312 427.2189

Williams, Lynn
5306 Tendilla Ave, Woodland Hills, CA 91364
818 346.0978

Williams, Marcia
84 Duncklee St, Newton Highlands, MA 02161
617 332.5823

Williams, Ron
7310 Bennington Dr, Dallas, TX 75214
214 348.6505

Williams, Susan
221 W Elmood Pl, Mpls, MN 55419
612 824.6103

Williams, Tim
520 Country Glen Ct, Alpharetta, GA 30202
404 475.3146

Williams, Will
239 Prince George St, Annapolis, MD 21401
410 626.1029

Williamson, Robert
4602 14th Ave NW, Seattle, WA 98107
206 782.4860

Wills, Tom
3443 Wade St, L.A., CA 90066
310 390.9595

Wilson, Dick
7517 Manchester Ave, L.A., CA 90045
310 578.2191

Wilson, James Harvey
2681 Snow Mountain Dr, Sandy, UT 84093
801 942.6208

Wilson, Jim
4184 W Highway A, Waubeka, WI 53021
414 692.9039

Wilson, Lin
1236 W Carmen, Chicago, IL 60640
312 275.7172

Wilson, Lisabet
2570 Tokalon Ct, San Diego, CA 92110
619 276.1091

Wilson, Rob
4729 Eighth Ave, Sacramento, CA 95820
916 368.2781

Wilson, Ron
14702 Danborough Rd, Tustin, CA 92680
714 544.0201

Wilson, Russ
1420 Flagler Ave, Jacksonville, FL 32207
904 398.0018

Wilson, Ty
Seven Cornelia St, NYC, NY 10014
212 627.5703

Wilson, Will
5511 Knollview Ct, Baltimore, MD 21228
410 455.0715

Wilson-Eversz, Kim
268 Union St, Brooklyn, NY 11231
718 237.8546

Wilton, Nicholas
220 Alta Ave, Algunitas, CA 94938
415 488.4710

Wimmer, Mike
3905 Nicole Cir, Norman, OK 73072
405 329.0478
fax 405 329.0478
page 81

Wimmer, Mike
420 Lexington Ave, NYC, NY 10170
212 986.5680
fax 212 818.1246
page 81

Winborg, Larry
731 N 24th St, Phila, PA 19130
215 232.6666
fax 215 232.6585
page 336

Wind Tunnel
4171 Buckingham Ct, Marietta, GA 30066
404 924.1241

Winemiller, Valerie
121 Monte Vista Ave, Oakland, CA 94611
510 653.4552

Winger, Jody
1117 Xerxes Ave S, Mpls, MN 55405
612 377.4838
fax 612 377.7505
page 95

Wink, David
1391 Willivee Dr, Decatur, GA 30033
404 325.4895

Winn-Lederer, Ilene
986 Lilac St, Pittsburgh, PA 15217
412 421.8668

Winners, Margo
15421 Rushmoor Ln,
Huntington Beach, CA 92647
714.373.2040

Winnett, Peter
805-1330 Hornby St, Vancouver, BC,
Canada V6Z 1W5
604 685.8475

Winsor, Barbara
PO Box 401, Concord, NH 03302
603 224.8311

Winter, David
903 W Gunnison, Chicago, IL 60640
312 275.9529 312 527.3900
page 436

Winter, Judeanne
711 W Ortega, Santa Barbara, CA 93101
805 962.6885

Wintermute
5113 Pastura Pl NW, Albuquerque, NM 87107
505 344.8220

Winters, Greg
2139 Pinecrest Dr, Altadena, CA 91001
818 798.7666

Wirta, Lauri Leo
55 W 92nd St, NYC, NY 10025
212 866.3668

Wisenbaugh, Jean
41 Union Sq W, NYC, NY 10003
212 929.5590
page 248

Wisniewski, David
12415 Chalford Ln, Bowie, MD 20715
301 776.1006

Witmer, Keith
8106 N Lake Blvd, Kings Beach, CA 96143
916 546.6006

Witschonke, Alan
68 Agassiz Ave, Belmont, MA 02178
617 484.8023

Witte, Michael
108 E 35th St, NYC, NY 10016
212 889.3337

Wofford, Terry
15951 El Lago Blvd, Fountain Hills, AZ 85268
602 837.9821

Wohnoutka, Michael
216 Lake Ave N, Spicer, MN 56288
612 796.5749

Wojkovich, Ron
900 W Jackson Blvd, Chicago, IL 60607
312 944.5680
fax 312 421.5948
page 426

Woksa, Marshall
203 School Ave, Rochelle, IL 61068
815 562.3702
page 428

Wokuluk, Jon
1301 S Westgate Ave, L.A., CA 90025
310 473.5623

Wolek, Guy
2700 S Narcissus Ct,
Broken Arrow, OK 74012
918 451.2546

Wolf, Elizabeth
3717 Alton Pl NW, Wash, DC 20016
202 686.0179

Wolf, Lee Edward
41 Belknap St, Somerville, MA 02144
617 776.3523

Wolf, Matt
2100 W Big Beaver, Troy, MI 48084
810 643.6000

Wolf-Hubbard, Marcie
1507 Ballard St, Silver Spring, MD 20910
301 585.5815

Wolfe Design & Illustration
1836 Catherine St, Phila, PA 19146
215 545.0605

Wolfe, Bruce Leslie
206 El Cerrito Ave, Piedmont, CA 94601
510 655.7871

Wolfe, Corey
302 N La Brea, L.A., CA 90036
213 655.0998

Wolfe, Deborah
731 N 24th St, Phila, PA 19130
215 232.6666
fax 215 232.6585
pages 42, 44, 325-339

Wolfgang, Sherri
95 Kingshighway S, Westport, CI 06880
203 454.4518

Wolfle, Vivi
848 Green St, San Francisco, CA 94133
415 346.0462

Wolter, Ted
1243 W Sherri Dr, Gilbert, AZ 85234
602 545.9349

Wong, Gwendolyn
760 Dawson Ave, Long Beach, CA 90804
310 438.1506

Wong, Joshua
76-12 113th St, Forest Hills, NY 11375
718 520.8490

Wong, Pat
1728 E Third St, Long Beach, CA 90802
310 439.6572

Woo, Don
205 Crystal Springs Ctr, San Mateo, CA 94402
415 340.9714

Wood Ronsaville Harlin Inc
17 Pinewood St, Annapolis, MD 21401
301 261.8662

Wood, Alan Graphic Design
57-22 163rd St, Flushing, NY 11365
718 321.7864

Wood, Clare
16 Heusted Dr, Old Greenwich, CT 06870
203 698.1113

Wood, Joan
141 N St Andrews Pl, L.A., CA 90004
213 463.7717

Wood, Jonathan
28 Shelton St, London,
England WC2H 9JN
011 44.71 240 2077
fax 011 44.71 836 0199
page 121

Wood, Judith
580 Washington, San Francisco, CA 94111
415 362.8280

Wood, Katina
11928 Chandler Blvd, N Hollywood, CA 91607
818 753.0539

Wood, Rob
17 Pinewood St, Annapolis, MD 21401
410 266.6550

Wood, Virginia
383 Silk St RD Three,
Newark Valley, NY 13811
607 642.9974

Woodcuts by Malloy
817 Westwood Dr S, Mpls, MN 55416
612 338.8940

Woodend, James
420 Lexington Ave, NYC, NY 10170
212 697.8582

Woodle, Arthur
169 Forest Ave, Marietta, GA 30060
404 429.1432

Woodman, Dave
7517 Manchester Ave, L.A., CA 90045
310 578.2191

Woodruff, Tom
29 Cornelia St, NYC, NY 10017
212 924.4192

Woodward, Joanne
24820 Perkins Rd, Harvard, IL 60033
815 943.0409

Woodward, Teresa
544 Paseo Miramar, Pacific Palisade, CA 90272
310 459.2317

Woolf, Jeanette
1164 E 820 N, Provo, UT 84606
801 377.3958

Woolf, Marie Ward
4051 Old Hwy, Mariposa, CA 95338
209 742.5228

Woolley, Janet
11 Kings Ridge Rd,
Long Valley, NJ 07853
908 813.8718
fax 908 813.0076
page 34

Woosley, Brigitte
106 E Graham, McKinney, TX 75069
214 562.2085

Worcester, Mary
2670 Marshland Rd,
Wayzata, MN 55391
612 449.4850
fax 612 449.8975
page 96

Workman, June
PO Box 8032, Fremont, CA 94537
510 792.1449

Wortsman, Wendy
729 E 11th Ave, Vancouver, BC,
Canada V5T 2E4
604 873.0565

Wray, Wendy
194 Third Ave, NYC, NY 10003
212 475.0440

Wright, Amy Bartlett
227 Old Mill Ln, Portsmouth, RI 02871
401 849.4680

Wright, Bob Creative Group
Carnegie Pl, Rochester, NY 14607
716 271.2280

Wright, Candace
3447 Glenrose Ave, Altadena, CA 91001
818 794.8284

Wright, Carol
2500 Angie Way, Rancho Cordova, CA 95670
916 635.4705

Wright, Jane Chambless
Nine Babbling Brook Ln, Suffern, NY 10901
914 368.8606

Wright, Janie
262 Connecticut Ave, Atlanta, GA 30307
404 373.2696

Wright, Malinda Cowles
2550 Date Cir, Torrance, CA 90505
310 534.2315

The Write Direction
110 Alpine Way, Athens, GA 30606
404 546.5058

Wrobel, Cindy
415 Alta Dena, St Louis, MO 63130
314 721.4467

Wu, Benjamin
654 Pier Ave, Santa Monica, CA 90405
310 392.4877

Wunderlich, Dirk
5110 Biloxi Ave, North Hollywood, CA 91601
818 763.4848

Wunsch, Marjory
16 Crescent St, Cambridge, MA 02138
617 492.3839

Wynes, Joyce
137 Williams St, Newark, NY 14513
315 331.7539

Wynne, Bob
815 S Central Ave, Glendale, CA 91204
818 241.9903

Xaiko
600 N Bishop Ave, Dallas, TX 75208
214 946.6569

Xavier, Roger
23200 Los Codona Ave, Torrance, CA 90505
310 373.7049

Xu, John
674 Fortuna Common, Fremont, CA 94539
510 651.7855

Yabut Inc
6601 Fifth Ave, Richfield, MN 55423
612 798.5977

Yaccarino, Dan
41 Union Sq W, NYC, NY 10003
212 929.5590
page 246

Yalowitz, Paul
3416 Baugh Dr, New Port Richey, FL 34655
813 372.9444

Yamada, Jane
13480 Contour Dr, Sherman Oaks, CA 91423
818 995.6883

Yamada, Kenny
1360 Reynolds Ave, Irvine, CA 92714
714 724.9236

Yamashita, Nob
12121 Wilshire Blvd, L.A., CA 90025
310 826.9378

Yamashita, Taro Hiroshi
211 E 53rd St, NYC, NY 10022
212 753.3242

Yang, James
2214 Washington Ave, Silver Spring, MD 20910
301 565.3091

Yaniger, Derek
3848 W Nancy Creek Ct, Atlanta, GA 30319
404 256.0781

Yanish, Mary
3887 Bostwick St, L.A., CA 90063
213 263.6040

Yankus, Marc
570 Hudson St, NYC, NY 10014
212 242.6334

Yanson, John Michael
211 Eighth St NE, Wash, DC 20002
202 546.0600

Yayo
3509 rue de Bordeaux, Montreal, QU,
Canada H2K 3Z2
514 596.1551

Yee, Josie
155 W 15th St, NYC, NY 10011
212 206.1260

Yee, Ray Graphics
424 N Larchmont Blvd, L.A., CA 90004
213 465.2514

Yelchin, Eugene
1400 N Hayworth Ave,
West Hollywood, CA 90046
213 851.7737

Yemm, Dale
2419 S 11th St, St Louis, MO 63104
314 481.2964

Yenne, Bill
681 Alvarado St, San Francisco, CA 94114
415 826.6749

Yerkes, Lane
11471 Persimmon Ct, Fort Myers, FL 33913
813 561.1055

Yiannis, Vicki
159 W Fourth St, NYC, NY 10014
212 242.0077

Yip, Gene
559 Pacific Ave, San Francisco, CA 94133
415 788.7074

Yodanis, Bruce
1130 SW 17th St, Ft Lauderdale, FL 33315
305 524.8467

Yoe, Craig
97 Croton Ave, Ossining, NY 10562
914 762.2009

Yost, Cindy
45 Pettom Rd, Norwalk, CT 06850
203 853.8163

Youll, Stephen
296 Pegasus Rd, Piscataway, NJ 08854
908 985.0086

Young & Lynch Design
1328 Emerald St, San Diego, CA 92109
619 270.4214

Young, Doyald
13957 Valley Vista Blvd,
Sherman Oaks, CA 91423
818 788.5562

Young, Eddie
520 N Michigan Ave, Chicago, IL 60611
312 527.0351

Young, George
Seven Birch Hill Rd, Weston, CT 06883
203 227.5672

Young, Paul
PO Box 1973, NYC, NY 10013
718 783.5022

Yourke, Oliver
525A Sixth Ave, Brooklyn, NY 11215
718 965.0609

Youssi, John
17 N 943 Powers Rd, Gilberts, IL 60136
708 428.7398

Yule, Susan Hunt
176 Elizabeth St, NYC, NY 10012
212 226.0439

Yurcich, Tom
11 Waters Rd, Sutton, MA 01590
508 865.3355

Yurkovic, Mike
5234 N Leamington, Chicago, IL 60630
312 282.7445

**Zabowski, Lulu
4645 Colfax Ave S, Mpls, MN 55409
612 825.7564
pages 99, 109**

Zafuto, Charles
285 E Main St, Tustin, CA 92680
714 731.3366

Zakroczemski, Daniel
126 Sycamore St, E Aurora, NY 14052
716 652.4224

Zalewski, Todd
1446 Van Kirk St, Philadelphia, PA 19149
215 831.9565

Zamchick, Gary
56 Hillside Ave, Tenafly, NJ 07670
201 568.3727

Zammarchi, Robert Illustration
32 Rugg Rd, Boston, MA 02134
617 787.9513

Zann, Nicky
155 W 68th St, NYC, NY 10023
212 724.5027

Zarins, Joyce Audy
19 Woodland St, Merrimac, MA 01860
508 346.8994

Zaruba, Ken
967 Wampler Ln, Westminster, MD 21158
410 876.8447

Zauss, Barry & Associates
2700 Ellison Dr, Beverly Hills, CA 90210
310 550.6107

Zeltner, Tim
203 Ellsworth Ave, Toronto, ON,
Canada M6G 2K7
416 653.2065

Zeto, Toni
901 Tenth St, Santa Monica, CA 90403
310 393.5431

Zick, Brian
1233 S La Cienega Blvd, L.A., CA 90035
310 855.8855

Ziducky, Barb
233 E Ontario St, Chicago, IL 60611
312 943.7311

Zielinski, John
411 N Fourth Ave, Maywood, IL 60153
708 343.7733

Ziemienski, Dennis
19176 Old Winery Rd, Sonoma, CA 95476
707 935.0357

Ziering, Bob
108 E 35th St, NYC, NY 10016
212 889.3337

Zilberts, Ed & Associates
5690 DTC Blvd, Englewood, CO 80111
303 220.5040

Ziller, Barbara
330 Fell St, San Francisco, CA 94102
415 621.0330

Zimmerman, Jerry
80 Eighth Ave, NYC, NY 10011
212 620.7774

**Zimmerman, Robert
Asheville, NC
704 252.9689
pages 8-9**

Zingarelli, Mark
8217 Cedarhome Dr, Stanwood, WA 98292
206 629.3696

Zingone, Robin
654 Pier Ave, Santa Monica, CA 90405
310 392.4877

Ziobro, Anita
11659 Swinton Ave, Granada Hills, CA 91344
818 366.7503

Zislis, Roberta
3400 Ben Lomond Pl, L.A., CA 90027
213 669.8170

Zito, Andy
135 S LaBrea Ave, L.A., CA 90036
213 931.1182

Zoppa, Cynthia
37 Salisbury Rd, Brookline, MA 02146
617 734.6034

Zuba, Bob
105 W Saylor Ave, Plains, PA 18705
717 824.7399

Zuber-Mallison, Carol
4323 Bluffview Blvd, Dallas, TX 75209
214 352.9192

Zuckerman, Craig
108 E 35th St, NYC, NY 10016
212 889.3337

Zudeck, Darryl
35 W 92nd St, NYC, NY 10025
212 663.9454

Zunk, Ingrid Illustration
2201 S Carmelina Ave, L.A., CA 90064
310 454.2662

Zuver, Alexander
32 Leroy St, NYC, NY 10014
212 727.3072

Zwarenstein, Alex
155 E 38th St, NYC, NY 10016
212 697.6170

Zwicker, Sara Mintz
98 Stetson St, Braintree, MA 02184
617 848.8962

Zwolak, Paul
211 E 89th St, NYC, NY 10128
212 289.5514
fax 212 987.2855
pages 196-197

NOTES

NOTES

RICH MAHON

REPRESENTED BY RIVOLI
5775 FOOTHILL DRIVE, LOS ANGELES, CA

COCO MASUDA

REPRESENTED BY JAN COLLIER: 415. 383. 9026 IN NORTHEAST CALL STUDIO: 212. 753. 9331

marty braun | illustrator

265 PLEASANT AVE

PEAKS ISLAND

MAINE 04108

207·766·9726

ILLUSTRATOR

JAMIE
HOGAN

265 PLEASANT AVENUE
PEAKS ISLAND, ME 04108
(207) 766-9726

THINK

BEEP BEEP BEEP

5

Margaret Hewitt

516-427-1404

Margaret Hewitt

516-427-1404

SAME DAY DELIVERY BY MODEM
EPS AT 9600 BPS
R ZIMM@AOL.COM

ART DIRECTORS I Have WORKED foR

WADE KNEEDEEP

VANA T. CASE

LES MEGS

OLIVE DRAB

ROBERT ZIMMERMAN (704) 252-9689

BARRY JACKSON

(818) 769-7321

JACKSON ◆ DOKTOR
STUDIO
4118 BECK AVE. STUDIO CITY, CA 91604

LOS ANGELES: ROSEMARY 310-396 1213

5775 FOOTHILL DRIVE LOS ANGELES CALIFORNIA 90068

CHICAGO: RENEE KALISH 312 704 0010

PATRICIA DOKTOR

(818) 769-7321

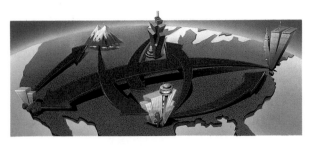

JACKSON ◆ DOKTOR
STUDIO
4118 BECK AVE. STUDIO CITY, CA 91604

CHICAGO: RENEE KALISH 312-704-0010

11

BILL MAYER, 240 FORKNER DRIVE, DECATUR, GA 30030 (404) 378-0686 FAX (404) 373-1759

BILL MAYER, 240 FORKNER DRIVE, DECATUR, GA 30030 (404) 378-0686 FAX (404) 373-1759

  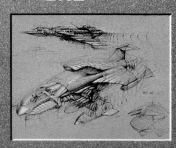

DAVID UHL ILLUSTRATION
1501 Boulder Street • Denver, Colorado 80211 • 303 455 3535 • FAX 455 1603

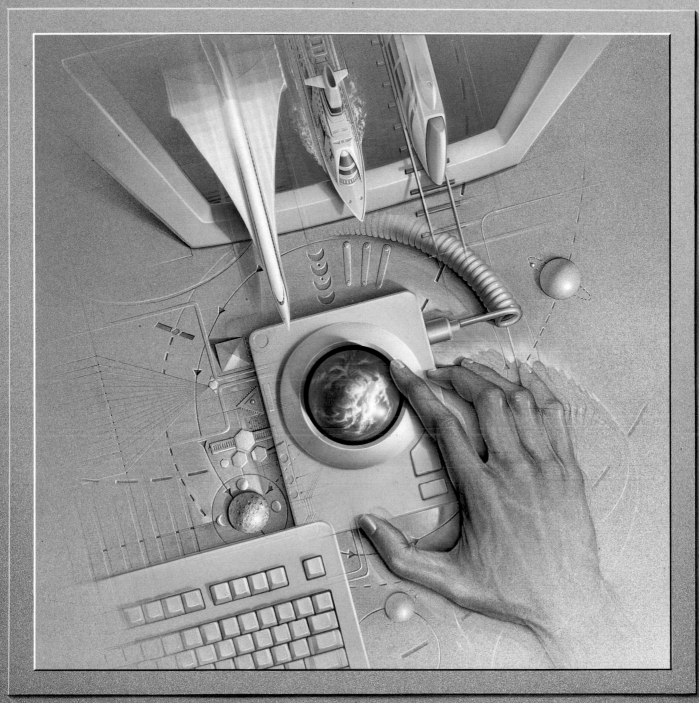

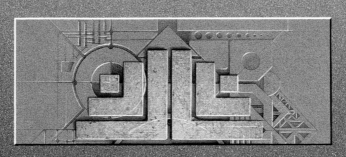
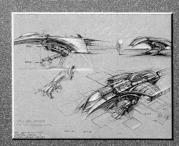

DAVID UHL ILLUSTRATION
1501 Boulder Street • Denver, Colorado 80211 • 303 455 3535 • FAX 455 1603

Philippe Beha

Joanne Palulian
Representative
212 581 8338
203 866 3734
Fax 203 857 0842

Joanne Palulian
Representative
212 581 8338
203 866 3734
Fax 203 857 0842

18

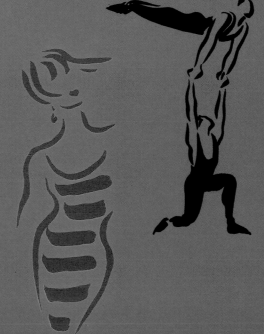

Chenille

Kabaker

Art Bank

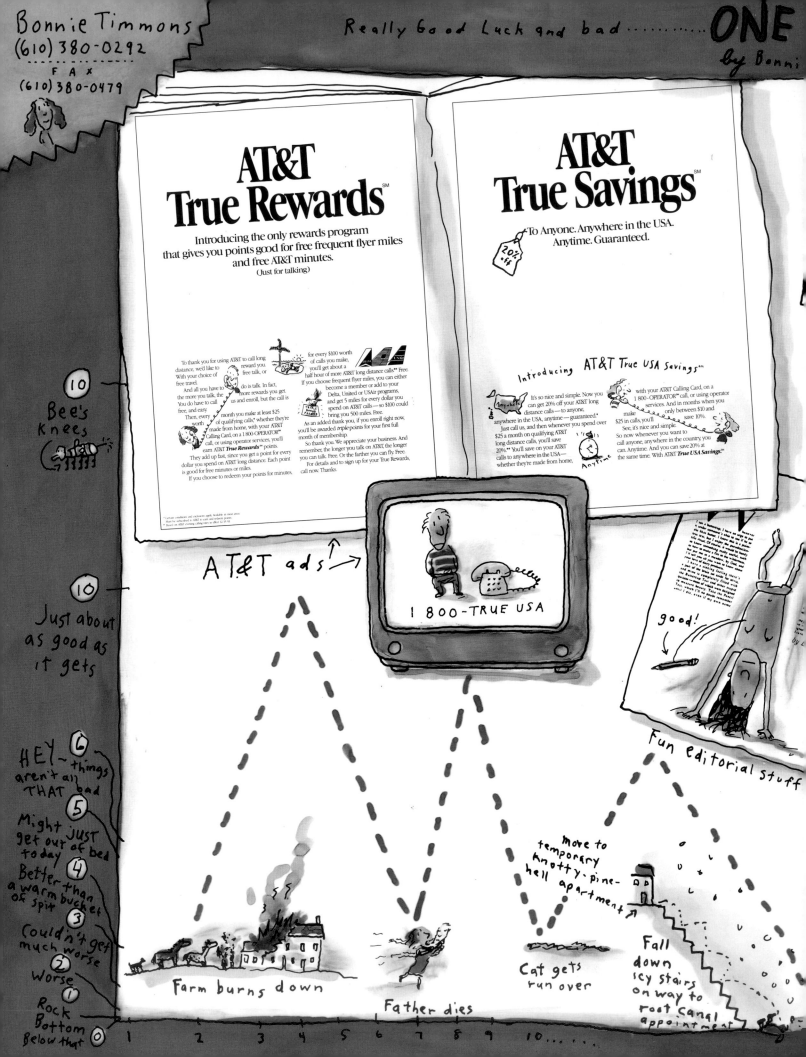

All It Takes Is Imagination.

Yours and Mine.

If you have any questions,
or would like additional
samples, please call.
Thank you.

David Lesh

317.253.3141

FAX 317.255.8462

Represented in the East
by **Joanne Palulian**

1.203.866.3734

1.212.581.8338

DAVID GOLDIN
COLLAGE

STUDIO: 212·529·5195
REPRESENTED by JOANNE PALULIAN
212·581·8338 OR 203·866·3734 FAX:203·857·0842

25

HOFKIN

Bonnie Hofkin

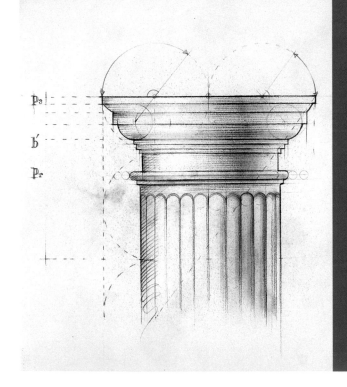

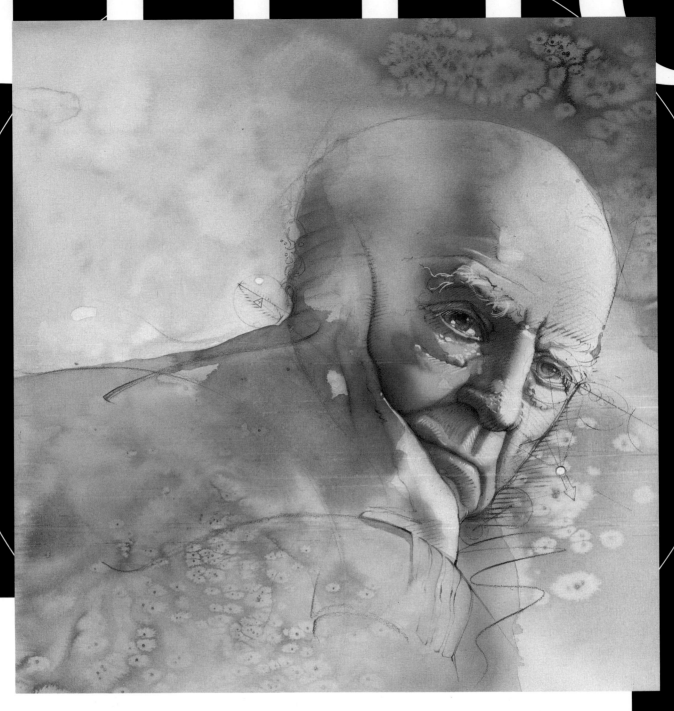

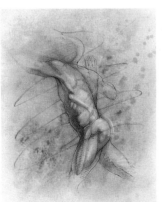

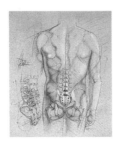

Bonnie Hofkin

Joanne Palulian
Representative
212 581 8338
203 866 3734
Fax 203 857 0842

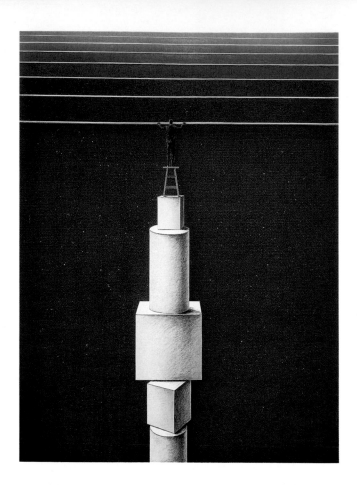

Dick Palulian

Joanne Palulian
Representative
212 581 8338
203 866 3734
Fax 203 857 0842

Greg Couch

Joanne Palulian
Representative
212 581 8338
203 866 3734
Fax 203 857 0842

In San Francisco & NW
Betsy Hillman
415 391 1181

tel: 415-291-0963

BORIS ЛЮБНЕР
БОРИС **LYUBNER**

Fax: 415-291-0726

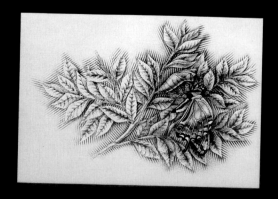

tel: 415-291-0963

**BORIS ЛЮБНЕР
БОРИС LYUBNER**

Fax: 415-291-0726

JOHN CLEMENTSON

JANET WOOLLEY

ALAN
LYNCH
ARTISTS
REPRESENTATIVE

34

EDWARD MILLER

JENNY TYLDEN-WRIGHT

BRIGID COLLINS

FARANAK

ALAN
LYNCH
ARTISTS
REPRESENTATIVE

11 KINGS RIDGE ROAD/ LONG VALLEY, NJ 07853

TEL (908) 813-8718 / FAX (908) 813-0076

REPRESENTED IN EUROPE BY ARENA:

TEL (071) 267-9661 / FAX (071) 284-0486

travis Foster
ILLUSTRATION

1209 SHELTON AVE, NASHVILLE, TENNESSEE 37216
Studio 615.227.0895   Fax 615.227.2996

L I N D A   F E N N I M O R E
I L L U S T R A T I O N

808 WEST END AVE. #801
NEW YORK, NEW YORK 10025
(212) 866-0279

MATTHEW HOLMES

TONY MORSE

Ivy Glick
& ASSOCIATES

TEL: 415•543•6056   FAX: 415•543•6075

41

JERRY DADDS

Studio:	West Coast	Chicago/Midwest	Philadelphia
Eucalyptus Tree	Ivy Glick & Assoc.	Dan Sell	Deborah Wolfe
410-243-0211	415-543-6056	312-578-8844	215-232-6666
Fax 243-0215	Fax 543-6075	Fax 578-8847	Fax 232-6585

DEREK GRINNELL

Indian-Vincent, an Anglicised edition of the famous
Hendee-Indian concern, of Springfield Mass. they
produced some of the finest motorcycles in the world.
Their V-twin side valve models enjoyed wide sales
in Great Britain, and eventually became Anglicized
around 1953—

RICHARD L. WALDREP

15804 ENSOR MILL RD., SPARKS, MD 21152, TEL 410-472-2328, FAX 410-472-1288

REPRESENTED IN CHICAGO BY:
DAN SELL, INC., 312-578-8844, FAX 312-578-8847

REPRESENTED IN PHILADELPHIA BY:
DEBORAH WOLFE, LTD., 215-232-6666, FAX 232-6585

44

Need
quick
turnaround
on
spot
illustrations?

Piece
of
cake.

Jeanne de la Houssaye

400 N. Peters • 206D

New Orleans LA 70130

1-800-524-4981

(504) 581-2167

FAX 581-1138

Represented in the mid-west by Tom Maloney (312) 704-0500 FAX 236-5752

45

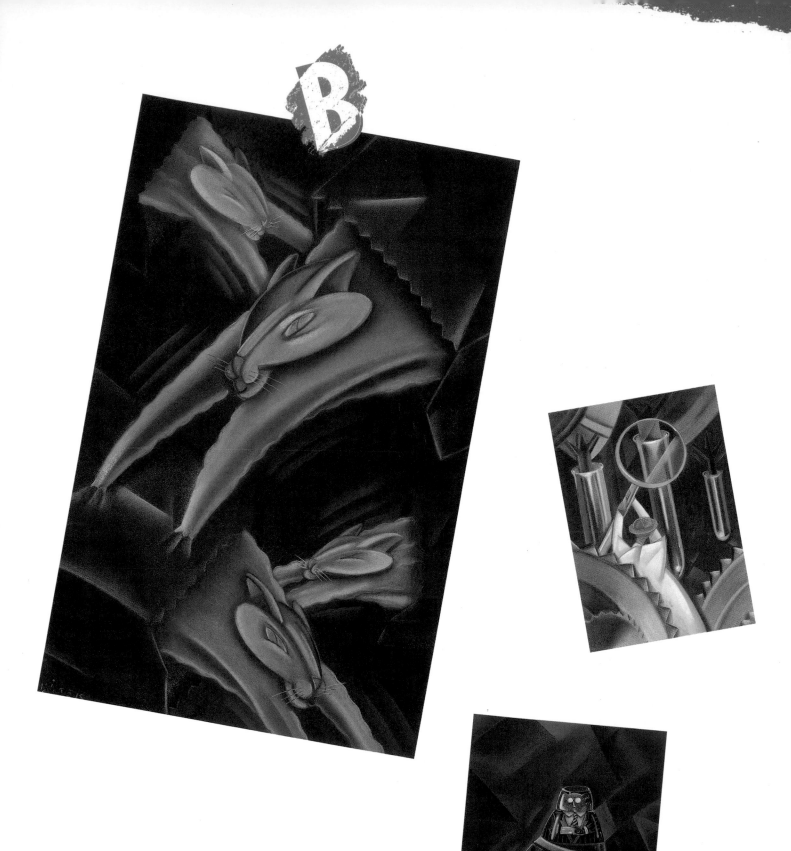

LORI**BILTER**

(615)**297-3930**

NASHVILLE**TENNESSEE**

NEVERNE COVINGTON ◆ REPRESENTED BY JOANNE SCHUNA (612)343-0432 ◆ FRANK SCHUNA (612)343-0104

DON BAKER

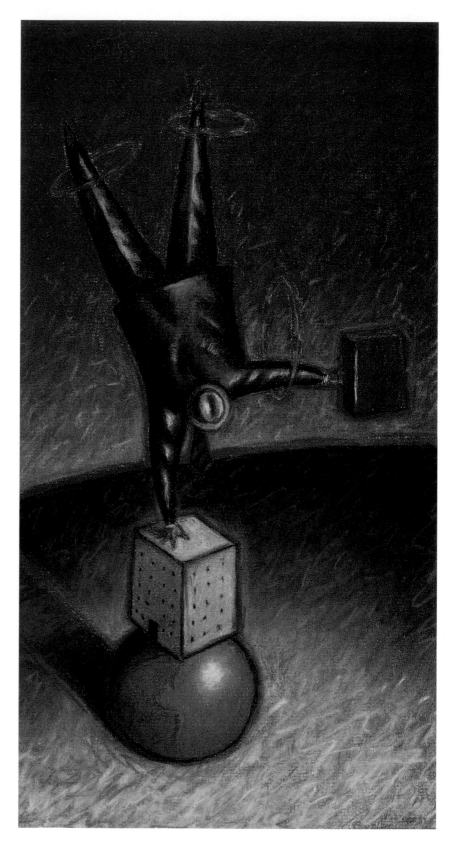

GREG
TUCKER
ILLUSTRATION

FRANCES MIDDENDORF / 212·473·3586 / 800·536·8287

DAVID OLMSTEAD

1300 NICOLLET MALL
SUITE 3046
MINNEAPOLIS, MINNESOTA 55403
612 339-2112
FAX 612 339-2233

REPRESENTED IN CHICAGO BY:
TOM MALONEY
312 704-0500 • FAX 312 236-5752

International Dairy Queen

52

SHARON WATTS
201 EASTERN PARKWAY • BROOKLYN, NY • 11238
718•398•0451

AMOCO OIL CO—Trial graphics, the plasma cell shooting antibodies

ASTD—Troubleshooting the puzzle

The White House—The Health Security Card

HEALTH SECURITY

A. B. JONES
123 45 6789

UNITED STATES OF AMERICA

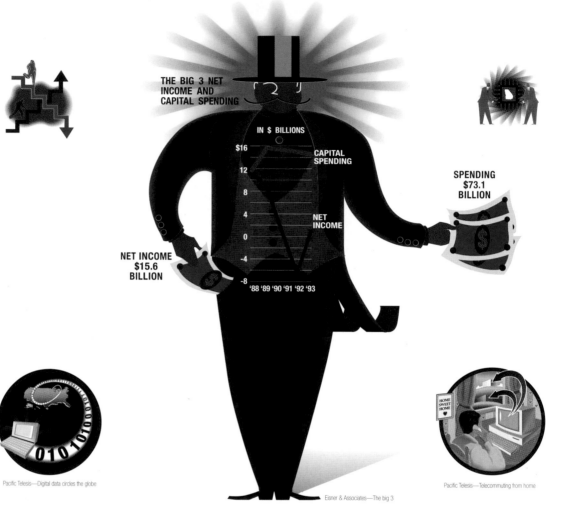

THE BIG 3 NET INCOME AND CAPITAL SPENDING

IN $ BILLIONS

$16

12

CAPITAL SPENDING

8

4

NET INCOME

0

-4

-8

'88 '89 '90 '91 '92 '93

SPENDING $73.1 BILLION

NET INCOME $15.6 BILLION

Eisner & Associates—The big 3

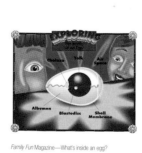

Pacific Telesis—Digital data circles the globe

Pacific Telesis—Telecommuting from home

Family Fun Magazine—What's inside an egg?

Georgia Trend Magazine—Top 100 companies in Georgia

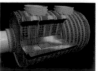

GEOTEK—Communications network

Nasa—Animation the shuttle & spacelab

MOST OF THE ART WE CREATE COMES FROM MACINTOSH COMPUTERS AND CAN BE MADE COMPATIBLE IN MOST FILE FORMATS INCLUDING PC, NEXT, SCITEX, SILICON GRAPHICS, SUN AND ALSO INCLUDING VIDEO.

American Medical Assoc.—Healthy Heart Video

G&A—Animation of endangered species chart

Sprint—French partnership in telecommunications

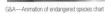

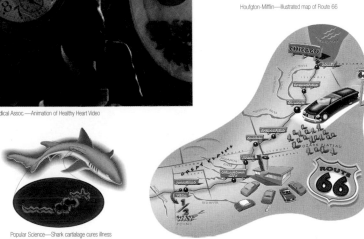

PERSONAL USES

Tele desic

EDUCATION

The Teledesic Network will offer a means of providing a wide range of information services, from high quality voice channels to broadband channels supporting videoconferencing, interactive multimedia, and real-time two-way digital data. It will provide "bandwidth on demand" allowing users to adjust their channel capacity from one moment to the next to accomodate various applications.

ECONOMIC DEVELOPMENT

MEDICINE

Teledesic—Worldwide communications via satellite

Barnette Design—Smokers that have quit smoking

Houfgton-Mifflin—Illustrated map of Route 66

American Medical Assoc.—Animation of Healthy Heart Video

ASTD—How managers can be profitable

Popular Science—Shark cartialage cures illness

MOST OF THE ART WE CREATE COMES FROM MACINTOSH COMPUTERS AND CAN BE MADE COMPATIBLE IN MOST FILE FORMATS INCLUDING PC, NEXT, SCITEX, SILICON GRAPHICS, SUN AND ALSO INCLUDING VIDEO.

DALE GLASGOW & ASSOC.
INFORMATION GRAPHICS

Dale Glasgow & Assoc.
4493 Andy Court
Woodbridge,
Virginia 22193

Voice
(703) 590-1702

FAX
(703) 590-8855

MODEM /
BULLETIN BOARD
(703) 590-0338

COMPUSERVE
72142,1625

To View More Work:
• Adweek Portfolios, 1988, '89, '90
• Creative Illustration Book. 1990, '91, '92, '93, '94
• American Showcase, 1991, '94
• New Media Showcase 1992, '93, '94
• Step By Step Graphics, Jan. 1990
• Personal Publishing, March1991,
• Washington Sourcebook, 1991, '93, '94
• Forthcoming book INFORMATION ILLUSTRATION, 1994

FOR A
OF COMPUTER ART

FOR

CALL US FOR A
OF COMPUTER ANIMATION

DOWNLOAD
FREE SAMPLES
BBS—703-590-0338

JOSEPH TAYLOR

ILLUSTRATION

708/328-2454

Brian Jensen

RKB Studios Minneapolis

call Rosemary Merrill or Diane Larson

612•339•7055

fax 612•339•8689

816-561-8045 **JIM PAILLOT** FAX 561-6201

To View Additional Work See The Workbook Or Call For Portfolio

59

VICTORIA ALLEN

ILLUSTRATOR
31 Walker Street
New York N.Y. 10013
(2 1 2) 3 3 4 - 0 1 2 0

CLIENT LIST: Ballantine Books •
Bloomberg Magazine • Boston Globe
Magazine • Business Week •
Business Tokyo Magazine • CBS
Records • Chicago Tribune Magazine
• Crown • Delicious Magazine •
Detroit Free Press • E Magazine •
Earth Day 1990 • GQ Magazine •
Global Finance Magazine • Knopf •
Lexicon Press • Macmillan/McGraw-
Hill • Mademoiselle Magazine • New
York Magazine • PAJ Publications •
Prentice Hall Press • Psychology
Today • Rolling Stone • Savvy
Magazine • Simon & Schuster •
Stereo Review • St. Martins Press
• TIME Magazine • Whittle
Communications • and many
more...

Lane Dupont

JOHN
BREWSTER
CREATIVE
SERVICES

[203]226.4724
fax [203]454.9904

Alan Neider

JOHN
BREWSTER
CREATIVE
SERVICES

[203]226.4724   [203]454.9904 *fax*

Sharif Tarabay

JOHN
BREWSTER
CREATIVE
SERVICES

[203] 226.4724
fax [203] 454.9904

Roger Chandler
Online illustrations

Represented by

JOHN
BREWSTER
CREATIVE
SERVICES

[203] 226.4724
FAX 454.9904

Seth Larson

JOHN BREWSTER CREATIVE SERVICES

[203]226.4724

fax[203]454.9904

Nan Rossiter

JOHN
BREWSTER
CREATIVE   [203]226.4724
SERVICES   [203]454.9904 *fax*

Miles Parnell

JOHN
BREWSTER
CREATIVE
SERVICES

[203]226.4724   [203]454.9904*fax*

JEFF NORWELL

Illustration

416/483-6225 EXT 651

David Milgrim

212 673 - 1432

Tom DuBois

Represented by David Montagano Telephone 312 527 3283 Facsimile 312 527 9091

© Crestley Collection

Happy Happy Joy Joy

Crush Crush Destroy Destroy

Mary Jones

Represented by David Montagano   Telephone 312 527 3283 Facsimile 312 527 9091

Licks

LAUREN SCHEUER • 617 924 6799

Bethany Gully

Boston MA

617. 350. 3089

CHRIS REED

17 EDGEWOOD RD. EDISON, N.J. 08820 (908) 548-3927 • FAX 603-0842

DANUTA JARECKA ❀ 114 E. ST 7 STREET #15 ❀ NEW YORK · NY 10009 ❀ 212·353 3298

MENDOLA ARTISTS

FOR 34 YEARS, CREATIVE DECISION MAKERS HAVE TRUSTED MENDOLA ARTISTS AS THEIR SOURCE FOR SUPERIOR ILLUSTRATION TALENT. OUR CURRENT GROUP CONTINUES THAT TRADITION WITH CONTEMPORARY AND CLASSIC ILLUSTRATION STYLES. IN ADDITION, WE CAN HELP AT THE EARLY STAGES OF A PROJECT WITH DESIGNERS AND SUPERCOMP ARTISTS. THE FOLLOWING PAGES REPRESENT A SAMPLING OF OUR 70 ARTISTS. YOU CAN SEE MORE OF THE MENDOLA ARTISTS IN THE AMERICAN SHOWCASE, THE WORKBOOK, AND THE CHICAGO SOURCEBOOK. AND IF YOU DON'T SEE WHAT YOU ARE LOOKING FOR ON OUR PAGES, CALL US UP AND ASK. WE CAN USUALLY HELP. TO RECEIVE YOUR COPY OF OUR LATEST PROMOTION BOOK, SEND OR FAX US A COPY OF THIS AD.

MICHAEL HALBERT

SEND ME THE 1995 MENDOLA ARTISTS PROMOTION BOOK

SEND TO:

MENDOLA ARTISTS
420 LEXINGTON AVE.
PENTHOUSE
NEW YORK NEW YORK
10170
(212) 986-5680
ATTN: TIM MENDOLA

MY ADDRESS:

NAME: _____
TITLE: _____
COMPANY: _____
STREET: _____
ADDRESS: _____
PHONE: _____

DUCKS ON THE POND

DAPHNE HEWETT

212 986-5680   FAX 212 818-1246   MENDOLA LTD.

GRAYBAR BLDG. 420 LEXINGTON AVE. PENTHOUSE NEW YORK N.Y. 10170   ARTISTS REPRESENTATIVES

LiiSA CHAUNCY GUIDA

MIKE WIMMER

3905 NICOLE CIRCLE, NORMAN, OK 73072, 405-329-0478

Represented in the east by:

MENDOLA LTD.

GRAYBAR BLDG., 420 LEXINGTON AVE., PENTHOUSE,
NEW YORK, N.Y. 10170, (212) 986-5680
FAX (212) 818-1246

KEVIN BEILFUSS

GOTTA BE-LEAF!*

BillVANN
SPORTS, ILLUSTRATED

"WORLD CUP FEVER" '94

ATTILA HEJJA

DON WIELAND

ROBERT KROGLE
STUDIO 1 800 653 6536

STEVE CHORNEY

BILL SILVERS

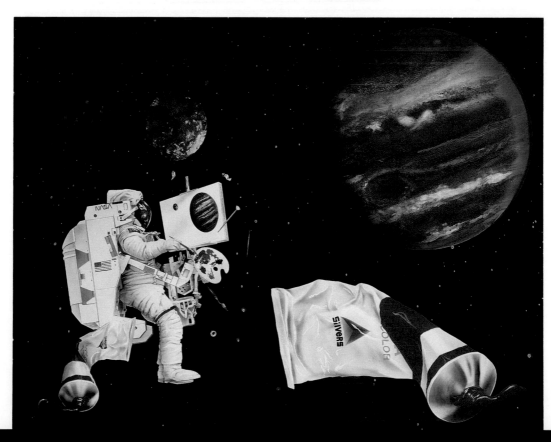

RON BERG
Illustration

Represented by
MENDOLA LTD.

CATHY DIEFENDORF

CATHY CHRISTY O'CONNOR

Don Sullivan
ILLUSTRATION
303-671-9257

212·580·9299

212·580·3030

DAVID FEBLAND
670 WEST END AVENUE #11B NYC NY 10025

ADVERTISING · PACKAGING · EDITORIAL ART

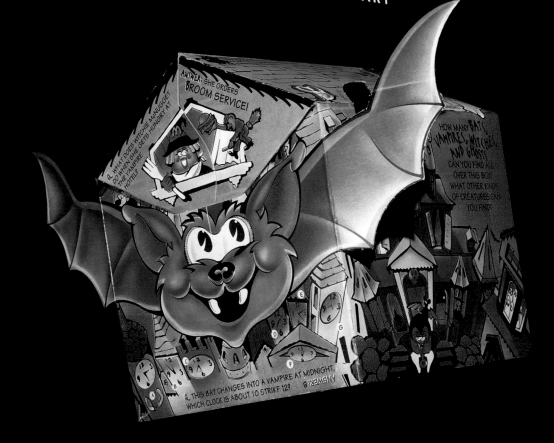

CALL

FOR

THE

B+W

STOCK

IMAGE

BOOKS

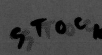

Minneapolis
612•377•4838

Represented by;
Gretchen Harris & Associates 612•822•0650
Freda Scott 415•621•2992 San Francisco

Saatchi and Saatchi, London, National Society for the Protection of Children

Clients; French Government, Minnesota Orchestra, Catholic Eldercare

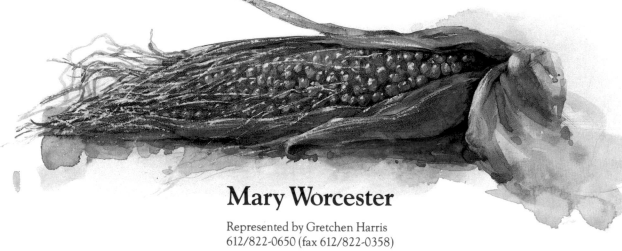

Mary Worcester

Represented by Gretchen Harris
612/822-0650 (fax 612/822-0358)

GENERAL MILLS/ BUÑUELITOS CEREAL

TOYOTA MOTOR CORPORATION

Kristen miller

CUT PAPER AND CALLIGRAPHIC ILLUSTRATION

REPRESENTED BY GRETCHEN HARRIS • PHONE 612.822.0650 • FAX 612.822.0655

SCOTT ROBERTS *illustrator*

Bachman Information Systems, Inc.

SCOTT ROBERTS *illustrator*

Phone & Fax 410.879.3362. Call for complete portfolio. Stock images available.

Scratchy Studio P.O. Box 716   Prudential Station   Boston, MA   02199

617-267-9215

Midwest Representative LuLu 6 1 2 - 8 2 5 - 7 5 6 4

New York London Tokyo Frankfurt

BONNIE RIESER   Tel. 503-452-2210

N A D I N E
REPRESENTS
PHOTOGRAPHY

C H A R L E S B U S H

ILLUSTRATION

JEANETTE ADAMS
REBECCA ARCHEY
MARTHA ANNE BOOTH
MERCEDES McDONALD
CRISTINE MORTENSEN
LIZ WHEATON

4 ◆ 1 ◆ 5
4 5 6 - 7 7 1 1
FAX 415-454-9162

NADINE REPRESENTS   415•456-7711 FAX 454-9162

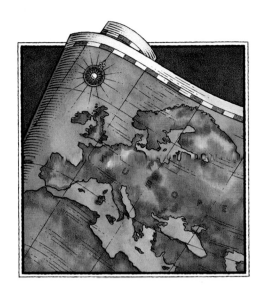

MERCEDES McDONALD

NO. CALIFORNIA: NADINE HUNTER 415-456-7711 FAX 415-454-9162

SO. CALIFORNIA: LAURIE PRIBBLE 818-574-0288 FAX 818-574-3940

ALL OTHER AREAS: FRIEND & JOHNSON 214-559-0055 FAX 214-559-0724

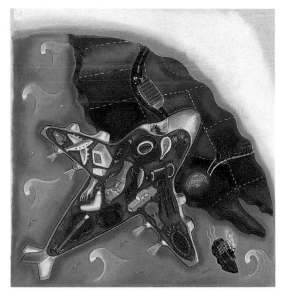

TUKO FUJISAKI ILLUSTRATION

ST. LOUIS
TEENUH FOSTER
314·821·2278

STUDIO
NY 718·789·7472
CA 619·276·0566

SAN FRANCISCO
JANE KLEIN
510·535·0495

Jannine Cabossel
ILLUSTRATION

Studio: 505-983-4099 Midwest: LuLu: 612-825-7564 San Francisco—Jane Klein: 510-535-0495

FABRICIO **VANDEN BROECK**

ROSARIO **VALDERRAMA**

GERARDO **SUZAN**

ROSARIO **VALDERRAMA**

FABRICIO **VANDEN BROECK**

FABRICIO **VANDEN BROECK**

GERARDO **SUZAN**

GERARDO **SUZAN**

ROSARIO **VALDERRAMA**

FABRICIO **VANDEN BROECK**

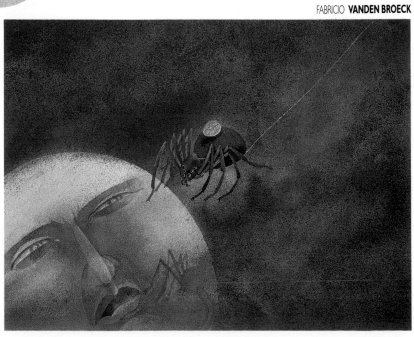

© Universal Studios

M.E.N.C.

Specializing in lifeforms in both real & surreal environments. Call for additional samples including illustrated poster design, character portraits, and surreal worlds of hightech.

See also The Creative Illustration Books 1991 - 1994

© The Bradford Exchange

Mark Stutzman

100 G. Street
Mt. Lake Park, MD 21550

301 334 4086
FAX 334 4186

Eloqui

Eloqui is a studio devoted exclusively to illustration. A complete portfolio is available upon request.

O.V.F.D.

Specializing in painted images in an impressionistic form. Call for samples of figures, sports, landscapes & still life for editorial, advertising and collateral.

U.S.F. & G.

Laura Stutzman

100 G. Street
Mt. Lake Park, MD 21550

301 334 4086
FAX 334 4186

Consultant Pharmacist

Eloqui

Eloqui is a studio devoted exclusively to illustration. A complete portfolio is available upon request.

JEFFREY OH
410·661·6064

Also see American Showcase, Volume 14 page 848, Volume 15 page 863, and Volume 16 page 879.

I am nine years old and still afraid of the dark.

JAMES KACZMAN

ILLUSTRATION

7 CHESTER ST
WATERTOWN, MA
02172-4002

617-923-4605

 REPRESENTED IN NEW ENGLAND BY LEIGHTON & COMPANY 508-921-0887

 REPRESENTED IN NEW ENGLAND BY LEIGHTON & COMPANY   508-921-0887

DONNA RUFF

18 Crockett St. Rowayton CT 06853

203 866 8626 Fax 203 866 8005

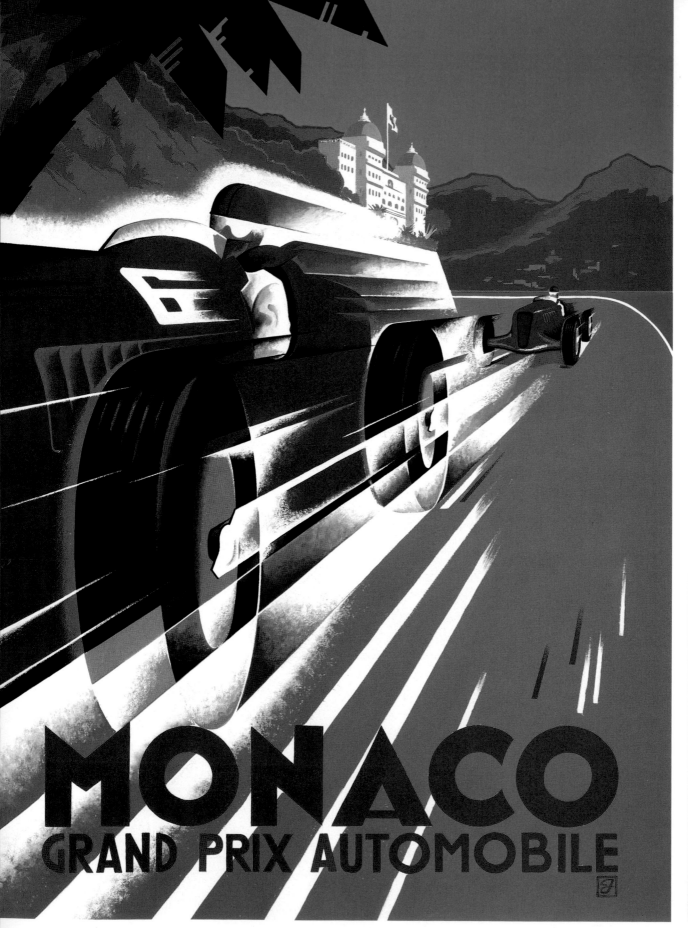

MONACO
GRAND PRIX AUTOMOBILE

ZIG PETERSON

ZIG PETERSON

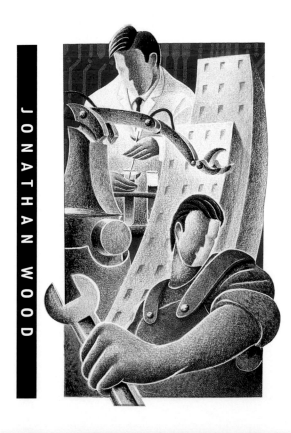

JONATHAN WOOD

JONATHAN WOOD

FRANK FRISARI

FRISARI

718 · 848 · 5007

Julie Paschkis

see also '94 Creative Illustration Book, page 192

Christopher Baldwin

Represented by Jaz & Jaz

(206) 282 8558   fax 285 4304

see also '94 Creative Illustration Book, page 196

Debbie Hanley

Represented by Jaz & Jaz  (206) 282 8558 fax 285 4304

Lina Chesak

Kevin O'Shea

Represented by Jaz & Jaz **JAZ** (206) 282 8558 fax 285 4304

see also '94 Creative Illustration Book, page 194

John Fretz

Artist's studio & fax (206) 623 1931

Represented by Jaz & Jaz (206) 282 8558 fax 285 4304

see also '94 Creative Illustration Book, page 190

Todd Connor

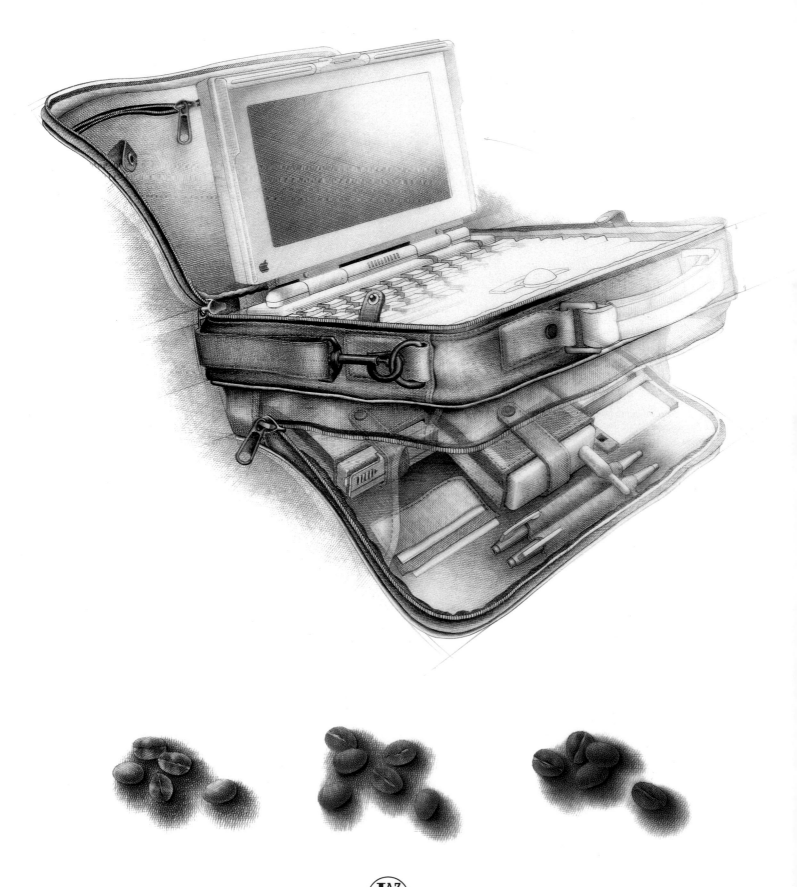

Represented by Jaz & Jaz **JAZ** (206) 282 8558 fax 285 4304

see also '94 Creative Illustration Book, page 197

Jim Frisino

Artist's studio & fax (206) 523 9593

Stephen Konz

Fred Saunders

Heather Scholl

Represented by Jaz & Jaz  (206) 282 8558 fax 285 4304

Dale Nordell

Represented by Jaz & Jaz (206) 282 8558 fax 285 4304

see also '94 Creative Illustration Book, page 191

Kim Drew

Represented by Jaz & Jaz (206) 282 8558   fax 285 4304

Dev Madan

Todd Nordling

Represented by Jaz & Jaz JAZ (206) 282 8558 fax 285 4304

Larry Milam

Artist's studio & fax (503) 236 9121

138 WEST 25TH STREET

BALTIMORE, MD 21218

STUDIO: **410 889 0703**

FAX: 410 889 5498

JIM STARR

© 1994 JIM STARR

NEW YORK
AMERICAN ARTISTS
212 582 0023

THE WEST
MARLA MATSON REPRESENTS
602 252 5072

WASHINGTON, D.C.
PAM CLARE REPRESENTS
301 365 5422

138 WEST 25TH STREET
BALTIMORE, MD 21218

STUDIO: **410 889 0703**
FAX: 410 889 5498

JIM STARR

NEW YORK
AMERICAN ARTISTS
212 582 0023

THE WEST
MARLA MATSON REPRESENTS
602 252 5072

WASHINGTON, D.C.
PAM CLARE REPRESENTS
301 365 5422

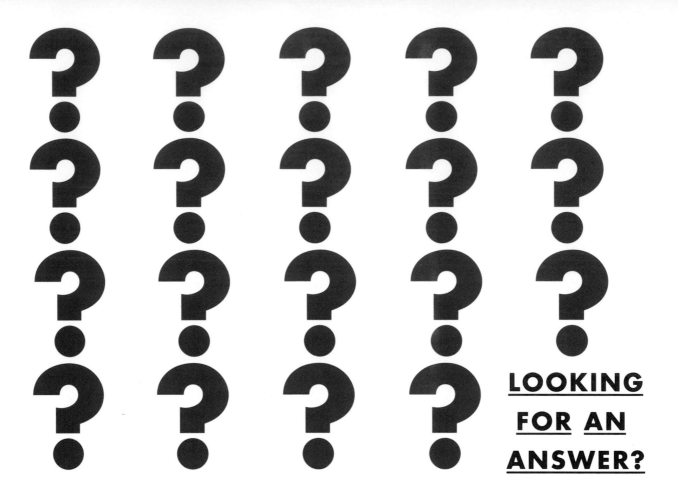

ANIMAL

DICK THORN

JANE GASTON

GARTH GLAZIER

FRUIT &VEGETABLE

DON ALMQUIST

MALCOLM FARLEY

KAREL HAVLICEK

PLACE

JOHN HULL

CHUCK PASSARELLI

JERRY LoFARO

THINGS

TONY RANDAZZO

NICKY DuPAYS

R.J. SHAY

CAFFEINE WithDRAWAL

POWER

NOT BORING!

Lipton BRISK ICED TEA

WALL ST

STUDIO X
3301 SOUTH JEFFERSON AVENUE ■ SAINT LOUIS, MISSOURI 63118
314.773.9989 ■ FAX 314.773.6406
OTHER SAMPLES MAY BE SEEN IN CREATIVE ILLUSTRATION 94, P. 403
AND AMERICAN SHOWCASE 13 THROUGH 17

Childrens Hospital

MATT
BROWNSON

Basin Exploration

DK Wheater-South Africa

Classified Records

McDonalds

Scott Towels

CAROL GUENZI AGENTS   Fax 303-733-8154 Call 303-733-0128

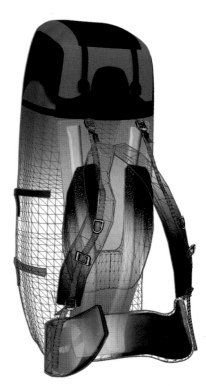

FINISHED ART... WHAT'S THAT?

JACQUES DEVAUD

A ART DIRECTOR'S THUMBNAIL

A PENCIL ILLUSTRATION

A COMPREHENSIVE ILLUSTRATION

Companion Software

A COLOR ILLUSTRATION

Sir Speedy

 CAROL GUENZI AGENTS   Fax 303-733-8154   Call 303-733-0128

ADDITIONAL WORK CIB 94

151

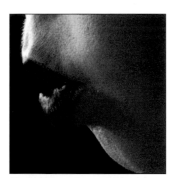

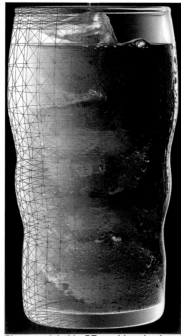

AGENTS

TODD
LOCKWOOD

KRONENBOURG

Dell Publishing

CAPCO

CAROL GUENZI AGENTS   Fax 303-733-8154   Call 303-733-0128
ADDTIONAL PAGES CIB 93-94

155

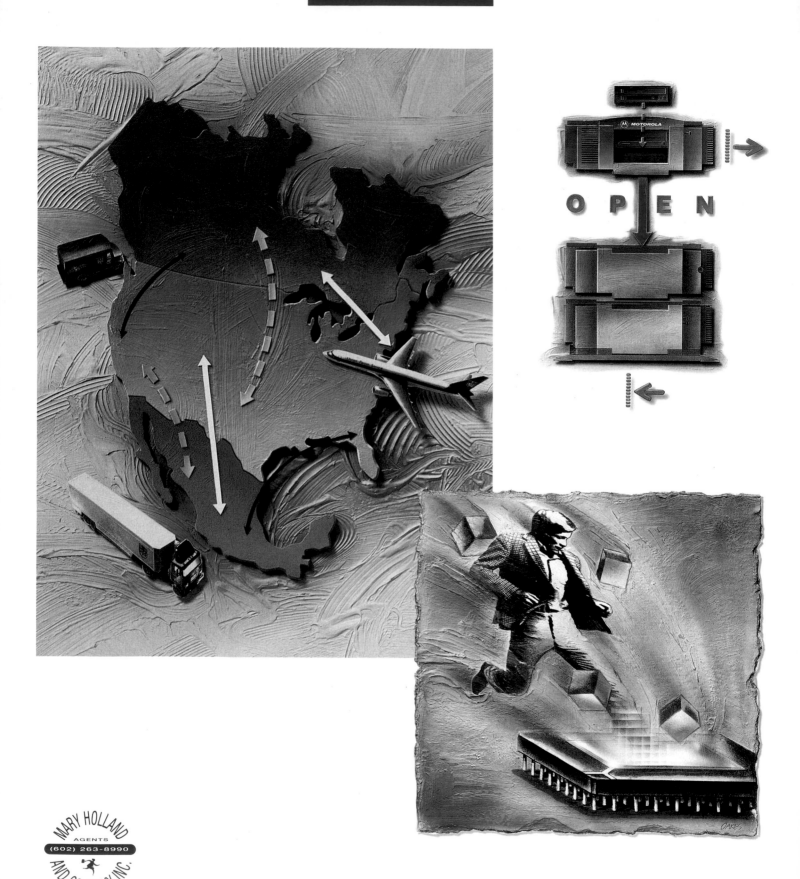

Susan Smith

537 CHESTNUT STREET   NEEDHAM, MASSACHUSETTS 02192   PHONE 617.449.7761   FAX 617.449.9092

ZITA ASBAGHI

(718) 275-1995

JEFF SANSON

ARTIST REPRESENTATIVE   KAREN WELLS   713·293·9375   FAX: 713·688·9988

RANDY ROGERS

L I N D Y   B U R N E T T

ELIZABETH TRAYNOR

CHRIS ELLITHORPE

Represented by **Alexander/Pollard** *Toll Free:* **800-347-0734** *Atlanta:* **404-875-1363** *Fax:* **404-875-9733**

D
I
A
N
E

B
O
R
O
W
S
K
I

Represented by **Alexander/Pollard** *Toll Free:* 800-347-0734 *Atlanta:* 404-875-1363 *Fax:* 404-875-9733

RAY AMEIJIDE

STUART BRIERS

LOU BORY ASSOCIATES

MICHAEL DAVID BROWN

LON BUSCH

AARON COLE

JACK DAVIS

BOB DESCHAMPS

BILL DEVLIN

ROBERT DE MICHIELL

LEE DUGGAN

THE DYNAMIC DUO

JACKI GELB

RANDY GLASS

THOMAS HART

CELIA JOHNSON

LIONEL KALISH

STEVE KELLER

LASZLO KUBINYI

SHARMEN LIAO

BERNARD MAISNER

ALLAN MARDON

HAL MAYFORTH

BRUCE MORSER

ALEX MURAWSKI

MARLIES NAJAKA

SIGMUND PIFKO

JERRY PINKNEY

CAMILLE PRZEWODEK

MARC ROSENTHAL

DREW STRUZAN

MICHAEL WITTE

BOB ZIERING

GERALD & CULLEN RAPP

We represent usually friendly somewhat DEMENTED wonderfully TALENTED illustrators. And have for over 50 years.

ABSOLUT SUMMER.

ROBERT de MICHIELL

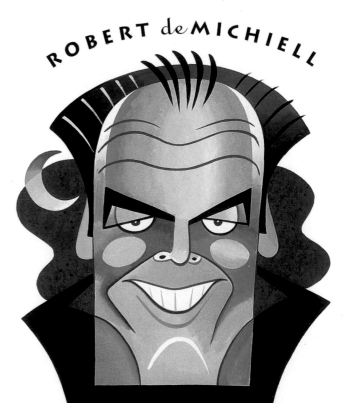

250 WEST 85 STREET · 3D · NEW YORK CITY 10024 · *phone* 212.769.9192

JAN-WILLEM Boer

MIN JAE HONG 914 · 986 · 8040

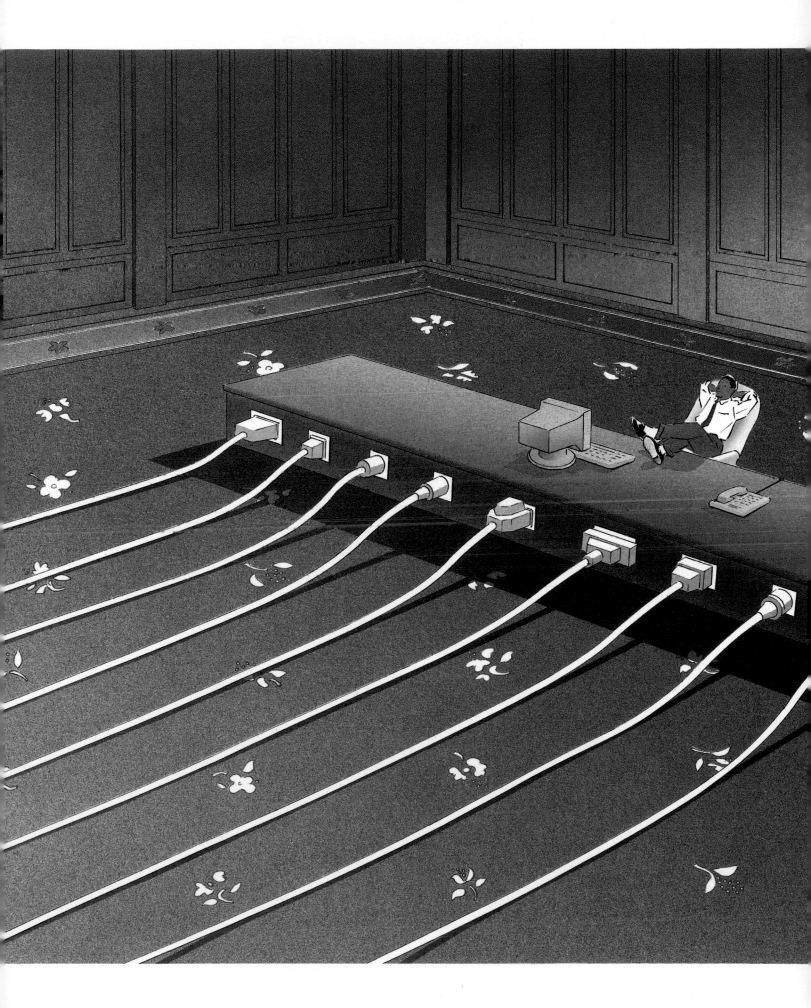

175

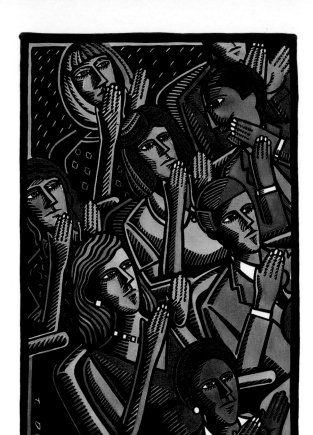

TOM DUCKWORTH
10109 RAIN DROP CIRCLE
GRANGER, IN 46530
219-674-6226

DUCKWORTH

Lori Osiecki

Lorio·123 West 2nd Street Mesa, Arizona 85201 Phone & Fax 602·962·5233

JOHN S. DYKES

17 Morningside Dr. S. ☐ Westport, CT 06880 ☐ (203) 222-8150 Fax 222-8155

"The ABC's of Amiga Fonts" for *AmigaWorld*

A professional development brochure cover for *Marsh & McLennan*

"Keeping a Lid On Higher Taxes", a poster for *Xerox Life*

179

Abe Gurvin Festive Illustrations for All Occasions   **(714) 499·2001** Studio & Fax

NATURAL GROWTH

CHARLIE MINGUS

AGORAPHOBIA

WARMTH OF KNOWLEDGE

Scott Laumann Illustration   619.743.3910

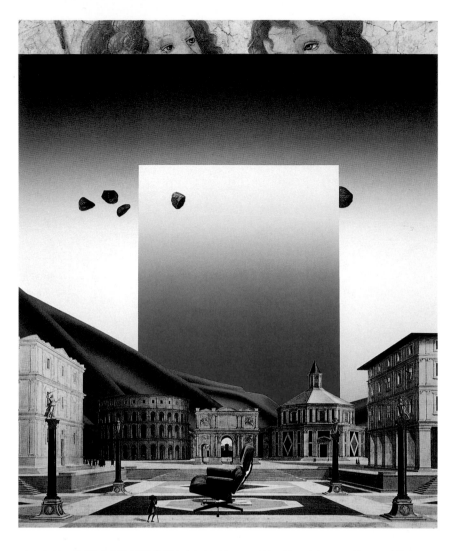

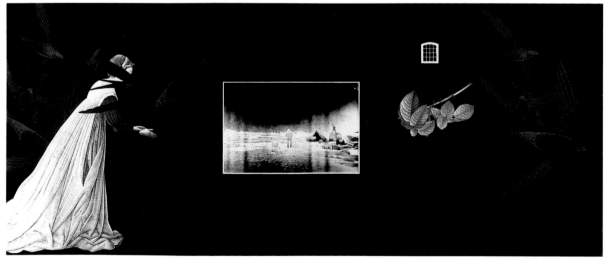

RICHARD KEHL

DONNA JORGENSEN ANNIE BARRETT ARTISTS REPRESENTATIVES
206 634-1880 FAX 206 632-2024

STEPHANIE LANGLEY

DONNA JORGENSEN ANNIE BARRETT ARTISTS REPRESENTATIVES
206 634-1880 FAX 206 632-2024

MITS KATAYAMA

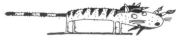

DONNA JORGENSEN ANNIE BARRETT ARTISTS REPRESENTATIVES
206 634-1880 FAX 206 632-2024

DAVID LUND

· Scott Medlock ·

· Greg Shed ·

· Tanhauser ·

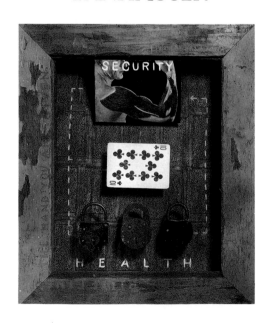

Richard · W · Salzman

ARTIST · REPRESENTATIVE

San Francisco 415/285-8267 Fax 415/285-8268

New York 212/997-0115   Chicago 312/252-2244   Los Angeles 310/276-4298

·DOUG BOWLES·

RICHARD·W·SALZMAN
ARTIST·REPRESENTATIVE

SLOAN

MICHAEL SLOAN STUDIO
Brooklyn, N.Y.C.

718·788·5437   fax 718·499·8958

Illustration in Fabric

Kate Edwards, 11126 Manhatten Mine Lane, Nevada City, CA 95959 / Fax: 916.265.8118 / Studio: 916.265.4502

phone 916-265-5666 fax 916-265-8118   11126 manhatten mine lane, nevada city, california 95959

BILL HALL

CREATIVE FORCE STUDIO   1235-B COLORADO LANE   ARLINGTON, TX 76015
817-467-1013   FAX 817-274-4011

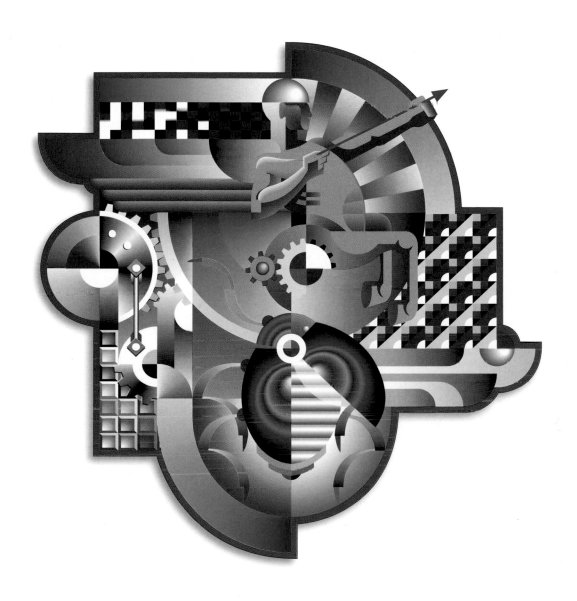

AUGUST  STEIN

DOUGLAS C. KLAUBA

RODIN'S MUSE [CLAUDEL]

312.943.4676

SCOTT McKOWEN

MARLENA TORZECKA REPRESENTS SCOTT McKOWEN • 211 EAST 89 STREET • SUITE A-1 • NEW YORK • NY 10128
TELEPHONE: 212•289•5514 / FAX: 212•987•2855

PAUL ZWOLAK

MARLENA TORZECKA REPRESENTS PAUL ZWOLAK • 211 EAST 89 STREET • SUITE A-1 • NEW YORK • NY 10128
TELEPHONE: 212•289•5514 / FAX: 212•987•2855

Gérard dubois

MARLENA TORZECKA REPRESENTS GERARD DUBOIS • 211 EAST 89 STREET • SUITE A-1 • NEW YORK • NY 10128
TELEPHONE: 212•289•5514 / FAX: 212•987•2855

ferruccio

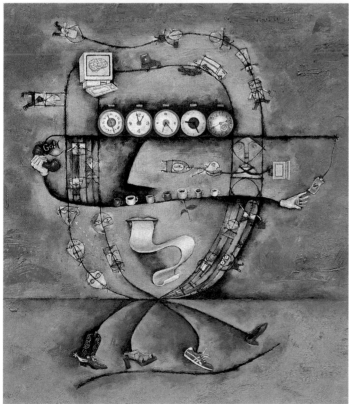

MARLENA TORZECKA REPRESENTS FERRUCCIO SARDELLA • 211 EAST 89 STREET • SUITE A-1 • NEW YORK • NY 10128
TELEPHONE: 212•289•5514 / FAX: 212•987•2855

MARLENA TORZECKA REPRESENTS MARC MONGEAU • 211 EAST 89 STREET • SUITE A-1 • NEW YORK • NY 10128
TELEPHONE: 212•289•5514 / FAX: 212•987•2855

VICTOR SADOWSKI

MARLENA TORZECKA REPRESENTS VICTOR SADOWSKI • 211 EAST 89 STREET • SUITE A-1 • NEW YORK • NY 10128
TELEPHONE: 212•289•5514 / FAX: 212•987•2855

Josée Morin

MARLENA TORZECKA REPRESENTS JOSEE MORIN • 211 EAST 89 STREET • SUITE A-1 • NEW YORK • NY 10128
TELEPHONE: 212•289•5514 / FAX: 212•987•2855

MASSICOTTE

ALAIN

ALAIN   MASSICOTTE

1121, West Ste-Catherine,
4th floor, Montreal,
Canada, H3B 1J5
Phone: 514-843-4169
Fax: 514-849-5955

WALTER PORTER

MARLA MATSON

REPRESENTS

PHOENIX 602-252-5072 FAX 602-252-5073

ADAIR PAYNE

MARLA MATSON

REPRESENTS

PHOENIX 602-252-5072 FAX 602-252-5073

BOB LYNCH

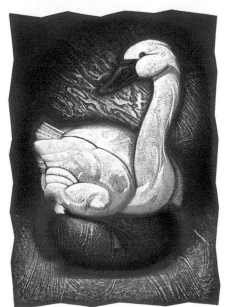

MARLA M MATSON

R E P R E S E N T S

PHOENIX 602-252-5072 FAX 602-252-5073

MARLA MATSON

REPRESENTS

PHOENIX 602-252-5072 FAX 602-252-5073

Cameron Wasson
4 1 5 4 5 5 8 8 7 4
p a i n t   n ' m a c
illustrations

SUSAN M. BLUBAUGH
212-406-3652

LISA MANNING
TELEPHONE 508 281-3983

LISA MANNING · CREATIVE CONCEPT ILLUSTRATION · 12 LEDGE LANE · GLOUCESTER · MA 01930

NACHREINER BOIE ART FACTORY LTD

925 ELM GROVE RD ELM GROVE WI 53122

TEL 414.785.1940 FAX 414.785.1611

NACHREINER BOIE ART FACTORY LTD

925 ELM GROVE RD ELM GROVE WI 53122

TEL 414.785.1940 FAX 414.785.1611

215

NACHREINER BOIE ART FACTORY LTD
925 ELM GROVE RD ELM GROVE WI 53122
TEL 414.785.1940   FAX 414.785.1611

NACHREINER BOIE ART FACTORY LTD

925 ELM GROVE RD   ELM GROVE WI 53122

TEL 414.785.1940   FAX 414.785.1611

CHRIS PYLE

Lisa Freeman Inc · 770 East 73rd Street, Indianapolis, IN 46240 · 317-255-1197, Fax 317-254-9693

Moon

Popcorn

Microscope

Nightclub

Firecracker

Peas

Dining Guide

Bird

Books

Chair

Bowling

Thief

Cleaning Supplies

MATT WAWIORKA

Lisa Freeman Inc · 770 East 73rd Street, Indianapolis, IN 46240 · 317-255-1197, Fax 317-254-9693

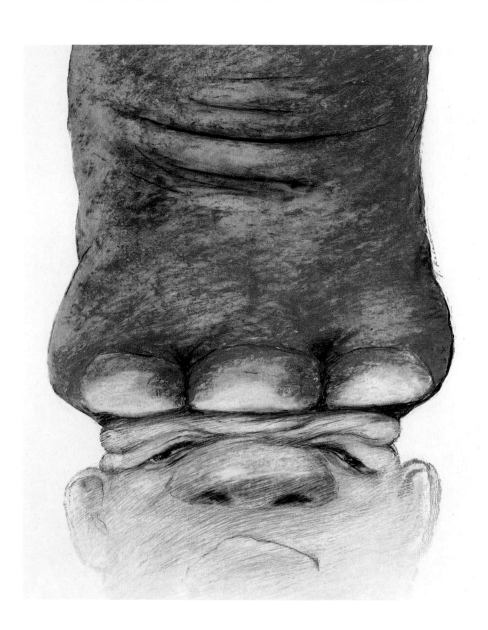

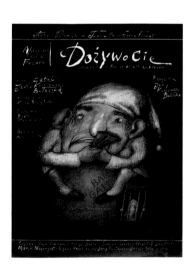

TELEPHONE 415-474-4159

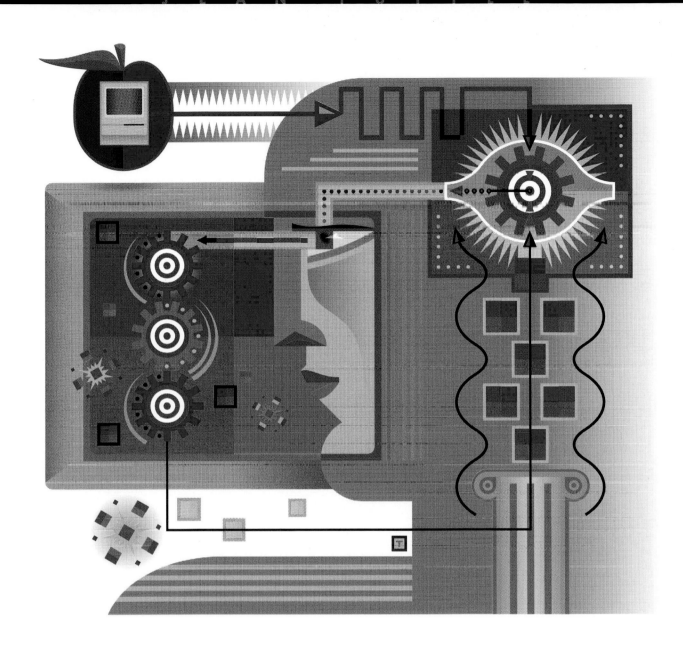

Robert Soulé

THE DEFENDANT

Janet Malcolm

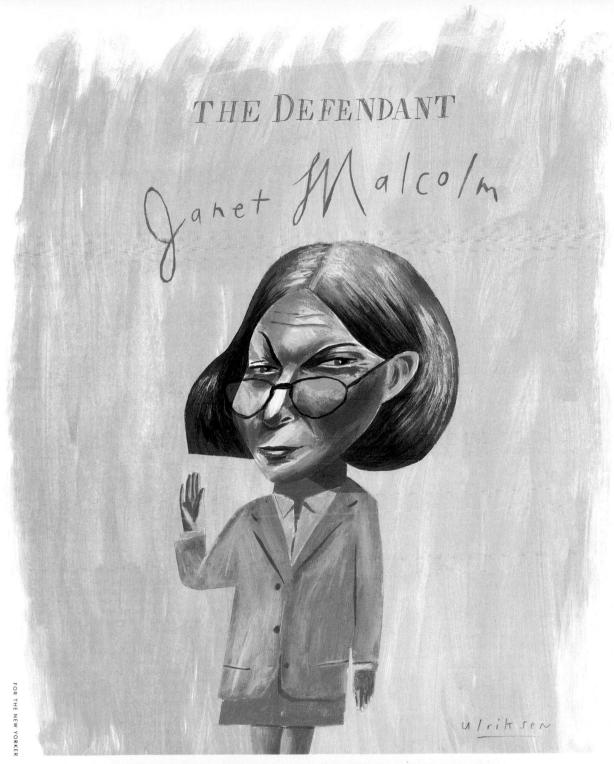

MARK ULRIKSEN

phone (415) 387 0170   *fax* (415) 387 1913

William Eisner Advertising

Francisco Communications

Scholastic Inc.

Murrie, White, Drummond & Assoc.

JOHN HAYES
(312) 787-1333
FAX (312) 975-0956

LOU M. POLLACK

STUDIO

TELEPHONE AND FAX
503 • 228 • 1658

LOU M. POLLACK

(ärt) THE AGENCY

Represented by Cindy Schumock (503) 225-9687 Fax (503) 228-6030

Roxana Villa

Studio 818.906.3355 Represented by Celestial Talent 214.443.9111

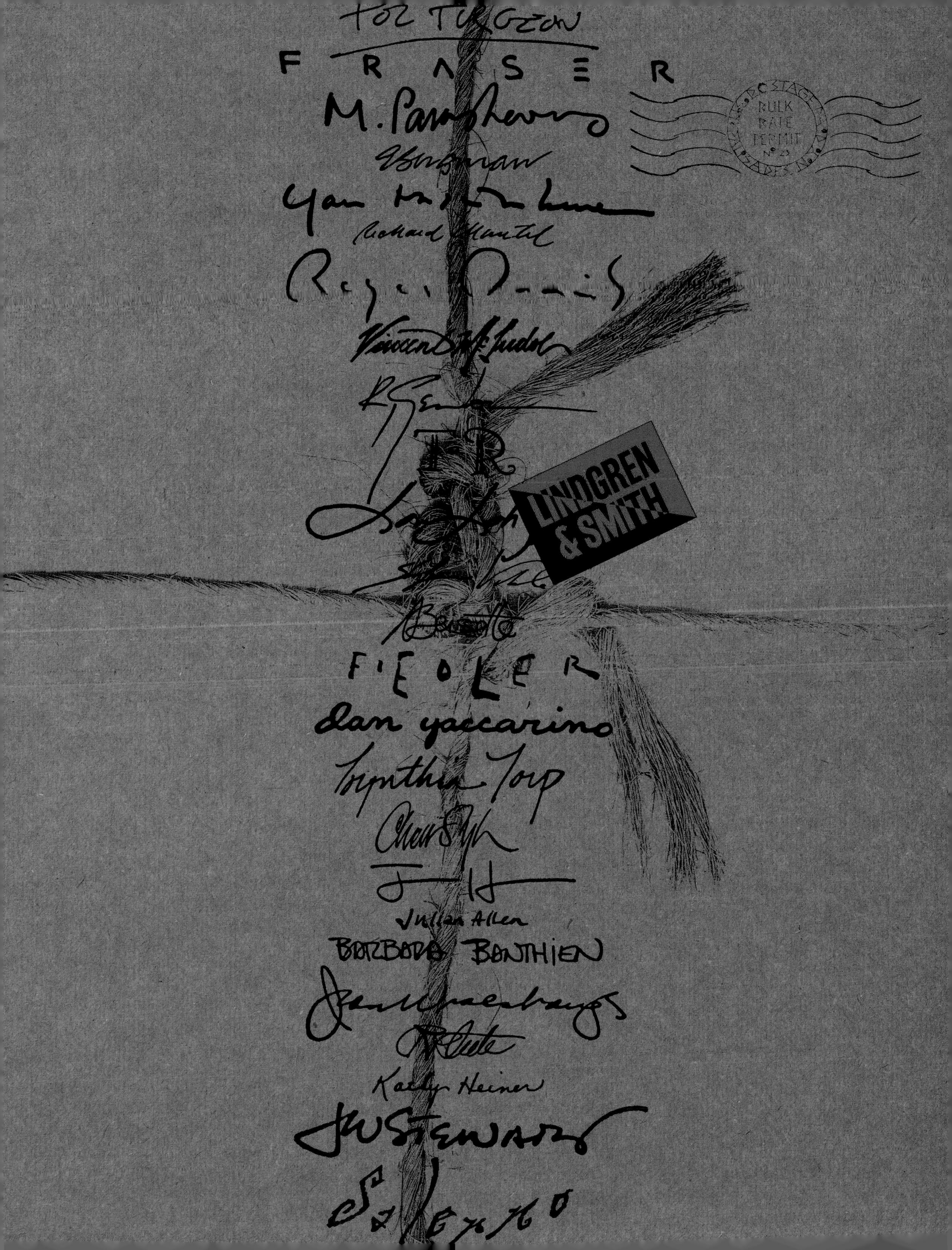

FOR TURGEON

F R A S E R

M. Paraskevas

Housman

Yan ??? Lee

Richard Mantel

Roger ???

Vincent McIndoe

R ???

??? ???

??? ???

Bruetti

F I E D L E R

dan yaccarino

Cynthia Torp

Chris Styh

??? H

Julian Allen

BARBARA BANTHIEN

Jean ???

R. Tate

Karelyn Heiner

J W STEWART

S. B. ??? O

LINDGREN & SMITH

Promotional image for a printer, AD Carmen Dunjko.

Pharmaceuticals brochure, AD Sylvie Clouthier.

J. W. STEWART

REPRESENTED BY PAT LINDGREN & PIPER SMITH 212.929.5590 · CHICAGO 312.819.0880 · SAN FRANCISCO 415.788.8552

Memory Thief album by Lost and Profound, poster version, AD JWS.

J.W. STEWART

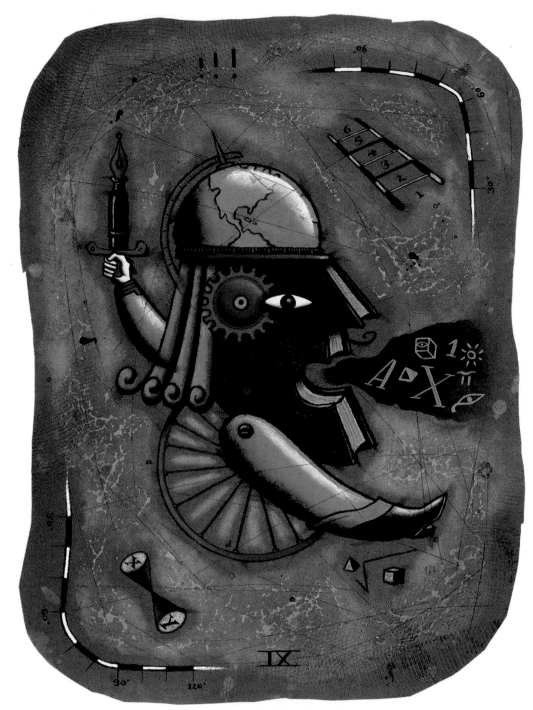

WASHINGTON POST

POL TURGEON

REPRESENTED BY PAT LINDGREN & PIPER SMITH 212.929.5590 · CHICAGO 312.819.0880 · SAN FRANCISCO 415.788.8552

JOSEPH DANIEL FIEDLER

REPRESENTED BY PAT LINDGREN & PIPER SMITH 212.929.5590 · CHICAGO 312.819.0880 · SAN FRANCISCO 415.788.8552

LORI LOHSTOETER

Steven Salerno

REPRESENTED BY PAT LINDGREN & PIPER SMITH 212.929.5590 · CHICAGO 312.819.0880 · SAN FRANCISCO 415.788.8552

ELIOT BERGMAN

JOE & KATHY HEINER

REPRESENTED BY PAT LINDGREN & PIPER SMITH 212.929.5590
CHICAGO JOEL HARLIB ASSOC. 312.329.1370 · LOS ANGELES MARTHA PRODUCTIONS 310.204.1771 · SAN FRANCISCO MISSY PEPPER 415.543.6881

DAN YACCARINO

REPRESENTED BY PAT LINDGREN & PIPER SMITH 212.929.5590 · CHICAGO 312.819.0880 · SAN FRANCISCO 415.788.8552

YAN NASCIMBENE

JEAN WISENBAUGH

Represented By Pat Lindgren & Piper Smith 212.929.5590 · *Chicago* 312.819.0880 · *San Francisco* 415.788.8552

VINCENT MCINDOE

BRISSETTE · GENDRON

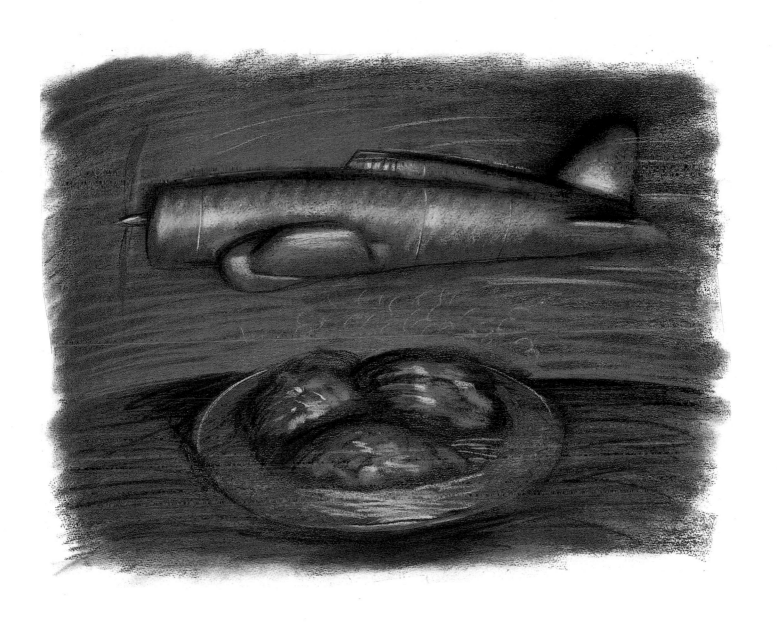

REGAN DUNNICK

Represented By Pat Lindgren & Piper Smith 212.929.5590 · Chicago 312.819.0880 · San Francisco 415.788.8552

ABSOLUT AUTUMN.

STEFANO VITALE

REPRESENTED BY PAT LINDGREN & PIPER SMITH 212.929.5590 · CHICAGO 312.819.0880 · SAN FRANCISCO 415.788.8552

ROBERT GANTT STEELE

DOUGLAS FRASER

REPRESENTED BY PAT LINDGREN & PIPER SMITH 212.929.5590 · OUTSIDE THE NORTHEAST JAN COLLIER 415.383.9026

Douglas Fraser

JOSE ORTEGA

212-772-3329

GRAPHICS + ILLUSTRATION TELEPHONE: 312 525-2081  FAX: 312 525-3114

KATHY PETRAUSKAS
312 642 • 4950 • FAX 312 642 • 6391

"Whether an artist's tools are
made from computer chips or
hog bristles is beside the point;
either you connect with the
subject's spirit or you don't.
For me, that struggle to connect is
where the energy comes from."

TOM EDGERTON

VICKI PRENTICE ASSOCIATES INC. 1888 CENTURY PARK EAST
SUITE 1900 LOS ANGELES CA 90067 **310.826.1332** FAX 310.284.3290

MARY SPENCER

TOM VOSS

ROBERT BYRNE

JOAN FARBER

ROCCO BAVIERA

LAWRENCE WALKER

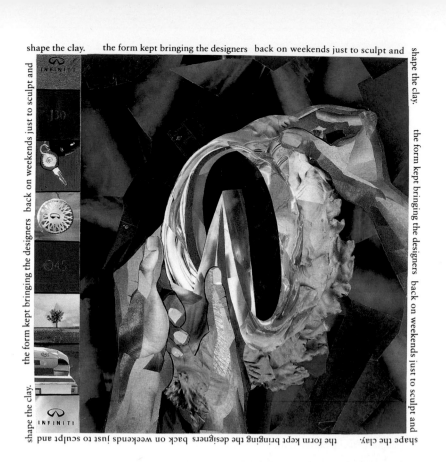

the form kept bringing the designers back on weekends just to sculpt and shape the clay.

THE WONDERS OF THE WORLD

MARJORIE E. PESEK

SUSAN MELRATH
3100 Jackson Ridge Court • Phoenix MD 21131

410•785•0797
410•785•1196 FX

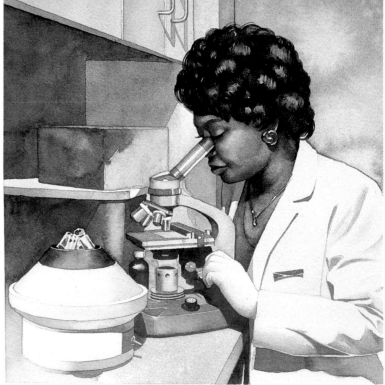

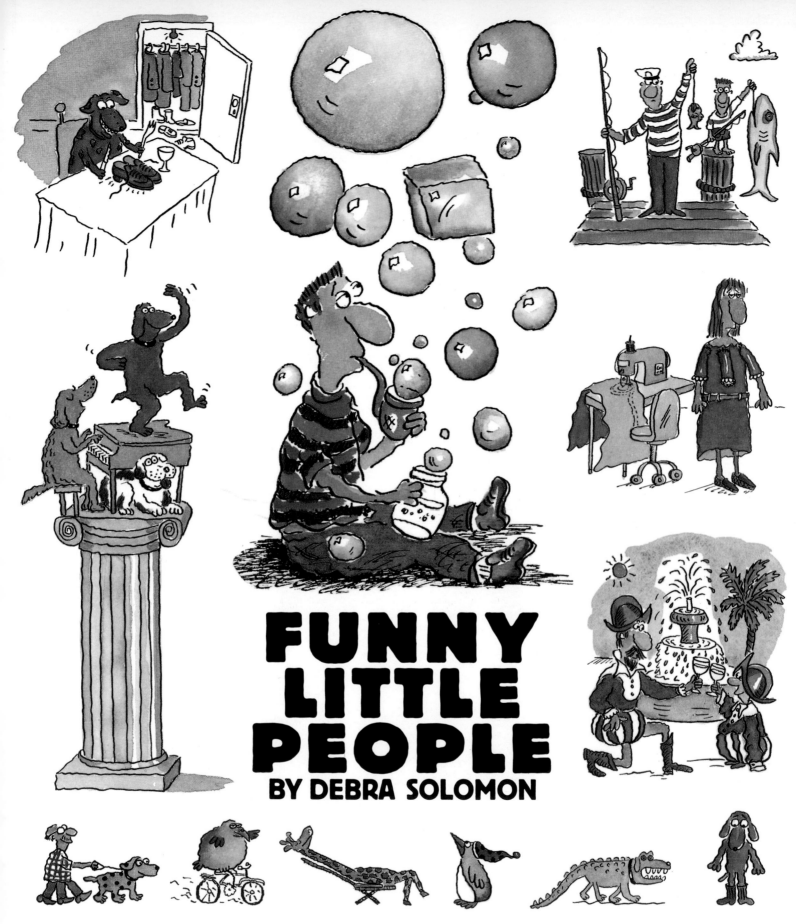

FUNNY LITTLE PEOPLE
BY DEBRA SOLOMON

(ANIMALS ALWAYS AVAILABLE)

143 GREENE STREET APT. 3 NEW YORK, NY 10012 TEL. (212) 473-0060 FAX (212) 473-7163

CLIENTS INCLUDE: IBM • AMERICAN EXPRESS • HALLMARK • PROCTOR & GAMBLE
UNION CARBIDE • NEW YORK TIMES • VOGUE • GLAMOUR • BANTAM • RANDOM HOUSE
NEW AMERICAN LIBRARY • PUTNAM • SIMON & SCHUSTER • WARNER • WORKMAN PRESS

LORRAINE SILVESTRI

122 PLIMPTON STREET, WALPOLE, MA 02081
PHONE/FAX: 508-668-0111

Clients include: Harcourt Brace, Ligature Inc., Blackstone Research Associates,
Brigham and Women's Hospital, St. Jude Medical Center, The Rheinner Group

To view more samples, see also: CIB '93, p. 426 and CIB '94, p. 427

TISH
TENUD
3427 folsom boulevard
sacramento · ca
9 · 5 · 8 · 1 · 6
fax · 451 · 6037
916 · 455 · 0569

Roses

peonies

tEA
time

CUCUMBER watercress sandwich

VALERIE SPAIN • STUDIOS • 617-923-1989

SCHOLASTIC

BOSTON GLOBE

GLAMOUR

AMSCO INTERNATIONAL

JULIETTE BORDA

114 CARNEGIE PLACE   PITTSBURGH, PENNSYLVANIA 15208   *phone* 412 441 7188   *fax* 247 9908

Represented by Jim Lilie / tel 415.441.4384 / fax 415.395.9809

MARY ROSS

RITA GATLIN REPRESENTS

2350 TAYLOR STREET • SAN FRANCISCO, CA 94133 • 415.776.3833

kirk richard Smith

FIREHOUSE 101 art + design
studio - 614 · 464 · 0928
492 armstrong street · Columbus, Ohio 43215

Sheldon Greenberg

Represented by Michèle Manasse

200 Aquetong Road
New Hope, PA 18938
Phone: (215) 862-2091
Fax: (215) 862-2641

The Discovery Channel

Maxine Boll

Represented by Michèle Manasse

200 Aquetong Road
New Hope, PA 18938
Phone: (215) 862-2091
Fax: (215) 862-2641

Berlitz Language, Inc.

Sweet Adelaide

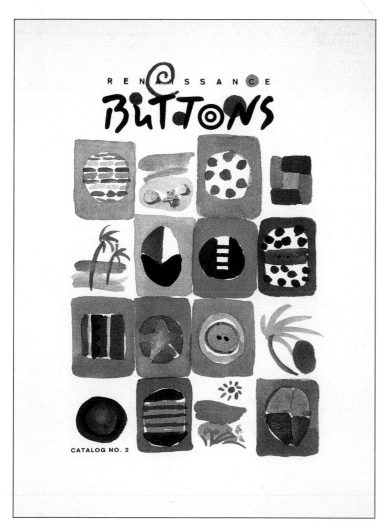

Renaissance Buttons, Inc.

Milwaukee Magazine

1995 © Maxine Boll

NEW Work

Carol Inouye

Represented by Michèle Manasse

200 Aquetong Road
New Hope, PA 18938
Phone: (215) 862-2091
Fax: (215) 862-2641

Angel In The Wood

1995 © Carol Inouye

Mike Reagan

Represented by Michèle Manasse

200 Aquetong Road
New Hope, PA 18938
Phone: (215) 862-2091
Fax: (215) 862-2641

Islands

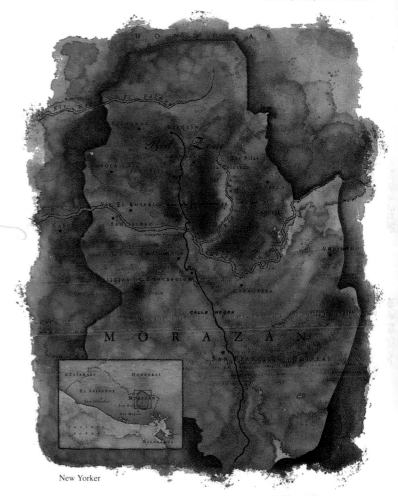

New Yorker

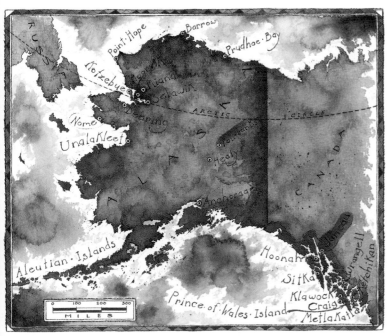

Sports Illustrated

Outside

1995 © Mike Reagan

Geneviève Claire

Represented by Michèle Manasse

200 Aquetong Road
New Hope, PA 18938
Phone: (215) 862-2091
Fax: (215) 862-2641

Nordstrom

I love

my pets

Playskool

Unpublished

BAR CAT

Holiday Greetings

1995 © Geneviève Claire

 **Work**

Jacques Cournoyer

Represented by Michèle Manasse

200 Aquetong Road
New Hope, PA 18938
Phone: (215) 862-2091
Fax: (215) 862-2641

Guernica Publishing

Interface Magazine

Unpublished   1995 © Jacques Cournoyer

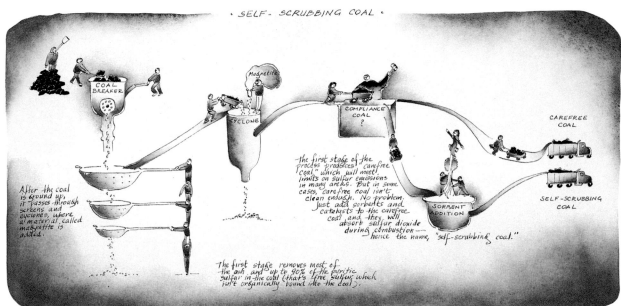

· SELF- SCRUBBING COAL ·

COAL BREAKER

Magnetite

CYCLONE

COMPLIANCE COAL ?

SORBENT ADDITION

CAREFREE COAL

SELF-SCRUBBING COAL

After the coal is ground up, it passes through screens and cyclones, where a material called magnetite is added.

the first stage of the process produces "carefree coal," which will meet limits on sulfur emissions in many areas. But in some cases, "carefree coal isn't clean enough. No problem. Just add sorbents and catalysts to the carefree coal and they will absorb sulfur dioxide during combustion — hence the name, "self-scrubbing coal."

The first stage removes most of the ash and up to 90% of the pyritic sulfur in the coal (that's free sulfur which isn't organically bound into the coal).

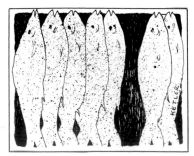

RUTH SOFAIR KETLER

101 BLUFF TERRACE
SILVER SPRING MD 20902
301 • 593 • 6059

REPRESENTED
BY KATHY HAYES
212 • 925 • 4340

284

RENARD
REPRESENTS
212.490.2450
FAX 697.6828
NEW YORK

288

JONATHAN
HERBERT

Renard Represents
Tel: (212) 490-2450
Fax: (212) 697-6828

**State-of-the-Art 3D
Modeling for Print
and Animation**
■

Call for book or reel

ROGER
HILL

Renard Represents
Tel: (212) 490-2450
Fax: (212) 697-6828

ROGER
HILL

Renard Represents
Tel: (212) 490-2450
Fax: (212) 697-6828

STEVE BJÖRKMAN

Renard Represents
Tel: (212) 490-2450
Fax: (212) 697-6828

© 1994 Steve Björkman

Available for Print and Film

MICHAEL McGURL

Renard Represents
Tel: (212) 490-2450
Fax: (212) 697-6828

Available for Print and Film

JAMES
BOZZINI

Renard Represents
Tel: (212) 490-2450
Fax: (212) 697-6828

JUD GUITTEAU

Renard Represents
Tel: (212) 490-2450
Fax: (212) 697-6828

VALERIE
SINCLAIR

Renard Represents
Tel: (212) 490-2450
Fax: (212) 697-6828

THEO RUDNAK

Renard Represents
Tel: (212) 490-2450
Fax: (212) 697-6828

JOHN
MARTIN

Renard Represents
Tel: (212) 490-2450
Fax: (212) 697-6828

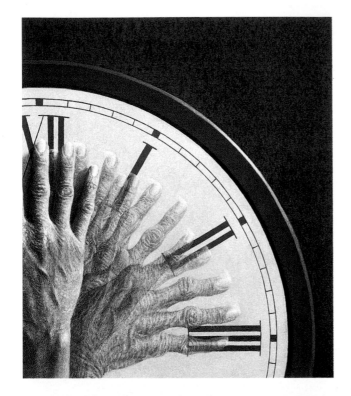

GARY ELDRIDGE

Renard Represents
Tel: (212) 490-2450
Fax: (212) 697-6828

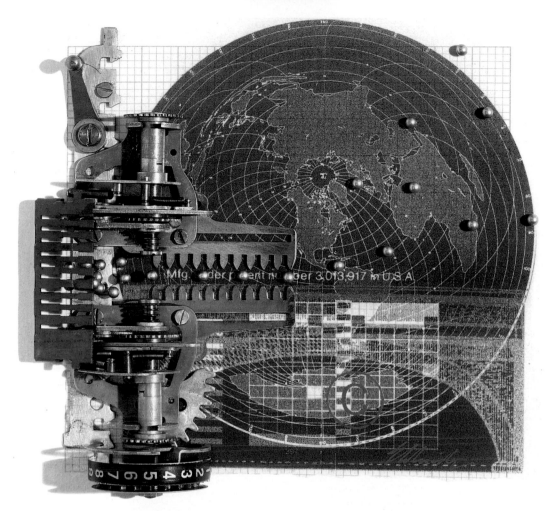

RENÉ
MILOT

Renard Represents
Tel: (212) 490-2450
Fax: (212) 697-6828

WAYNE McLOUGHLIN

Renard Represents
Tel: (212) 490-2450
Fax: (212) 697-6828

WILLIAM
HARRISON

Renard Represents
Tel: (212) 490-2450
Fax: (212) 697-6828

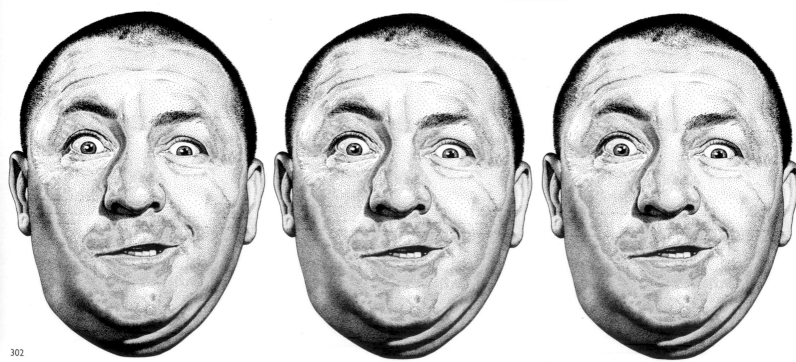

BILL
CIGLIANO

Renard Represents
Tel: (212) 490-2450
Fax: (212) 697-6828

DAN
GARROW

Renard Represents
Tel: (212) 490-2450
Fax: (212) 697-6828

Available for Print and Film

ROB
BROOKS

Renard Represents
Tel: (212) 490-2450
Fax: (212) 697-6828

KAZUHIKO
SANO

Renard Represents
Tel: (212) 490-2450
Fax: (212) 697-6828

ROBERT RODRIGUEZ

Renard Represents
Tel: (212) 490-2450
Fax: (212) 697-6828

STÉPHAN DAIGLE

Renard Represents
Tel: (212) 490-2450
Fax: (212) 697-6828

SUSAN GROSS

696 8th AVE
S.F. CA 94118
415.751.5879

Clients Include: Harper Collins, Nordstrom, BBDO, Hewlett Packard, Sassy, LA Times, Chronicle Books, Oracle, The Washington Post, Phillips Electronics, Crown Books, Tandem Computers & more!

 Anne Johnstone phonefax: 617 666-8120

GREGORY
DYE

Studio / Denver
303.933.0340

Tom Maloney / Chicago
312.704.0500

JENNY SACHS

JENNY SACHS DESIGNS 157 EAST 32ND STREET
SUITE 22B NEW YORK NY 10016 **212.684.0565**

PAUL VISMARA

 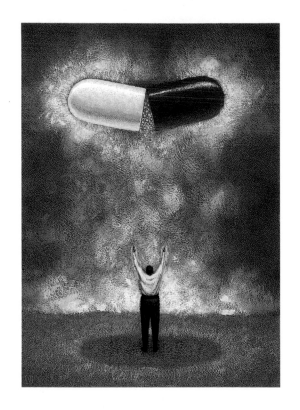

CHICAGO, IL   TEL/FAX 312.248.7084

NEW SUMMER SALADS

rick allen

represented by JANET VIRNIG · *tel* 612 926 5585 · *fax* 612 926 3347

Jerry Blank

Telephone: 408 289 9095
Facsimile: 408 289 8532

james f. kraus

art guy studios

[617] 437-1945

boston, ma

JOEL HARLIB ASSOCIATES   312-329-1370   FAX 329-1397

318

NATURE GARDEN COLLECTION™

CROCUS BULB KIT

Includes Two Premium Dutch Crocus Bulbs, Two Glass Vases & Instructions

THE NATURE COMPANY

NATURE GARDEN COLLECTION™

NARCISSUS BULB KIT

Includes Premium Dutch Narcissus Bulb, Glass Vase & Instructions

THE NATURE COMPANY

NATURE GARDEN COLLECTION™

HYACINTH BULB KIT

Includes Premium Dutch Hyacinth Bulb, Glass Vase & Instructions

THE NATURE COMPANY

"SAVORING PARADISE" : ORIGINAL LITHOGRAPH PUBLISHED BY JACKSON PRESS, LA

CYNTHIA FITTING

415 567 3353   FAX 415 474 6935

REPRESENTED BY: FREDA SCOTT   TEL 415 621 2992   FAX 415 621 5202 / DIANN ROCHE   TEL 816 561 0590 FAX 816 531 5103

Joe Baker

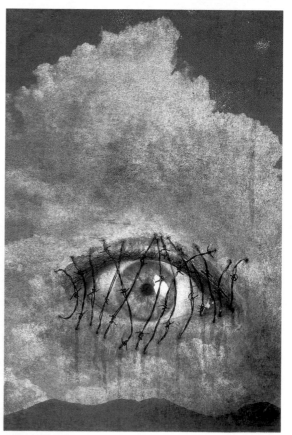

Joe Baker

Matt Foster design studio Fax: 215.1257 510.215.1251

SF · Freda Scott 415.621.2992
NY · Daniele Collignon 212.243.4209
Midwest · Lulu 612.825.7564

Matt Foster **design studio** Fax: 215.1257 510.215.1251

SF · Freda Scott 415.621.2992

NY · Daniele Collignon 212.243.4209

Midwest · Lulu 612.825.7564

AMY L. WASSERMAN
COLLAGE ILLUSTRATION
PHONE 816-561-2757
FAX 816-561-9776

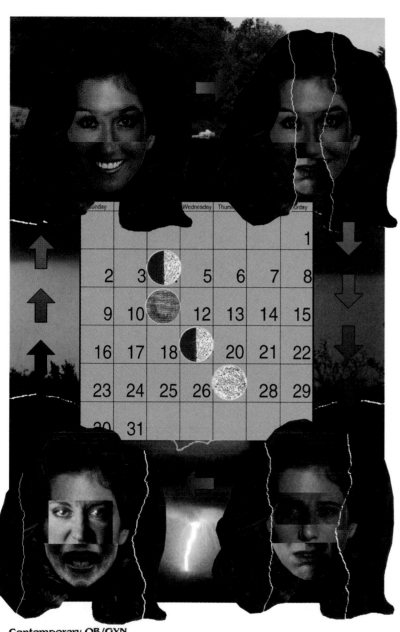

Contemporary OB/GYN

Smithsonian

Time

LISA POMERANTZ

DEBORAH
WOLFE
LIMITED

731 N. 24TH STREET   PHILADELPHIA, PA 19130   215 232 6666   FAX 215 232 6585

SKIP BAKER

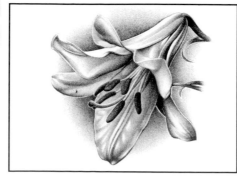

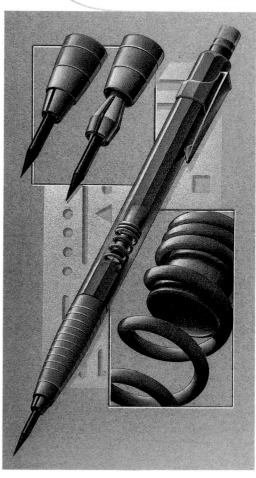

DEBORAH
WOLFE
LIMITED

MARIANNE HUGHES

LEIF PENG

DEBORAH
WOLFE
LIMITED

731 N. 24TH STREET   PHILADELPHIA, PA 19130   215 232 6666   FAX 215 232 6585

LEIF PENG

ANDY LENDWAY

DEBORAH
WOLFE
LIMITED

731 N. 24TH STREET   PHILADELPHIA, PA 19130   215 232 6666   FAX 215 232 6585

MARK WICKART

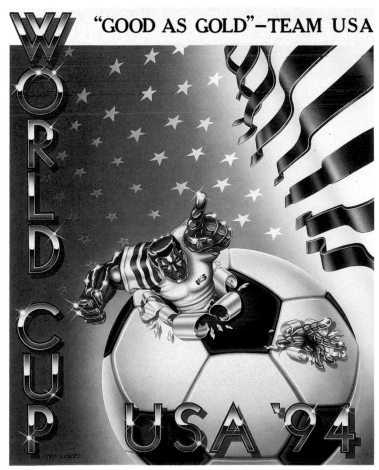

"GOOD AS GOLD"—TEAM USA

WORLD CUP USA '94

DEBORAH
WOLFE
LIMITED

731 N. 24TH STREET   PHILADELPHIA, PA 19130   215 232 6666   FAX 215 232 6585

RANDY HAMBLIN

DEBORAH
WOLFE
LIMITED

332   731 N. 24TH STREET   PHILADELPHIA, PA 19130   215 232 6666   FAX 215 232 6585

ANDY MYER

BILL MORSE

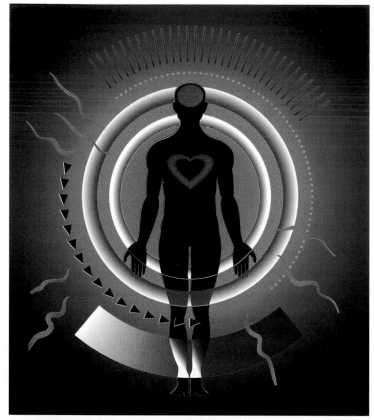

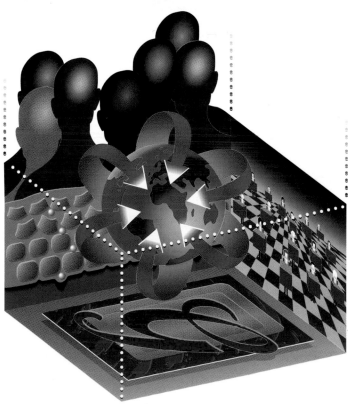

PATRICK GNAN

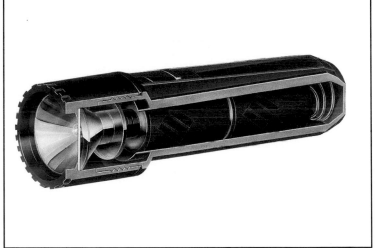

DEBORAH
WOLFE
LIMITED

731 N. 24TH STREET   PHILADELPHIA, PA 19130   215 232 6666   FAX 215 232 6585

LARRY WINBORG

JOE DORETY

DEBORAH
WOLFE
LIMITED

731 N. 24TH STREET   PHILADELPHIA, PA 19130   215 232 6666   FAX 215 232 6585

JENNY CAMPBELL

DEBORAH
WOLFE
LIMITED

731 N. 24TH STREET   PHILADELPHIA, PA 19130   215 232 6666   FAX 215 232 6585

STEVEN NAU

DEBORAH
WOLFE
LIMITED

731 N. 24TH STREET   PHILADELPHIA, PA 19130   215 232 6666   FAX 215 232 6585

MICHAEL W. MARTIS

ILLUSTRATOR

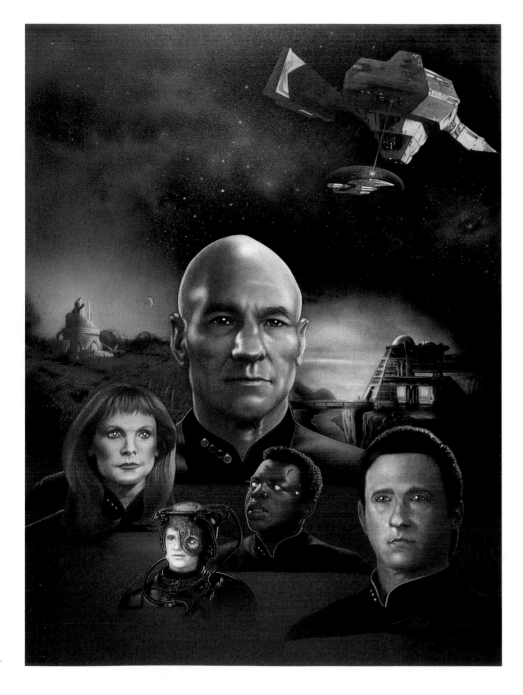

phone
(515) 285-8122

fax
(515) 287-6483

W.B. JOHNSTON

(204) 582-1686

K.D.

KEN DUBROWSKI

ILLUSTRATOR

49 FREEMAN STREET · WOLLASTON, MA 02170 · PHONE / FAX 617 · 328 · 1198

SCOTT POLLACK 516•921•1908 FAX 516•921•2383

RICHARD

Elmer

RICHARD ELMER, 504 EAST 11 STREET, N.Y.C. 10009, (212) 598-4024

344

LINDA BLECK

ITESM

Santa Cruz Operation

642 West Aldine Street, Suite One
Chicago, Illinois 60657

312 281 0286 telephone
312 281 4955 facsimile

Microsoft

IMAGINE ONE ADVERTISING / OIL ON BOARD

OIL ON BOARD

OIL ON BOARD

jeff LABBÉ

christine prapas

GATX 1993 ANNUAL REPORT / SANDRA DUBOIS DESIGN

northwest territory
P 503.246.9511
f 503.246.6016

COMPLIMENTARY BUGATTI

artist studio *jeff labbé*
phone 909.621.6678
fax 909.621.6678

represented in California by:
das grüp
phone 310.540.5958

represented by -- *brian* **BATTLES**

christine prapas

 northwest territory
p *503.246.9511*
f *503.246.6016*

artist studio *brian battles*

phone 619.267.3182
fax 619.267.6649

stephen f. **HAYES**

stephen f. **HAYES** -------------------------------- **represented by**

christine prapas

northwest territory

p *503.246.9511*
f *503.246.6016*

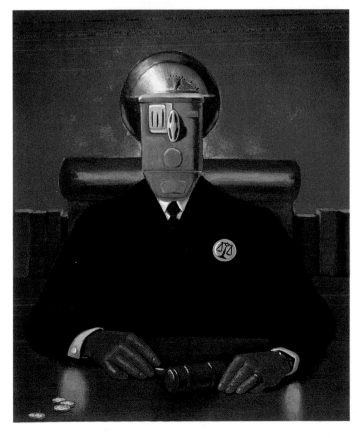

artist studio *stephen f. hayes*
phone 503.524.6726

represented by —————————————————————————— steve **KENNEVAN**

christine prapas

🎿 **northwest territory**
p *503.246.9511*
f *503.246.6016*

BANANA CREME/NORDSTROM BATH LINE

DONNA KARAN FRAGRANCE/NORDSTROM

BIKER/UNPUBLISHED

lydia j. **HESS** -- **represented by**

christine prapas

northwest territory ❄
P *503.246.9511*
f *503.246.6016*

THE NAMES PROJECT/AIDS MEMORIAL QUILT

HEALTH AND FITNESS MAGAZINE

HEEKIN GROUP LITERARY FOUNDATION

WIDMER BREWING COMPANY

christine prapas

northwest territory
p *503.246.9511*
f *503.246.6016*

R A C I N G   T E A M

ROLAND CORPORATION US
3-D SPORTS
RAMIREZ TRAVEL

IT CAN BE DONE ELECTRONICALLY
OR THE OLDFASHIONED WAY

christine prapas

Cosmopolitan

El Torito Restaurants

A northwest territory
p 503.246.9511
f 503.246.6016

Created
in
Aldus
Freehand
by a
playful
mind.

Wendy's

artist studio *olivia*
phone 714.252.1147
fax 714.252.1260

represented in New York by:
bernstein & andriulli
phone 212.682.1490

christine prapas

madeline **VASQUEZ** ------------------------------

--- **represented by**

mike **WEPPLO** -----------------------------

northwest territory
p *503.246.9511*
f *503.246.6016*

N

Mass./Conn.	**Chicago**	**New York**	**California**
lauri pribble	*patrice bockos*	*dennis godfrey*	*das grup*
phone 203.455.0811	phone 312.661.1717	phone 212.807.0840	phone 310.202.7675

MIKE SCHROEDER

WATER COLOUR
5801 LA VISTA COURT
DALLAS, TEXAS 75206
214.821.9834

JIM DARNELL

RANDY FISHER

RICK WHIPPLE

ELLIOTT PARK

DAVID DANZ

ADDITIONAL WORK CAN BE SEEN IN THE WORKBOOK '92-'95, CREATIVE ILLUSTRATION BOOK '93-'94, AMERICAN SHOWCASE VOL 18
PLEASE CALL FOR AVAILABLE STOCK

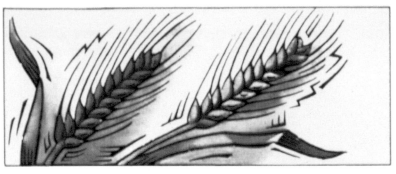

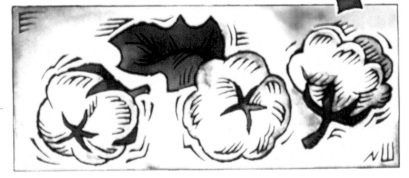

AMY BRYANT
STUDIO / FAX 214·902·0163

REPRESENTED BY ANDREA LYNCH
5521 GREENVILLE AVE. 104-338, DALLAS, TEXAS 75206
TEL: 214·369·6990 FAX: 214·369·6938

RAMUNE
(r rä/moo/nê)
617-444-1185

DOROTHY REINHARDT

San Francisco 415.584.9369

DAVID GROVE

382 Union Street
San Francisco California 94133
415 · 433 · 2100

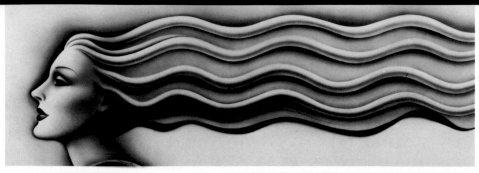

MK MONTGOMERY
707 829-2135

O'NEILL SPORTSWEAR

CALIFORNIA CAFE RESTAURANTS

PRIVATE COMMISSION

Michel Bohbot

510 · 547 · 0667

MARK NAGATA

MARK NAGATA ILLUSTRATION
1948 Leavenworth Street
San Francisco CA 94133
415 922 6612

Represented by: **PETER AND GEORGE LOTT**
60 East 42nd Street
New York NY 10165
212 953 7088

NOBU KAJI

Studio
(415) 343-7331

**BARBARA
MELODIA**

Fax
(415) 347-2352

Clients include:

Lucasfilms, Ltd.
Joseph A. Wetzel Associates
World Wildlife Fund
Elfinlight Press
The Oakland Zoo
Determined Productions, Inc.
Sierra Magazine
Nakashima and Associates
Willitz Designs
Vera Scarves
Silvestri
Rubber Stampede
Diablo Valley College

Terryl Whitlatch

Animals Real and Imagined

Phone 510 • 228 • 7675 □ Fax 510 • 372 • 7613

ROB SAUNDERS

TEL (617) 566-4464   FAX (617) 739-0040

© ROB SAUNDERS 1994

James Swanson (708) 352-3081 Fax (708) 352-3082

RICH BOWMAN

DIANN ROCHE REPRESENTS (816) 561-0590

MARTY ROPER

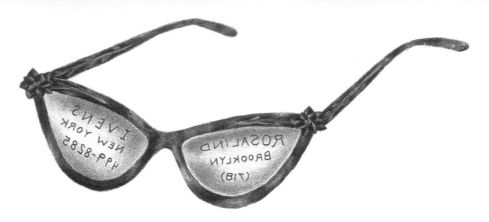

AMERICAN HEALTH, THE ATLANTIC, AUDIO, THE BOSTON GLOBE, IBM, LIFE, McGRAW-HILL, THE NEW YORK TIMES, R.H.COSMETICS, TRAVEL HOLIDAY, WINDOWS

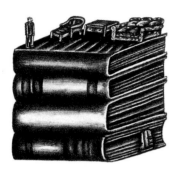

SCOTT PECK 214·422·7438

Tie
One
On.

Wilfred Spoon

Lawrence W. Duke

Nick Backes

Ben Perini

Mary Carter

Paul Kratter

Ed Lindlof

Miro Salazar

Fred Hilliard

Tracy Britt

Try One On.

PAUL
KRATTER

MIRO
SALAZAR

(212) 677-9100 / FAX: 353-0954

Carol Chislovsky Design Inc.
853 Broadway New York, New York, 10003

CHISLOVSKY

SANDRA SHAP

CHRIS GALL

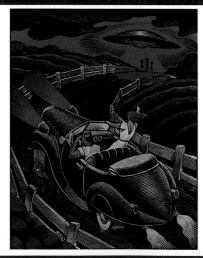

JACK GRAHAM

(212) 677-9100 / FAX: 353-0954

Carol Chislovsky Design Inc.
853 Broadway New York, New York, 10003

CHISLOVSKY

SUSAN FOSTER

Harry Pulver Jr.

PHONE • 612 • 377 • 1797 • FAX

CLIENTS ℞ LEVI'S, PILLSBURY, ALLSTATE,
GENERAL MILLS, SCHOLASTIC, PIZZA HUT,
... ETC ...

studio: 415.344.2100
fax: 415.344.2300

MICHELE
LALLY

studio: 310.587.5873
fax: 213.655.4093

MINDY
OLIVER

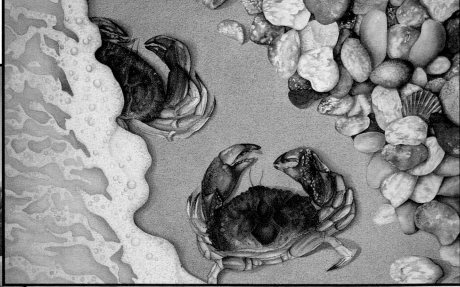

In NYC
Sid Buck and Barney Kane   studio: 415.964.1733
212.221.8090   fax: 415.967.8711

JOANIE
POPEO

studio: 904.358.1445
fax: 904.358.1445

OSCAR
SENN

studio: 310.590.0535
fax: 310.590.0535

DAVID
TURNER

ERIC JOYNER   707·769·1344

FLOOD

Represented by Sell Inc.
(312) 578-8844
FAX (312) 578-8847

JOHN FRANCIS ILLUSTRATION

1665 Logan Street
Suite 1046
Denver, CO 80203
303-894-8350
FAX 894-8343

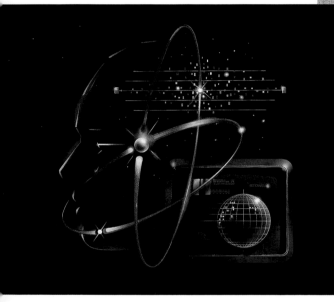

Clients Include

Gore Tex
Du Pont
Norelco
Infiniti
AT&T

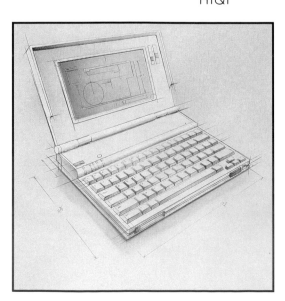

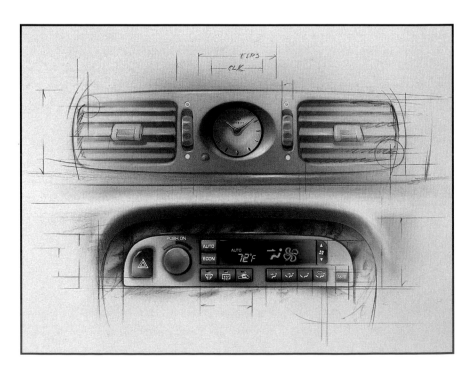

Thomas Dannenberg

Illustration • Graphic Design
Tel: (905) 731-8038   Fax: (905) 731-5689

AGNES ARU

illustrator

498 MANNING AVE.
TORONTO CANADA M6G 2V7
TEL•FAX (416)532-9861

Daphne McCormack, *illustrator*

Phone/Fax: (416) 868-0190

JACKIE SNIDER
613-475-4551

STEPHEN SNIDER

613-475-4551

IT'S ALIVE!

MARC GABBANA 2453 Olive Ct Windsor Ontario Canada N8T 3N4 Phone/Fax (519) 948-241

"PIZZA WARS", FOODSERVICE AND HOSPITALITY MAGAZINE

GiO VAN NiNA ILLUSTRATIONS AND DESIGN

"GOT THE WINTER BLUES", POSTER FOR GUARDIAN DRUG STORES, JW&R ADV.

"TENDING TO YOUR TEETH", GUARDIAN GOOD HEALTH GUIDE

"LOVES LABORS NOT LOST", COSMOPOLITAN MAGAZINE

"WORLD VISION", CANADIAN PHARMACEUTICAL JOURNAL

PATRICK FITZGERALD

ILLUSTRATION

PHONE/FAX (416) 429-2512

STEPHEN • QUINLAN • ILLUSTRATION • LTD
PHONE/FAX (416) 485-8277

Current clients include: The Addiction Research Foundation, Bell, Federal Express, Globe & Mail, Heinz, IBM, Kodak, Labatts Brewing Co., The Royal Bank, Somerville House Publishing, Sunlife Insurance Co. and Visa.

Sarah Jane English

(416) 247·7336

fax: (416) 247·5638

23 Hepworth Drive

Toronto, Canada M9R·3W1

JUDY MAYER GRIEVE
TELEPHONE / FAX (416) 502 - 3874

BARBARA SPURLL
ILLUSTRATION
416·594·6594
FAX 416·601·1010

Calvin
Nicholls

(705) 878·1640

MARC BURCKHARDT

ILLUSTRATION

Clients Include:

TIME WARNER ~ MORRISON RESTAURANTS ~ RANDOM HOUSE ~ FORBES

THE OLD FARMER'S ALMANAC ~ PARAMOUNT COMMUNICATIONS ~ MCI

BETTER HOMES & GARDENS ~ ARBITRON INC. ~ PSYCHOLOGY TODAY

(5 1 2) 4 7 4 - 9 7 8 1

FOR ADDITIONAL WORK, SEE CREATIVE ILLUSTRATION '94 & GRAPHIC ARTISTS GUILD DIRECTORY #10 & 11

JIMMY HOLDER

Phone (818) 244-6707   Fax (818) 244-6766

1507 Columbia Drive • Glendale, CA 91205

Harriet must go
Shopping!
Even though
there's an impending
Blizzard.

Where's
that taxi?

Suzette
Barbier

Phone:
617.527.8388

Fax:
617.244.0266

STUDIOS

joani
PAKULA

©joani

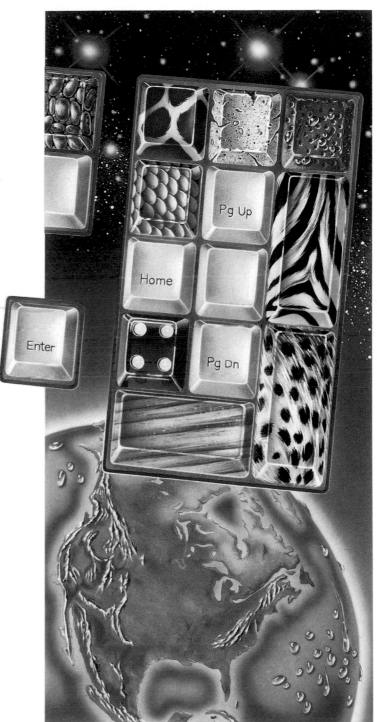

816 734 4344

illustration

MARLA

MARLA SHEGA
ILLUSTRATOR

4 4 0 1
EDINBURG LANE
HANOVER PARK
IL 60103
708-830-4745
FAX 708-830-4745

REPRESENTED BY
TOM MALONEY

•

307 NORTH
MICHIGAN AVENUE
SUITE 1008
CHICAGO, IL 60601
312-704-0500
FAX 312-236-5752

DAVID CHEN

CREATIVE ILLUSTRATION
301-460-6575

15013 EMORY LN. ROCKVILLE, MD 20858

CONRAD REPRESENTS   T·(415)921-7140 F·(415)921-3939

RogEr RotH

7227 Brent Road
Upper Darby, PA 19082
Tel./Fax 610-352-3235

THE NEW YORK TIMES

MONEY MAGAZINE

WALL STREET JOURNAL

CALIFORNIA LAWYER

THE NEW YORK TIMES

WALL STREET JOURNAL

WALL STREET JOURNAL

CHEMICAL BANK

©1994 Roger Roth

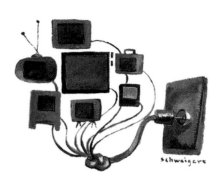

EAST AFRICA

KENYA

TANZANIA

carol schweigert
9 lawnwood place, charlestown, boston ma 02129
phone/fax 617-242-3901

STEPHANIE OSSER 617-237-1116

The Boston Globe Magazine
Doubleday
Horticulture
Little Brown
Random House
The New York Times Magazine
Unicef Greeting Cards
WGBH-TV

Del Monte Corporation
Harper Collins
Alfred A. Knopf
McCann-Erickson
The New England Aquarium
Simon & Schuster
Warner Books

THE BRIDGE
SITS ON SOLID
MAHOGANY TO
ELIMINATE
FEEDBACK

150 Winding River Road Needham, MA 02192

413

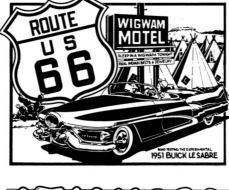

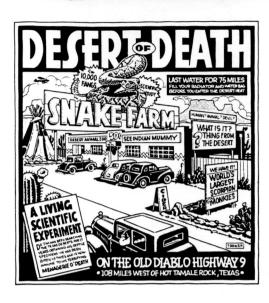

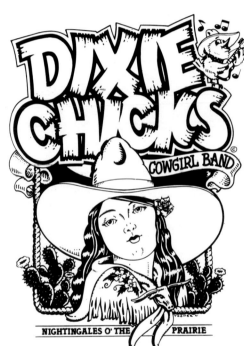

GEORGE TOOMER
3923 COLE AVE • DALLAS, TX 75204
214 522-1171 • FAX: 214 528-3588

FRIEND OF THE FRIENDLESS • PROMOTER OF THE SHY • CHAMPION OF LOST CAUSES • GYNOPHILE • PRACTICING DESIGNER, ILLUSTRATOR AND GARDENER.

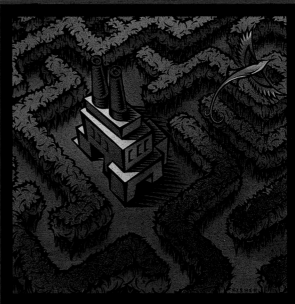

MIKE FISHER

1620 CAROL SUE AVENUE • SUITE 309
GRETNA, LOUISIANA • 70056
TEL/FAX 504 • 393 • 8947

417

H e l e n D'S o u z a

416-466-0630

DESIGN GROUP

Paseo Castellana 179, 4D1, 28046 Madrid, España 571 8183 Fax 571 8055

GUIA DE LA BUENA VIDA 1994

EL PAIS • COVER DESIGN

NEW YORK LOTTERY • LOGO

SONY MUSIC • MINIDISC PROMOTION

DISCOVERY • EDITORIAL ILLUSTRATION

VAUGHAN FILMS • IDENTITY

**CELLULAR COMMUNICATIONS
ANNUAL REPORT • ILLUSTRATION**

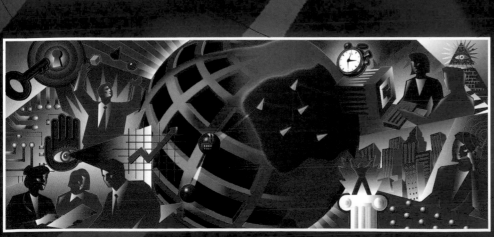

COMPUTER TASK GROUP • ILLUSTRATION

419

Abe Gurvin Festive Illustrations for All Occasions   **(714) 499·2001** Studio & Fax

FRANK LUX & ASSOCIATES

mac

REPRESENTING:

ALAN ARIAIL/MARC ROSS

DAN CLYNE

KARLA GINZINGER

TERRY JASINSKI

DAVE MILLER

JIM PRICE

EVAN SCHWARZE

MICHAEL STEPANEK

JOHN WALKER

DAVID WEHRSTEIN

THE SOURCE FOR ALL YOUR ILLUSTRATION
NEEDS AT ONE LOCATION.
WHETHER CONVENTIONAL, COMPUTER,
FULL COLOR OR BLACK AND WHITE,
WE REMAIN QUALITY DRIVEN AND
DEADLINE CONSCIOUS.
GIVE US A CALL.

REPRESENTED BY FRANK LUX   CHICAGO

FRANK LUX
AND ASSOCIATES
I · N · C

PHONE · 312 · 222 · 1361   FAX · 222 · 0753

421

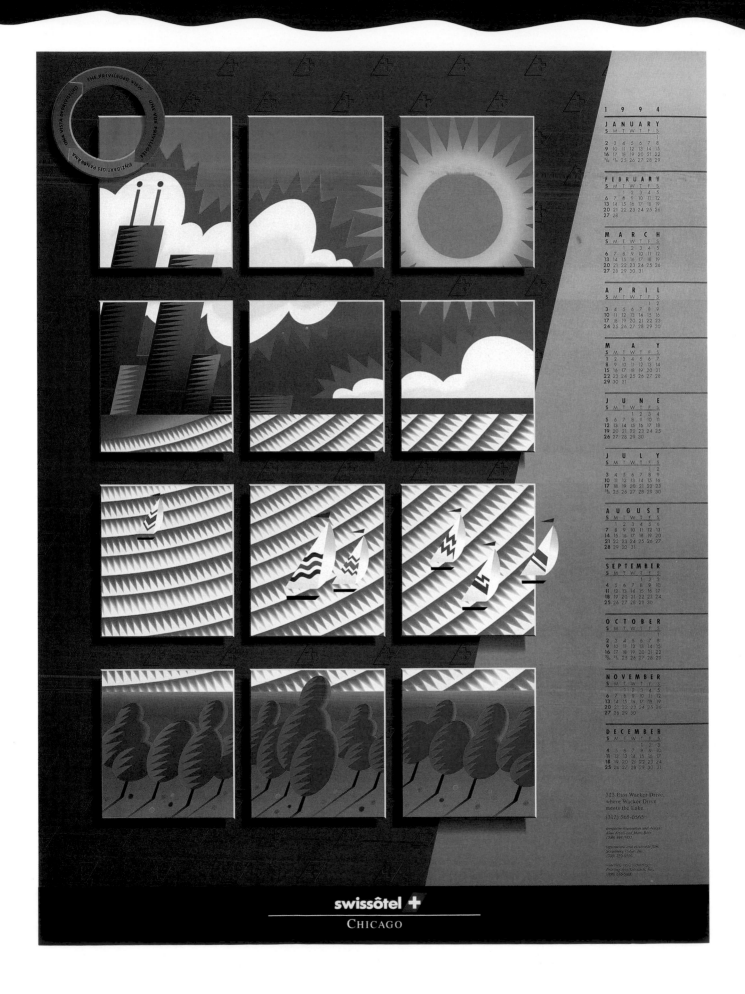

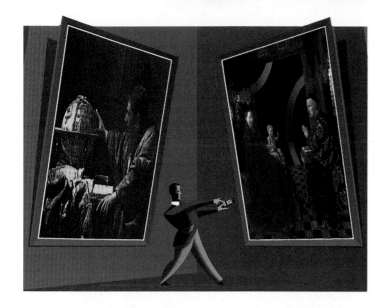

MITCH O'CONNELL

TOM MALONEY 312·704·0500

IN NEW YORK - DANIELE COLLIGNON 212·243·4209

Computer illustrations
3-D Modeling & Animation
Multimedia Presentations

Shawn Egan

314 227-7770

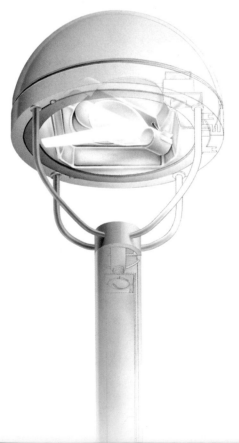

METROPOLIS

MARSHALL
wōk·sa

815 • 562 • 3702

ROD
THOMAS
617·449·0480

16 GRASMERE RD
NEEDHAM MA
02194

429

Lynx

FEEL · THE · THUNDER

6878 fry rd · middleburg hgts., ohio · 44130

(216) 234-1808

5375 SKYWAY DRIVE• MISSOULA, MONTANA 59801• FAX & PHONE 406-251-3587

Cosmetics&Toiletries

CLARKE
TATE
800-TATE-008
301 WOODFORD STREET
GRIDLEY, IL 61744

•ATLANTA•
WILL SUMPTER & ASSOC.
404.874.2014
•MINNEAPOLIS•
MARIETTA & JERRY MASON
612.729.1774

COMPUTER ILLUSTRATION

DARYLL COLLINS
Humorous Illustration

PHONE/FAX
(513)683-9335

• 2969 Ensley Ct. • Maineville, OH 45039 •

Jefrey Gunion

ILLUSTRATION & DESIGN

408/336.3300 TEL

408/336.3309 FAX

8100 Harvard Drive • Ben Lomond • California • 95005

For more illustration examples refer to: The 1991, 1992, 1993 Bay Area Creative Source Books & The 1993 Creative Illustration Book.

GWEN CONNELLY
S T U D I O S

STUDIO 1• 312.943.4477
708.869.8643
F A X • 708.869.8653

REPRESENTED BY JERRY LEFF ASSOCIATES, INC. ■ 420 LEXINGTON AVE. ■ NEW YORK NY 10170 ■ TEL: 212-697-8525 ■ FAX: 212-949-1843

435

DAVE WINTER IS REPRESENTED BY DAVE WINTER ☎ 312-527-3900, 275-9529

TODD TREADWAY

Todd Treadway Illustration
778 S. Swadley St.
Lakewood, CO 80228
(303) 763-9288

Kathy O'Connell

Cold Springs Design 1494 Cold Springs Road, Pottstown Pa. 19464

Call For: Sample Disk of Computer Cartoons.

Tel: (610) 326-8038
MODEM /FAX: (610) 326-6173
Same Day Delivery By Modem

Clients Include: M & M / Mars, Sunshine Cookies, Johnson & Johnson, Atlantic Oil, Burpee Seeds, Ore-Ida, Bachman's, Holiday Inn, Nutri-System, Salerno, Sun Oil

JANICE GOLDBERG
(416) 410-0848

• HEDY KLEIN •
ILLUSTRATION
718-793-0246

JIM CARSON
617 661.3321

ICON GRAPHICS INC. • **34 ELTON STREET** • **ROCHESTER, NEW YORK 14607** • **716 271-7020** • **FAX 716 271-7029**
All illustrations are produced electronically. Call for more illustration samples.

LORRAINE RABL
201·836·4283

MIKE TOFANELLI
I L L U S T R A T I O N

1100 Howe Avenue #246
Sacramento, CA 95825
Phone/Fax 916.927.4809

DAVID SCANLAN

TEL: (310) 545-0773 • FAX: (310) 545-7364

Los Angeles Rep.: Rosemary Morales - (213) 467-4674
Chicago Rep.: Robin Stevens - (312) 689-3442

E. Stark Studio

Clients include: • Brazos Valley Museum of Natural History • Texas A&M University College of Veterinary Medicine • Safari Club International • American Heritage Center and National Cowboy Hall of Fame • World Hockey Association • Chronicle of the Horse • Messina Hof Winery • Casa Ole Restaurant • Steak & Ale
EMMA STARK   (409) 779-0722

448

The Bottomless Bowl of Bits!

Win a lifetime supply of Kibbles 'n Bits.

TAKE ONE

J. WALTER THOMPSON ADV.

SMITH, BADOFSKY + RAFFEL ADV.

HRMagazine

IF HAVING A RED NOSE IS NOT IN YOUR JOB DESCRIPTION, SEE WALGREENS.

If constant nose blowing and wiping is making you look more and more like a certain reindeer, fly on over to your neighborhood Walgreens. From our selection of over 200 cold and flu remedies there's bound to be one that will help get you and your nose back to normal in no time. Of course, if you're bucking to be leader of Santa's team, that's a different story. Call 1-800-WALGREENS toll-free for the Walgreens or 24-hour location nearest you.

Walgreens
The Pharmacy America Trusts

TSIRRELL
708·213·9003
AVAILABLE FOR PRINT AND ANIMATION

CALL! CALL! CALL!

©TERRY SIRRELL

450

Nicholas J. DiBlasio

207 Commonwealth Ave. Boston, Ma. 02116
Phone & Fax **617 - 266 - 2650**

451

Jackie Urbanovic

illustration • character creation • concepting

420 N. 5th St., Suite 950, Mpls., MN 55401 • **(612) 673-9323**

Julie Pace
Computer Imagery / Hand Drawn
909 337-0731
fax 337-5703

Sing·a·Long

I don't think so

454

SUGAR BOWL / FRENCH ROAST ESPRESSO BAR

WHEN A LAYOFF HITS HOME / WHITTLE COMMUNICATIONS

MEETING HER KIDS FOR THE FIRST TIME

THE MOTHER CHAIR / ALGONQUIN BOOKS

VIRGINIA HALSTEAD

4336 GAYLE DRIVE, TARZANA, CALIFORNIA 91356   818.705.4353

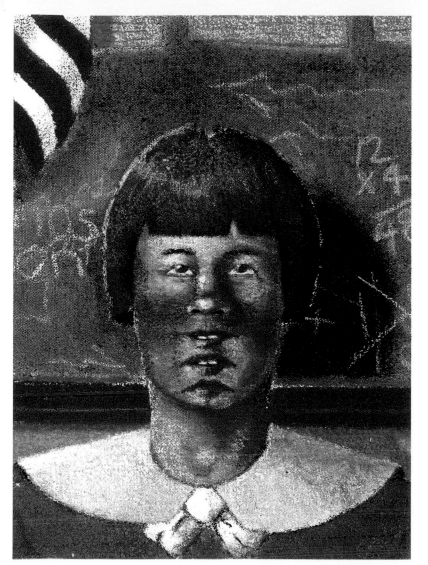

DENISE C. CRAWFORD

PHONE & FAX 713·663·7377

West Coast
Andrea Lynch/Repertoire
5512 Greenville, #104-338
Dallas, TX 75206
214·369·6990 Fax 214·369·6938

East Coast
Jerry Leff Associates, Inc.
420 Lexington Ave., Suite 2760,
New York, NY 10170
212·697·8525   Fax 212·949·1843

JOHN ALLISON
ILLUSTRATION
816-444-7782

CLANCY GIBSON

Represented by Link 416 530 1500 Fax 416 530 1401

NINA BERKSON

Represented by Link 416 530 1500 Fax 416 530 1401

GRANT INNES

Represented by Link 416 530 1500 Fax 416 530 1401

PAUL RIVOCHE

Represented by Link 416 530 1500 Fax 416 530 1401

Fred Hilliard

NEW YORK
JERRY LEFF ASSOC.
212·697·8525

CHICAGO
KEN FELDMAN
312·337·0447

SAN FRANCISCO
BARB HAUSER
415·647·5660

SEATTLE
DONNA JORGENSEN
206·634·1880

LOS ANGELES
MARNI HALL
310·652·7322

AIM Institutional Funds/The Hively Agency

206 842 6003 · 206 842 7528 FAX

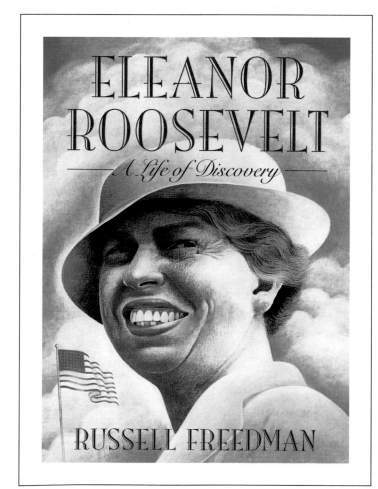

CYNTHIA
VON BUHLER
(617) 783-2421

Joe DiMaggio

Bob Cox '94

1/56

ROBERT RAYEVSKY   403 GARWOOD DRIVE   CHERRY HILL, NJ 08009   PHONE/FAX: 609-427-6970